D1488345

HOSTILES AND FRIENDLIES

About the *hostiles:* I've never heard it pronounced with anything but a long *i* as a noun meaning the hostile Indians, while they were effectively hostile. Curiously, old army men who fought them sometimes changed the *i* to a short one when they were captured. I recall old General Brown at Denver once speaking of the "captured hostiles"—short *i*—immediately after he had spoken of them with a long *i* while out under Crazy Horse at the Rosebud. I'm certain he wasn't conscious of this change in pronounciation.

—Letter from Mari Sandoz to Mamie J. Meredith (78)

HOSTILES
AND
FRIENDLIES

Selected Short Writings

of

MARI SANDOZ

UNIVERSITY OF NEBRASKA PRESS

LINCOLN: 1959

First Printing 1959
Second Printing 1959
Third Printing 1963

Publishers on the Plains
UNP
COPYRIGHT 1959 BY THE UNIVERSITY OF NEBRASKA PRESS

Library of Congress Catalog Card Number 59-6617

Manufactured in the United States of America

CONTENTS

ILLUSTRATIONS

Following page 103

Map of the Sitting Bull Country, 1831–1890, showing the relative fields of activity of the two Sitting Bulls. Drawn by the author.

Following page 106

Sioux Chiefs to Washington, D.C., 1875. Seated: Sitting Bull the Oglala; Swift Bear; Spotted Tail. Standing: Julius Meyer and Red Cloud. Photograph made at Omaha. Courtesy Nebraska State Historical Society.

Inscription on Henry Rifle presented to Sitting Bull the Oglala, at Washington, D.C., 1875. Now in the Museum of the American Indian. Courtesy the Museum of the American Indian.

Sitting Bull the Hunkpapa. Barry photograph, 1885. Courtesy the Smithsonian Institution.

The funeral procession of Crazy Horse passing through Camp Sheridan, Nebraska. *Frank Leslie's Illustrated Newspaper,* October 13, 1877. "This illustrates the complete ignorance of eastern artists about the accoutrements of the Sioux, of their appearance. The horse wouldn't have a white man's bridle, the mourners would be in tatters of mourning, the travois is wrong, the saddle is wrong, etc." (77).

INTRODUCTION

IN THE AUTOBIOGRAPHICAL SKETCH which begins on page xv, Mari Sandoz speaks of her liking for books which "were direct, didn't have long introductions, and weren't fooling the reader—it was clear what they were doing all the time." It has been our object to make this collection of Mari Sandoz' short writings just such a book.

The most direct way, it seems to us, of stating what we have intended to do in these pages is to present unvarnished excerpts from the record—from the editor's report to the author and publisher, and from the correspondence of the author and editor during the preparation of HOSTILES AND FRIENDLIES.

According to the editor's first report on the project, August 1957:

The various pieces fell naturally into three categories, of which the first two—Recollections and Indian Studies—pertain to sources of the author's material. In the Recollections, we are shown what she grew up with—family, neighbors, Indians; the fauna and flora of the sandhills; the physical environment and the shaping economic and social conditions; the violence—natural and human violence; the hard facts of life in a frontier region. "The Kinkaider" was written in 1929, "The Neighbor" more than a decade and a half later; yet the force of these early impressions is still a powerful stimulus, memory is still yielding up fresh detail. . . . But memory alone would not have sufficed for this author's work. There had also to be the material derived from exhaustive research; and it is to this source that the Indian Studies pertain. . . .

In the fiction group we see the two kinds of source material in action, so to speak—applied to achieve an artistic end. . . . This "sources-and-uses" line largely determined the plan of the book—to show how the author's subject-matter and point of view are rooted in her own experience, and to give some idea of the research preparation which enables her to write so surely and circumstantially—and also gave us a context in which all the material might be considered. . . .

In addition to the pieces selected to be run *in toto,* autobiographical sidelights and bibliographical data were extracted from occasional pieces, speeches, interviews, and letters. It was felt that this material contained pertinent and enriching information which, if incorporated into a running commentary, would add to the value of the collection as a source book for future studies as well as providing a further unifying element and generally

enhancing the readability, freshness, and character of the presentation.
. . . While the fiction is arranged chronologically by date of writing
(rather than date of publication), obviously this collection can hope to give
no more than a partial picture of Mari Sandoz' development as a writer.
For one thing, the short writings occupy a minor place in the Sandoz canon.
(Since the appearance of *Old Jules* in 1935, the author has written only
twelve articles and stories for magazines of general circulation as compared
to ten books.) Moreover, even though this group of stories written between
1925 and 1940 may fairly be classified as "early work," considered by
themselves they do not shed much light on the evolution of characteristic
themes, point of view, style, and technique—for the author already had
evolved her methods by the time she began to appear in national magazines. (She began to write "as soon as I could read"; wrote seventy-eight
short stories before her first acceptance; had planned the Trans-Missouri
Series before she was twenty.) But when read *in conjunction* with the
recollections and research pieces, I believe that these stories do tell us
something of the author as a craftsman—of the fusion of the remembered
and the imagined, of firsthand observation and creative historical vision,
of deeply-felt personal experience informing art. And I believe that this
collection—quite apart from its intrinsic interest and its value to social
historians and anthropologists—has something to say to anyone who is
interested in the making of a writer.

It was proposed in this report that the book include a foreword—
"an appreciation and appraisal"—by a leading critic, scholar, writer,
or other authority in the field of regional literature. The author replied in letters of August 8 and 10, 1957:

. . . I'm convinced that you can work out a plan to make the book seem
something like a whole. I am, however, uneasy about the critical introduction. . . . I am struck again with the inadequacy of my short writings
as any gauge of me as a writer, or at least I hope so. . . . Anyone with
reasonably good literary standards is going to find these pieces of minor
importance. If the critic is familiar with my books, he's going to have to
ask, if he's honest at all, why this inferior work was anthologized. Which
will be bad for your sales. If he doesn't say that my long works are superior
to this, then the first evaluation of any body of my work will tend to set the
critical tone of my work for all time— No one will want to evaluate my
writing as a whole because a partial examination found it so inadequate.

You know how these things go. It's true that I'm not afraid of the evaluation posterity will put upon my nonfiction—good or bad it is unique in its
field and those who come after me will have to depend upon it to a very
large extent. These books have always had critical acclaim even if not
always understanding, and one shouldn't expect the impossible. Besides,
I am too great an admirer of the Romance poets to have much respect for
critics as a tribe, although in the more esoteric fields I don't think ours are
too bad. . . . Anyway, I am uneasy about having the first criticism of a
body of my work made from the short pieces. . . .

The editor replied (August 14, 1957):

. . . A critical introduction was not at all what I intended to suggest—in fact, I thought it would be out of place. (See Report, pp. 19–20: "It would be silly . . . to attempt a broader picture by stuffing the introduction and commentary with a rundown of connections between the short writings and the books. The material should be 'placed' with respect to the whole Sandoz canon, yes; but to use this collection as the basis for a full-dress critical appraisal would be a case of tail wagging dog.") . . .

However, to characterize the collection as your minor writing is not at all to apologize for it. . . . Your short writings are worth collecting on their own merits: the interest which is inherent even—sometimes especially—in the minor writings of a major writer is a plus value. It is true that this collection will have greater import for a reader familiar with your nonfiction books and your novels, but it has something to say on its own—just as has each separate piece in it though they gain in interest and significance when read in the light of the whole collection.

With all the emphasis in the report on "plus values"—the scholarly contribution of the research articles, the interest as regional history and autobiography and so on—the first and most obvious reason for publication may have got overlooked or scanted: Articles and stories are collected and published because they contain information or tell a tale that will engage the attention of a reader.

Subsequently, the author was queried again about her feelings on the matter of a contributed foreword, and answered in a letter of February 18, 1958:

I'm against having one from the outside. I stood against this on the *Old Jules* and have never had any reason to regret my decision. Forewords from the outside are for newcomers in the field, for posthumous explanations, and for people venturing into a field in which they are definitely not expert. I maintain that so long as I am alive none of these hold.

These excerpts will, it is hoped, be sufficient to indicate the intention of Hostiles and Friendlies and to account for the absence of the customary salute to the author by a distinguished colleague in the world of letters.

From here on, all but a fraction of the editorial commentary is Mari Sandoz speaking.—Speaking, it should be added, in a conversational voice, for these observations about her life and work were made without any idea that they would ever find their way into a collection of her writings.

Virginia Faulkner
Assistant Editor
University of Nebraska Press

AUTOBIOGRAPHICAL SKETCH OF
MARI SANDOZ' EARLY YEARS

This account was derived from various articles, speeches, interviews, and letters as indicated in the text.* On reading it over, the author commented that it "seems to make my life entirely too difficult. It really wasn't; for whatever the life of a child, it is normal until one grows up enough to find out that others live in other circumstances" (79).

I GREW UP NEAR the Sioux Reservation at Pine Ridge, South Dakota, in the free-lands region of northwest Nebraska. I was the eldest of six children. Our father, a cripple, was less interested in routine physical labor than in his old Indian friends, and in providing good homes for the landless of the world, including experimentation in fruit and crops adapted to the new country. Our mother did most of the field and garden work, and so the care of the house and the children usually fell to me. When a baby was two weeks old it was put into my bed and was then my responsibility (62). I also learned to run father's trapline when necessary and to skin anything from a weasel to a cow (58). By the time I was ten I could bake up a 49-pound sack of flour a week, but I would let the bread sour and the baby cry if there was anything to read (65).

I was about nine when I started to school and made the wonderful discovery that little black marks were the key to wonderful stories. I knew about stories [before I knew how to read]. I lived in a storyteller region—all the old traders, the old French trappers, all the old characters who had been around the Black Hills—the Janises, the Bordeauxes, the Charbonneaus—told grand stories of their travels and experiences in the early days of the Missouri and around Fort Lara-

* To ascertain a source, see the corresponding number in the Bibliography, pages 241–244.

mie. The Indians were wonderful story-tellers. There was an old Indian woman who told of Sand Creek and the Washita and Fort Robinson, and of buffalo hunts, and of fights with the Snakes and the Crows—but not much of wars with the whites for these were still touchy and unhappy affairs. Many a night I sat in the woodbox and listened. As long as I kept still I didn't have to go to bed.

Father came from an upper-middle-class professional family. He didn't believe in fiction. That was for the hired girl and the hired man. So I had to borrow books and smuggle them into the house in the sloppy front of our low-belted dresses. Our area seemed overrun with retired Boston schoolteachers and Chicago widows. [Every lone woman too gay for quiet ways was called a Chicago widow. They were mostly brought in to take up homesteads for ranchers.—*Author's note*] The ex-teachers supplied Hawthorne and Shakespeare, but the Chicago widows had lighter reading, mostly paperbacks and magazines. I remember that one of the books was called *From Ballroom to Hell*, and it showed every step of the way. Then there was *St. Elmo* but I don't know how it began or ended, as both the front and back were gone. The one book my father had permitted me to have was *Robinson Crusoe*, but it, like the others I smuggled in, was read in the attic, hidden meanwhile in the straw tick. I could see the value of the two kinds of literature as I grew older. The books of the Chicago widows were direct, didn't have long introductions, and weren't fooling the reader—it was clear what they were doing all the time. [But I saw they were thin and artificial, without imagination. The books I reread many times were those of the Boston schoolteachers: Hawthorne, Conrad, Hardy, etc., even *Looking Backward.—Author's note*]

I knew some of the same kind of characters [as were in the Chicago widows' books] in real life. The country was full of road agents and hired killers. Doc Middleton was running a temperance bar.* One of the hired killers we knew quite well—in fact, he shot my uncle. [In addition there were the hideouts from cattle conflicts elsewhere: from the Olive lynchings in Custer County, Nebraska; the Lincoln County War of New Mexico; the Johnson County War in Wyoming. Many old Texas trail drivers and cowboys and cattlemen from everywhere had drifted into the sandhills because the region was one of the last pockets of free range left.—*Author's note*] I learned much

---

* David C. (Doc) Middleton, Nebraska's best-known cattle rustler and horse thief, ran a temperance bar in Gordon, Nebraska, for some years after serving a term in the State Penitentiary. He died in 1913 in the county jail of Douglas, Wyoming, while doing time for bootlegging.—*Editor's note*

from the talk of all these old timers, and perhaps more from the
Indians, for the Indians remembered better . . . (46).

I started writing when I started to school. While born in the Panhandle of Nebraska, I spoke only a few words of hybrid English at
the time, with an equal smattering of Polish and French mixed into
my mother tongue, Swiss-German (58). [When I was ten] I decided
to write a story—secretly, of course—and submit it to a newspaper
[Omaha *Daily News*] offering a book as a prize. It was published
but it didn't get first prize—somehow I never did get first prize. But
when it came home I found out that I belonged to a family that not
only did not read fiction, but certainly did not write it. Father put
me in a cellar. I believed that when a parent went to the trouble of
punishing a child, the least the child could do was act punished. I
howled to high heaven. I knew there were snakes in the cellar. I also
knew they were harmless. After some time Father came along and
asked if I wanted to go quail hunting. I sure did. . . . After that I
used a pen name * (46).

By sixteen I had gone to school [four and a half years], passed the
rural teachers' examination, and had a school. At twenty-one I decided that I must have a college education. I came to Lincoln and
sat around in the anterooms of various deans for two weeks between
conferences with advisers who insisted that I must go to high school.
Finally bushy-haired Dean Sealock got tired of seeing me waiting and
said, "Well, you can't do any more than fail—" and registered me
(58).

Father was interested in fossils, pottery, and remains of village
sites along the Niobrara, and as I studied history and geology, read
anthropology, the area we had explored as children took on greater
significance. With no fixed curriculum, I browsed around in all the
sciences except chemistry, the only one I ever made a living at—in
a drug laboratory (46). For . . . eight years I worked here and there,
attended University as I could, wrote seventy-eight short stories (and
didn't sell one), won honorable mention in a Harper's Intercollegiate
Contest in 1926, and wrote a bad novel that, fortunately, no one
would publish (46, 58). Years before I could do more than give away
my short stories I was selling articles on such unpromising subjects
as unusual holiday celebrations, mad dog cures, earning one's way

* "Although she had never heard of a pseudonym, she sought protection by
signing her name Alice McCall, Ruth Norris, and Anka Annis. Her first serious
stories written and published in her college days were signed Marie Macumber"
(66).

through college filling capsules, prairie fires, well accidents, bone pickers, early irrigation attempts, muskrats, Indians, and my own father and mother (28).

I don't know just when I thought of the topic for a book (57). The West changed irrevocably after the First World War, and it occurred practically outside my window. Questions arose: What happens when modern man comes into a stone-age region? What does he do to it? It to him? (64) I've always been interested in man and his way of life upon this earth and felt a strong urge to clarify my conclusions in writing. Early I saw that Old Jules and his community were by far the most promising material of my experience.*

As I worked with the material, three years in research and two in the writing, it gradually dawned upon me that here was a character who embodied not only his own strengths and weaknesses but those of all humanity—that his struggles were universal struggles and his defeats at the hands of his environment and his own insufficiencies were those of mankind; his tenacious clinging to his dream the symbol of man's undying hope that over the next hill he will find the green pastures of his desire. Further, I looked about me in life and in history and literature and I saw there were two kinds of men, the defeated and the undefeated, and that surely the last was the first.

About my life [during the writing of Old Jules]: There's little to say except what's in the book. I worked my way in the University . . . by afternoon jobs, one and a half years in a drug laboratory and one and a half years as English assistant, and the rest of the time four hours a day in the State Historical Society in research and nights on the proof desk of the State Journal. The years during which I wrote, approximately eight all together, I was sub proofreader on the two dailies here in the city [Lincoln] and did research for the State Historical Society in Sioux Indian history, or just existed, as one always does, somehow.

As for the book: The research and writing were surely a tremen-

---

* "Sometimes it seems that a quirk of fate has tied me to this father I feared so much, even into my maturity. The three crucial moments in his life after I could take part in our family life involved me as an unwilling participant. . . . Out of these came the need to write [Old Jules], augmented by the one line my father wrote me in 1926, when I received honorable mention in the Harper's Intercollegiate Short Story Contest, guarded by the name Marie Macumber. He discovered my activities, sent me one line in his emphatic up-and-down strokes: 'You know I consider writers and artists the maggots of society.' The book became a duty the last day of his life, when he asked that I write of his struggles as a locator, a builder of communities, a bringer of fruit to the Panhandle."—Foreword, Old Jules (11)

dous undertaking for an amateur but the real problem was finding a publisher. The ms was in most of the larger publishing houses in America. . . . It was usually held for months, came back with long letters of suggestions that would certainly make it acceptable. One wanted me to have the story told by the main character at one sitting and volunteered to send me a copy of *Journey of the Flame* as a guide. Another suggested that I make it a history of the Populist movement in Nebraska. Still another thought that it would seem like fiction to the reader anyway and should be labeled so. That would leave me free to elaborate one of the love stories and drop all the rest. One publisher called me a cross between Tolstoy and Hamsum but illiterate.

In 1933, after eight rejections, I submitted it in the Atlantic contest (57). When [it was] returned with a curt rejection letter, I quit.* Starved out, my confidence in even my critical faculties gone, I gave up writing permanently and sneaked back to the sandhills. There I hunted ducks and helped at the corral with the fall vaccination and dehorning. I found I could still take a dally round a post fast enough to keep my hands from being rope-burned and that I could still hold a steer down with a knee on his neck while I pushed the needle behind his shoulder blade. But in less than a month I was building myself a shack of privacy in which to write a novel that I had been thinking about doing for nine or ten years.** It was *Slogum House.* By the time the rough draft was done, I was offered more work at the State Historical Society in Lincoln. I made a new copy of *Old Jules,* and started it on its alphabetical round of the publishers again. On its fourteenth trip out it was accepted—and won the Atlantic nonfiction prize in 1935 (58).

---

* Mamie J. Meredith recalls the "last day and night in 1933 before Marie returned to the Sandoz ranch which she had left twelve years before for Lincoln, the State University, and a career in writing. Nebraska was hard hit by the depression; in Lincoln expert stenographers were being offered $35.00 a month. A rejection of the 'Old Jules' manuscript had come that day from Little, Brown and Company which had held it for eight months. She wrote them a letter predicting that the book *Old Jules* would be remembered after the judges of the Atlantic nonfiction contest were dead and forgotten. Then she began carrying out the stories she had been writing, rewriting, and submitting to editors during the dozen years in Lincoln. There were eighty-five of them and she watched them burn in the old galvanized iron washtub behind the apartment house. A few friends who had heard of her decision to go back to the Sandhills where there would be food and shelter at least, watched with her. She had silenced their protests with 'They are not good enough'" (67).

** The shack eventually was heated by a Topsy stove the author purchased with the fee—either five or ten dollars—which she received for her paper "Pioneer Women." See page 59.—*Editor's note*

The announcement was by telegram with the meaning veiled so that the news wouldn't leak out. It came to my desk at the Nebraska State Historical Society, Capitol Tower, Lincoln, on a very busy day, and I had no time to realize its import until half a week later when Volta Torrey, then on the staff of the Omaha *World-Herald,* called me for a statement. Apparently it was true. My heart began to pound so hard I could scarcely hear Volta's voice. Afterward I walked into the office of Dr. Sheldon, Superintendent of the Historical Society, to resign my little job. I walked very slowly, for I liked my work there very much (68).

The author's reactions to the success of Old Jules *were described by her in an article written at the time of its publication, October 1935.*

My German-Swiss grandmother had a saying for every occasion. One she found particularly useful was: "Setting a cur on a fine pillow doesn't improve the dog." Two years ago, when the last revision of *Old Jules* was completed and the manuscript started once more from publisher to publisher no one considered it an occasion for acclaim or commendation. I doubt very much whether two years' travel and a fine pillow have improved that dog very much.

There is, however, no denying that the fine pillow has given the dog's mistress considerably broadened opportunities and obligations. Certainly the opportunity to come and go with some freedom through editorial portals . . . might well be envied any beginning writer. And Eastern reporters, I discovered, are grand people to know when you can get them to tell you about the novels they are secretly writing, or, as one did me, lets you glimpse something of the vast mystical vista he calls his human soul. And there is the amazing way busy Nebraskans rush around to do things for you. . . .

Then there is the fan mail that any prize award always seems to bring, in my case over half from writers and would-be writers. . . . But the Slim Jim who used to dodge cactus and sandburrs out in Sheridan County could never have imagined half of what has happened to her during the last few months. Surely she never would have dared dream of "sitting" for a sketch by anyone, and certainly not by such a well-known artist as Georges Schreiber. . . . And certainly the little girl who sat on the flat-topped gate-post and watched, with considerable envy, the bunting-trimmed teams go by to the celebration at Palmer's Grove on the Niobrara never hoped to spend July 4, 1935, at Newport. Not Newport, Nebraska, in the hay-shipping center of the world, but Newport, Rhode Island. . . . Then there are the innumerable fine people I met, both in Nebraska and in the East through the prize award. . . .

But all these things have no more bearing upon the book than the fine pillow upon the cur. My writing falls just as far below the standard I have set for it as it did last June. I have gained a little leisure to write—no greater facility and certainly not one whit more of understanding or discernment of either literature or life. These things are beyond prizes, editorial offices, book-club selections, and critics. These things come, if they come at all, through effort and pain and the dark road of night; like death they come to the writer alone (16).

RECOLLECTIONS

There was, of course, no training school for the pioneer. He went out and was one or wasn't (8).

THE FATHER AND MOTHER who figure in these recollections are Jules Ami Sandoz and Mary Elizabeth Fehr, his fourth—and last—wife. Both were born in Switzerland, Jules Sandoz in Neuchatel in 1857, his wife nine years later in Schaffhausen. As a young man, Jules Sandoz studied medicine in Zurich. After a quarrel with his family, he came to America in 1881 and to western Nebraska in 1884, bringing with him his dream of building communities which would have political and economic freedom. He located colonists on homesteads in the Niobrara country, inducing them to immigrate and settle there with his descriptions of how the virgin land could be developed. In 1930 the College of Agriculture of the University of Nebraska conferred upon him posthumous membership in its Hall of Achievement for his pioneer horticulturist work (67).*

Not long after the publication of the biography which made Old Jules an American legend, his daughter wrote to a friend:

. . . I consider Old Jules not a pioneer so much as a frontiersman. And he was that. He had the skill, the violence, and the courage to cope with the unknown elements of a wild country; but not the patience for the dull road of the pioneer. As soon as the region was fairly well tamed, his taste for conflict made him restless and he turned to the frontier of experimentation in fruit and soothed his turbulent spirit in fights with his neighbors. He was a frontiersman who opened the way for the pioneers who lived with him (57).

---

* The source of material quoted or summarized in the commentary is indicated by the numbers enclosed in parentheses. To ascertain a source, see the corresponding number in the Bibliography, pages 241–244.

I

The Kinkaider Comes and Goes

The author wrote the following piece in 1929 as part of the semester's work in a course on magazine-article writing given by Professor Sherlock Bronson Gass at the University of Nebraska. Subtitled "Memories of an adventurous childhood in the sandhills of Nebraska," it appeared in the April and May 1930 issues of the *North American Review.*

On a gatepost twenty-five miles over the wind-swept hills from the nearest railroad hangs a tipsy sign. Many winter snows, many summer suns, have weathered it, mellowed it to a velvety gray. Precariously creaking on one nail, the first storm will cast it down, unlamented, into the jointed sandgrass.

While the boiling engine of the mail truck cooled from the long pull through the sandy gap, I shook the wrinkles from my skirt and idly inspected the blurred legend: "Pleasant Home." No pleasantness here to sun-blinded eyes. Only a little valley carpeted with russet bunchgrass tucked in between towering hills whose highest dunes are bald among clusters of green-black yuccas. Decidedly no home.

But in a clump of ragged sunflowers stood an old cookstove, the corroded oven door sagging to reveal hay and straw of a mouse nest where spicy cookies once baked. And suddenly it all came back; the little white beehive of a house with a green blind at the one window—the home of a spinster music teacher from Chicago and one of the first of a dozen of these "music boxes" as the cowboys dubbed them. A rare pleasantness, too, crept over me: the soft haze of a heat-dance on the far gap; brown shading to cream yellow on the hill slopes; the whitish horizon, streaked with wind, blending to deepest blue overhead. Memories relegated to mental attics by years at college and at work revived in my consciousness. This patch of sandhills stretching from the Niobrara River to the Platte was the Jötunheim of my childhood, spent upon its fringes. Out of this almost mythical

3

land, apparently so monotonous, so passionless, came wondrous and
fearful tales of gray wolves that leaped upon fat yearlings (probably
because of the scarcity of children)—and of rattlesnakes—and of cattlemen.

That the grays existed, my brothers and I knew. Once, when reports of unusual ravages reached our father, Jules Sandoz, pioneer
locator and trapper, he set out on a hunting trip with Jim, a convict
on parole to him. The diminutive buckskin team, through their fondness for spectacular runaways, pulled an odd wagon out of our yard
that midwinter morning. Piled high with equipment covered by a
huge calico feather tick roped down, it looked much like a fat blue
sausage on wheels.

Two weeks later the unwashed men came back, half-frozen, but
jubilant. They had poisoned one of the largest grays ever taken in
Nebraska; a difficult feat, for the gray wolf eats only his own kill.
Fortunately, they found a half-eaten rabbit on the animal's trail. A
large dose of strychnine did the rest. The pelt brought $110, mostly
cattlemen bounty, altogether a magnificent sum. But much to
Mother's consternation, the money went for more guns, traps, and
ammunition.

Such evidence of vulnerability reduced our respect for wolf stories
related before the wood-filled heater on winter nights. The cattlemen, however, remained fabulous beings, something like the capi-
talists pictured in the *Appeal to Reason,* our household paper in those
days, only their bellicosity was the result of gorging on public lands,
a sacred something that existed, apparently, only in the sandhills.
Specifically, we knew a boy, not much older than our own pre-school
years, whose father was said to have been shot from his own windmill by a hired killer. And the rifle the boy's mother drew upon the
murderer had proved empty! That catastrophe, my brother Young
Jules and I consoled ourselves, could not happen in our home. The
Sandoz arsenal was always loaded to the muzzle, or, rather, muzzles;
and Father had been a crack shot since the early eighties, when he
roamed the hills with the Indians.

The thin crust of security we thus built over our existence was
rudely and finally broken by a horseman who rode wildly into our
yard, his rifle balanced across his saddle. He had fenced a little Government land near a large ranch, and that morning he found an old
whiskey bottle on his doorstep. In it was a rifle shell wrapped in an
unsigned note telling him to get out or be carried out.

The smell of hot lead stung our nostrils that night as Father molded bullets and we children dipped the shiny slugs in melted beeswax and set them in rows like marching soldiers to cool. It was good fun, and not until one of the few indulgences Jules Sandoz permitted his family, and one valued accordingly, was forgotten did we sense the gravity of the occasion. That night there was no burning of a pinch of smokeless powder in Father's palm, accompanied by his usual explanation that the force of this explosive depended upon confinement. Instead we were marched off to bed early.

Through my crack in the wall I watched Father limp about on his stiff ankle, a reminder of his first dug well and the subsequent long months in the hospital at Fort Robinson. Now he took down one gun after another, ejecting the factory-loaded shells with steel-jacketed or soft-nosed bullets. Reloaded ammunition was used for target practice only.

Calculatingly, he rolled the heavy shells in his palm, his sharp eyes confident upon those of the nervous little man beside him. The two guns over his bed, a thirty-thirty and a twelve-gauge pump-gun "for close range," the forty-five–seventy over the lounge in the kitchen–living room, the thirty-thirty outside the door on the bleached deer antlers—all were examined; even the little group behind the door. Mother sat close to the lamp, bending over her glinting needle, mending socks. Once or twice she looked up, her mouth a thin line, but she dropped her head without speaking.

The next morning there was a great deal of target shooting. Father sent spurts of sand from the exact centre of a yellowish spot, little larger than a tablecloth, on a hillside across the Niobrara. Encouraged to loquacity, the frightened man of yesterday talked endlessly about "boring him full of daylight," meaning, we knew, the rancher suspected of sending the note. And finally the two men vanished into the hills together. A week later Father came back. The man stayed, unmolested.

Upon that prelude, the tempo of our life accelerated. Mysterious men, Government agents, Mother called them, came out in shiny top buggies. They carried rolls of semi-transparent, bluish maps, and after supper, with Father, they pored over them for hours, talking a meaningless jargon of figures, corners, correction lines, old soldiers' claims, and fictitious filings. Over the shoulder of a less formidable one we caught glimpses of these plats, ruled into squares through which ran funny black marks, indicating, the man told me, ridges of hills. Obliterated and faked corners, buried plow shares and sickle bars to detract the compass needle, and final delvings into Father's

deer hunting days in the eighties, when the corners were new, length-
ened the evenings.

Early in the morning the men usually started into the hills, the
Government man driving, while Father watched the roadside for a
grouse or a rabbit, his pump gun between his knees, the barrel against
his shoulder, brushing his unkempt beard. Now and then he pushed
the old cap, either of muskrat or of equally shapeless cloth, back
from his eyes as he scanned the horizon. The thirty-thirty rifle was
always across the buggy bed at his feet.

Rapidly one exciting event followed another: Government indict-
ment of the larger cattle outfits for fictitious filings and fraudulent
fencing of public lands; troops that cut the barbed wire fences when
the cattlemen refused to tear them down; Father gone to Omaha as
a Government witness; his picture in the daily papers, his rifle still
across his forearm.

Strange men came and went, men we were forbidden to mention
to our rare playmates. Always curious, I discovered that one of these
wore a revolver in his armpit and had a shiny button, like a star, that
he kept hidden. "Nosey brat!" he called me when I asked him why
he didn't carry his gun like the cowboys that stopped to water the
dusty, gaunt herds of cattle they were stringing into the hills. Once
or twice furtive ranch owners called, ostensibly to look over the few
Indian ponies we had for sale.

"We'll see you're taken care of, Jule," I overheard one of them
promise, flipping the end of a packet of bills.

But Father was stubborn in his contention that he wanted to build
up the country. The result was that several of the indictments led to
convictions. A couple of cattle kings went to prison. The fraudulent
filings that covered every desirable section were canceled and the
sandhills were now actually opened for settlement. Through the sudden effectiveness of the abused Kinkaid Act, some mysterious person
in Washington, surely a god! was doling out the land within these
soapweed marred slopes in 640 acre chunks to any apparently *bona
fide* homeseeker.

And now came our first covered wagon. True, there had been
others, dimly remembered, but this was tangible reality as it swayed
drunkenly down the hill, rumbled over the plank bridge, and climbed
the rise, drawn by two slow horses, followed by two colts and a lazy
yellow cow with her calf tied to her tail. Amid loud shoutings from
the black-bearded driver and nickerings from the horses, the wagon
stopped on the little level spot across the road from our house. Many

children tumbled out, leaping and playing in their release. What fine playfellows they were, and how interesting the wagon was, stacked up and dark, much like our attic.

That wagon was the vanguard of a long line of homeseekers that passed through our little world. Strange people, these, from far-away places, the men always seeking Paradise over the next hill, the women gaunt and silent or scolding in high, nervous voices. Impatiently they waited for Father or started out alone.

To take such people into the hills, run a line from a known corner to a desirable location, and then take them to the land office at Alliance to file or contest was the business of Jules Sandoz. For this service, requiring a week or ten days, he received $25. Usually the settler had only a portion of that sum or none of it, so he got his home "on tick" or "on pump," meaning, in sandhill parlance, he charged it. Most of the settlers paid eventually, often in rye or corn they grew from seed that also came "on tick" from the locator.

And every so often a well-meaning meddler would warn Mother that sooner or later, when the Government vigilance was lowered, the cattlemen would strike. Many homeseekers, too, were discouraged by tales of starvation spread by ranchers or were frightened by the stories of this or that settler who was hauled out of the hills by his widow after a sad "accident." But nothing really alarming had happened—probably nothing would.

Then, July 2, 1908, a young school teacher, new in the community, tore madly into our yard. His face was paper white and his day-old beard was like a black smudge along his chin. Mother ran to meet him, her hands under her apron, her face anxious.

"Emile's been shot!" he shouted.

Mother's hands dropped heavily to her sides.

"How?"

"While he was branding his calves in the corral, before the whole family.* Ralph Nieman, the damned skunk, rode up, shot him in the back, and then rode away!"

Weakly, Mother dropped to the woodblock in the front yard. So it had come! Father's brother, who never located a settler, who was, in fact, rather friendly to the small cattlemen about him. He lived only five miles away, on Pine Creek, with his wife and seven children.

And Father was locating in the hills, had been gone for three days!

All evening our barbed-wire telephone line was busy. The sheriff had been down; had the murderer. He didn't have him; he hadn't

* Later reports: he was milking a cow, the boys holding the calf off.

even gone out. The man had shot himself; no, he had shot someone else. By the next noon the situation was clarified. The sheriff had not sought the murderer until the next morning. Community feeling ran high; the young teacher talked of mobbing, of searching the upper ranch, located in a wet hay flat full of willows. Without able leadership the plan collapsed. They waited for Father, who had once been the leader of a vigilante-like group. But he was in the hills, in that land of endless dun-colored hills where chops and blowouts follow each other like waves of a wind-whipped sea. Across the road camped two groups of homeseekers, apparently not understanding the situation.

A day passed. Uncle Emile was still alive with a bullet in his lungs. Two days—three. Uncle Emile was dead. The settlers' wagons creaked away across the river. And still there were no signs of Father. A reward was offered for the murderer, who, some said, was surely across the border, north or south, by now. Or perhaps in the deeper hills. Maybe he would sneak up to a hilltop as hunters once did for deer and antelope, bareheaded, looking from behind a soapweed, only it would be a man he was stalking, a man in the valley, sighting through his compass, his back to the killer.

And then Father came home.

With my baby sister astride my hip I ran to tell him. He knew. Above the dark beard his face, commonly so ruddy from wind and sun, was greenish yellow. I dropped behind my mother, afraid.

The funeral was that afternoon.

"You ought to go," Mother reasoned. "What will people say?"

But Father didn't go. He lay on the couch under the window, watching the neighbors drive past, his rifle within reach. On their way back, several of them stopped, wondering, generally considering Father's caution wise. An associate of the murderer's, not debonair, handsome, as the killer, but stocky and red-faced, with whitish pig eyes, stood at the outskirts of the crowd a while; and then rode away. It was whispered that he was looking for the locator, also that Uncle Emile was killed because he gossiped, knew too much and told too much about the ranchers. I ran into the garden. Was there anything about them that Father didn't know?

That evening, while Mother was doing the chores and Father inspected the orchard, using his rifle as a cane, I nailed the three windows in their bedroom down with ten-penny nails. The house door had no lock, but I drove a spike diagonally into the casing and then worked it out with pinchers, leaving a hole ready for noiseless in-

sertion after everyone was asleep. Young Jules was told of my activities.

"I'll rip his belly open with my toadsticker!" he promised, flourish-
ing his one-bladed knife.

"I'll — I'll —" But I could not say that my tactics were aggressive.

That evening our father was careful not to sit between the lamp
and the unblinded window while he ate his supper. He found no
relish in the accumulation of daily papers, no interest in the new
Geographic, and contrary to all precedents, he went to bed early.
Mother and I cleared away the dishes, but every crunching step outside brought our eyes fearfully together. A belated pig came grunt-
ing to the sill; the forgotten cat scratched against the door for her
milk; even Keno, the pup, was gone, and I visualized him in the last
convulsions of poisoning. Finally everyone was in bed.

When the house began to crackle as old frame houses do if one
lies awake to hear, I sneaked out with the spike gripped in my hand.
In my horror of being too late—of having the door pushed open in
my face—I couldn't find the hole, and the spike slipped from my stiff
fingers to the floor with a tremendous clatter.

"Jule!" our mother whispered to her spouse.

But Father was awake, whispering too. "Keep low, keep low," he
commanded her, "so I dare shoot."

I was petrified; my legs like posts. They thought I was the killer!
Should I let a probable prowler know my whereabouts? But the
scrape of my Father's rifle on the wall as he took it down decided me.
Closing my eyes and gritting my teeth I took a dive into the unknown,
expecting to stop lead either way.

"It's only me!"

No one kindly shot me. In utter disgrace I was packed off to bed
and ordered to stay there, "or you'll get a hell of a licking!" Father
threatened. Disgusted, I covered my head with the sheet and hoped
we would all be killed.

The next morning even Keno made an appearance. Mother hoed
under the trees near the house; the boys hung about, something very
unusual for them; I puttered away at the housework, trying not to
disturb Father lying on the lounge staring at the ceiling.

After dinner, while searching the cherry trees for ripening fruits,
I glimpsed a horsebacker coming up through the young orchard.
There was no road; only an occasional hunter from down the river
came that way. Hard upon my announcement of his coming, the
horseman trotted into the yard. It was the white-eyed man.

He swung from his saddle * and stopped, his right hand free over the revolver in his holster. Just then Father limped into the doorway, his rifle across his arm.

"How, Jule!" The man used the old settler's Indian greeting in a surly growl. If there was an answer to the greeting it escaped me. Under his shaggy brows, Father's eyes were sharp as gray gimlets, his palm caressing the grip of his rifle, his forefinger in the trigger guard. Behind him I could see Mother's blue dress and behind her the white faces of the boys.

"What you want?" Jules Sandoz asked the question always demanded of friend or foe.

"Just riding through—" The man's voice was insolent. "This is the road to Pine Creek, ain't it?" As if he had every right in our yard!

The two men's eyes held, riveted.

"Yah!" Father spat, at last. "And take it—get off the place, and get damn quick!"

Slowly the man turned his back, mounting his horse deliberately, heavily. He held the impatient animal still, looking down upon the locator in the doorway, his hand resting on the butt of his revolver. Silence hung between them like a poised rattler. Almost imperceptibly Father's finger tightened on the trigger, the knuckles of his hand whitening.

With a laugh that was more a snarl, the man threw back his head, baring his teeth like a dog's. He jerked the reins and loped out of our yard, up the hill, and out of sight.

"They don't catch me unprotected," Father commented, lowering his gun. I went to bed with a sick headache.

A few weeks later we heard that an officer at Roswell, New Mexico, contrived to room with a man he suspected was the killer wanted in the hills. To make certain he tried that antique dodge, an uneasy conscience, exhibiting all the signs of relentless remorse. When the stranger asked him what the trouble was, he said that he had killed a man in a fight.

"Hell, that's nothing! I killed one in cold blood and you don't see me losing sleep over it!"

It all seemed too absurd, even then. The murderer, however, was actually captured there, returned, tried, found guilty of manslaughter, and sentenced to ten years in prison. With good behavior reductions he was out on parole before the bereaved family had adjusted them-

* While talking this over with the family for Old Jules later, we remembered that the man stayed on his horse.

selves. Even so, the conviction was a definite homesteader victory. In the past these killers had trumped up some sort of case and escaped even temporary detainment.

And just when we settled back into some semblance of normalcy, Father announced that he had filed upon an additional three quarters, his lawful allotment, twenty-five miles away, over the rolling, terrible hills.

"You are crazy!" Mother lamented.

Not until we learned that a residence must be established did we children sense the full significance of the calamity. Father had put up a small shack and nailed the door shut to prevent the scum that rides the first wave of population into a new country from stealing everything movable. Early in September we set out for the shack. Due to the buckskins' temperamental behavior at gates or during Father's lapses into absent-mindedness, I was commandeered to go along, much to my discomfort. But audible objections were never in order from the Sandoz family, and so, with all the seriousness of an eleven-year-old with responsibilities, I gripped the lines; Father swung the whip; and the buckskins shot ahead. We were off, into the dreadful hills.

Heat, sand, lizards, and undulations that blended into a perfect similarity stretched endlessly before us. Even game was scarce. We saw few birds, no grays, no cattlemen, only one rattler, and that one escaped into a prairie-dog hole. We passed an occasional dugout, a little soddy, or an old claim shack, all dull gray and alone in russet or sandgrass valleys. Often we left the wagon trail, only two dim yellowish streaks over the darker tan or obliterated entirely by the light wind in the sand cuts, and struck across the hills. Toward noon the buckskins began to lag. First one singletree and then the other ground the wheel. Squinting under his cap at the sun, Father pulled up to a windmill, scattering a bunch of ruminating Herefords. The team was watered; we lunched from a tin cookie box; and then we went on. The hills grew higher; the valleys harder, resounding under the small hoofs. Soddies were more frequent, with here and there a long gray strip of late breaking, a few anaemic sunflowers pushing up between the sods.

About five o'clock we arrived at Pete's place, where a preliminary school meeting was in session. The half-soddy, half-frame house was filled with gaunt, sun-bronzed men and women. Several slightly gray girl-women, "Boston old maids" Father dubbed them, sat primly on improvised benches, squeezed in between women nursing babies

and men chewing tobacco. Few of the men carried guns, although
Pete, a second cousin, had a rifle hung on his wall. Someone told
about a celebration given at the Spade ranch, with everything free
for the settlers, including ice cream. Were the cattlemen following
the gray wolves into mythology?

The next morning we bumped over trackless bunchgrass knolls and
finally rattled down over a steep hill. In a high grassy valley, a tiny,
new pine shack leaned against the south slope—our homestead. The
buckskins snorted and fidgeted about approaching it.

"Hold 'em. I'll walk over," Father warned as he started to see if
anything had been disturbed. Before I had the nervous team quieted,
he came running back, bobbing grotesquely in his limp, his mouth
to the back of his hand.

"Bit by a rattlesnake under the house while I reached for the hammer!"

The words came in jerks between spittings of clear saliva. The hills
did a queer dance—bit by a rattlesnake—a rattlesnake! But Father
pushed his pocket knife into my hand and jerked it away before I
really could open it, and slashed at the large, purplish swelling about
two pin-pricks. The dull blade sank into the puffy flesh but did not
cut even the skin. With a groan he flung the knife from him and
sucked fiercely.

"I may drop dead any minute!"

His eyes turned habitually to his constant companions in danger—
his guns. He grasped the pump-gun.

"Hold that team!" he commanded. I gasped, but before I could
form a coherent thought, he slapped his palm down on the rim of
the hind wagon-wheel, laid the muzzle against the swelling, holding
the gun steady between his body and the wagon bed. A shot echoed
up and down the hills. The buckskins plunged ahead. I fell off the
seat but clung to the lines. Bracing my feet against the dashboard,
I pulled and jerked until the ponies slowed to a short lope, to a trot.
When I finally turned them, Father was limping toward me. Black,
clotty blood dripped from the back of his hand where the swelling
had been. I tied the lines about my waist, ripped the blue shirt sleeve,
and made a handkerchief tourniquet just below the shoulder. Then,
gray-faced, Father lay down in the wagon bed.

"Drive for Pete's and drive like hell!"

Too terrified to ask the direction, I swung the whip over the
ponies, letting them take their heads. They sprang out; my sunbonnet flew off; the board seat went next as we bounced over the

bumpy knobs. I dared not look at the man in the wagon. I was afraid.

Foam from the ponies' mouths hit cold against my cheek. With my feet far apart, I hung to the lines as we tore at breakneck speed down a long hill and across a valley. It all seemed so strange, unreal. Surely this was not the way we came an hour ago, perhaps only fifteen minutes ago? We must be lost. And just when I was sure that we were, I saw the place. Pete came running out to stop what he considered just another runaway.

With his wife he helped Father into the house and then he ran to saddle a horse and ride to John Strasburger's homestead for whisky. I knew he was aggressively temperance; he would never have any. Even if he did, I had heard of a sheepherder who died from snake bite while dead drunk. By the time that Pete came back, brandishing a tall bottle about a quarter full, Father's arm was purple to the shoulder. He gulped the brown liquid.

"It's not enough," he mumbled hopelessly, and sank back.

Pete ran to hitch his team to the top buggy. I held the horses while he went to fetch Father, staggering, but not drunk. "Don't let them run away," he warned as the buggy sagged under his weight. I thought he meant the buckskins. Hold horses, hold horses! Would I really have to drive home alone? They would run away; the gates were too hard to open; I could never find the way. . . .

Pete cut my introspections short by swinging me into the buggy bed at his feet. We shot through the yard gate and were on our way home. After four or five miles of sand the fiery team slowed, their lathered sides heaving. Father's face was sunken into his beard, his eyes closed. He swayed a little. I reached my arm around his knees and held on to the seat to keep him from sliding forward. Once he looked down upon me.

"Swelling's spreading into the lungs," he panted thickly. Pete whipped the jaded team into an unbelievably slow run.

"If he kills his team getting me home, tell Mama to pay for them," Father instructed me. I pulled my skirt up to my face and cried, slowly, hopelessly. "Your mama's a good woman," he went on, his breath wheezing. "And you'll get like her. Marry a farmer and help build up the country."

This unprecedented sentiment from our father disorganized any resistance I might have had. I must have wailed, for Pete cautioned me.

"Hush, you'll have to keep steady. We may need you to drive before this day is done."

Biting the gingham of my skirt—I'll always remember the taste of the cotton and the dye on my tongue—I calmed myself. After all, violence was a constant specter at our elbows. . . . But the sun burned my unshaded eyes. My head ached. And still the wheels spun yellow sand into my lap, my face. Father did not answer our inquiries any more. At two claim shacks we stopped. Only frightened faces rewarded us. No one had anything. At last we were in sight of the blue ribbon of the Niobrara. Pete whipped up the gaunt, lathered team and in one last spurt we were in our own yard.

"Ah, now, you let the horses run away!" Mother scolded as she ran out to meet us. But when she understood she sent me flying on cramped legs into the house for a cup of whisky, a big cup. Father shot it into his mouth. Before they had him in the house, I was on my way to Sears's, for of course our telephone was out of order! It was clear that I could make the mile trip in less time than Pete's horses, already down in their harness in the yard.

Dropping into a dog trot which previous emergencies had taught me I could hold for the mile, I finally lived to cover the infinite distance. And Bachelor Charley was an eternity answering my knock on the screen door.

Long after dark that night, as I lay abed in a coma from exhaustion, I was awakened by Young Jules shouting into my ear: "The doctor's come—in a red automobile!"

And so he had, but I didn't get to see the mechanical contrivance. A funny, short man pushed me back to my pillow, telling me I must be still. Father would pull through. But he might have been dead long before this from the deadly September venom if he hadn't shot it off.

Thus ended our plans to take up a new homestead that fall. In the winter Father changed his filing for a more promising one.

II

When the time for residence establishment on Father's homestead in the sandhills arrived, James, my second brother, and I were delegated to spend the summer and fall in the new shack. We were to live alone in the terrible hills with only a twenty-two rifle for protection. But I was glad. Perhaps the hills seemed a worthy antagonist. Perhaps I was already one with that strange land.

To Jules Sandoz, living alone like that was nothing, and we tried to imitate him. But when the buckskin team disappeared through the west pass toward our old home on the Niobrara twenty-five miles away, we looked at each other a little frightened. And in our ears rang Father's last command:

"Watch your fires, or you'll be burning the country out. Ranchers don't plow the guards like they used to. Remember those kids that burned in the Osborn—and look out."

We had nodded soberly, appreciating the danger. Our homestead was cut by the old dividing line between the Spade and the Spring-lake ranches. North of our frame shack the line guards, two strips of plowing approximately eight or ten feet wide and sixteen feet apart, trailed over knolls and through draws. They were weedy, neglected. South of our little strip of breaking the reddening bunchgrass waved unbroken. We roamed about these knolls, hunting rabbits and young grouse for our frying pan, seeing almost no one, and losing our vigilance about fires.

Then one morning a vague, iridescent veil hung along the horizon— a prairie fire.

"But it's far away," I consoled James, and myself.

The veil changed to piling billows of sulphurous yellow. The southeast wind freshened. Three heavy wagons filled with men rattled past, the Springlake hay crew going to fight the fire. Now and then a horsebacker galloped over the hills. One stopped at our shack.

"You kids better stay clost to the breaking. Let the house and stuff burn. Lay face down on the plowing and you'll be all right."

So it was coming our way! The wind blew harder, trailing the pungent smoke in long, blue-black rolls over our heads. We tried to eat our dinner, but despite myself I kept talking about the three-month fire old-timers still recall. Only a heavy snowstorm had stopped that one. James, his blue eyes round, kept mentioning the two boys who had left their guard-protected sod house and ran into the swamp while their father and mother were away fighting the fire. They were burned to death in the tall rushes, only a mile north of our shack!

By two o'clock the smoke streamed along like a gray blanket just a few feet over our heads. We imagined red flames in the dark depths. Suddenly the strain of waiting was too much. We ran to the top of a hill, to another, and another. Only endless dunes and smoke. Even our little strip of breaking was lost.

While we stood, dumbfounded, a coyote tore past, not five feet away. Cattle bawled. We saw their flying feet below the smoke, heard the thunder of their hoofs. Now shouts cut the dull roar of wind and flames.

A gang plow broke from the smoke, almost upon us. A man was riding a horse in the lead, another was on the seat, hanging to the levers as the sod rolled out in ribbons. Behind them ran the "back-firers" scattering flames along the southeast side of the new guard. These little fires burned back into the wind very slowly, spreading along the guard and widening it materially. Singed men swung sacks and old chaps upon any backfire that got too vigorous. All worked frantically against time.

A curtain of flame shot up from the earth on a grassy knoll, crackling, leaping. The fire was upon us. We fled, as the cattle and the coyote had fled.

On a bare knoll we stopped, panting. The fire now was almost out. Cautiously we stole back to listen to the exploits of the day. Men were plodding wearily along the guard, beating out smoldering spots. Two groups closed in from the sides. They had tapered the fire and finally headed it, after contesting every step of the sixty miles between the starting spot near the railroad tracks and here. Then two women drove up with a cream can full of hot coffee. One of them, the music teacher, was vastly interested in the many settlers left homeless in that sixty mile strip. Grateful that the fire had been turned from her "Pleasant Home," she asked us who we were, and gave us cookies.

Thrillingly the memory of all this came back to me as I stood before the ruins of her old house and rubbed the velvety surface of the sign. I had almost forgotten the little woman, yet she had helped make the long months before Mother moved into the district less lonesome by sending me little notes and verses about the "purpled hills" and the "baptismal silences." And she had loaned me the novels of Conrad. How could I have forgotten that!

But she represented only one type of the strange folk we found in the sandhills. Coming from every corner and blind alley of the world, the settlers were sure to differ in their conception of a fitting mode of life and habitation. Some lived in their wagons or in the open, until the winter's early march forced them to dig into the ground. Hay from a rancher's meadow formed the roof of their dugouts and the pallets in the corners, and even filled the round barrel of the hay burners that smoked furiously and reddened the eyes. An occasional foreigner and his wife, refugees from a more bitter foe than cold or loneliness, lived content in a dugout for several years. Many an erratic bachelor, lacking the proddings of ambitious women folk, lived in the ground until a wandering range cow or his own horse fell unheralded into the dark and damp interior. Then there was the drifter who built himself a winter lodge of old rushes held together with barbed wire and posts pilfered from a rancher's hay corral. The penniless ate veal, stealthily but surely. And the cattlemen, suddenly "on the wrong side of the fence," could do nothing.

The music teacher, a little afraid of the rough-appearing men who rode past or stopped for a drink at her well, continued to live alone. Contrary to all predictions by the rougher women, she grew ruddy of skin; she liked the wind-ruffled grass about her door, the whistling curlew on a knoll, the yellow-breasted meadow lark singing his morning song on her plank pump, and the purples and yellows of the hills. The women who had sniffed at her ideas welcomed her when there was sickness or when a new baby came to a mother who needed coaxing to take up the weary burden once more.

Another kind of settler was the prosperous one who "shipped in" from Tulsa or Elmhill, or Cotter's Corners. Livery freighters planted dressers, incubators, cream separators, and rocking chairs on the bare prairie and went away. With the awkward breaking plow the man turned up smooth ribbons of gray earth in a low spot where the sod was densely rooted. With the help of the entire family a soddy was put up in two or three days. Plastered with gray mud from an alkali lake bed, it was cosy. Let the winter winds howl, the summer sun bake.

Different as these Kinkaiders were, we found them united by a common bond. Two of them, in fact. All these settlers wanted a railroad; held meetings, consumed enormous amounts of chewing tobacco, and went home optimistic. Nothing came of it. The other was, as most bonds are, a common need. Fuel. With no tree closer than the Niobrara River or the brush of the Snake, with little money and wretched roads over twenty to forty miles of sun-drenched or snow-glazed hills to the nearest railroad, wood and coal were out of the question. Cow-chips were the solution. Most of the settlers had lost all the qualms that curse the fastidious long before they reached the hills. Barehanded they took up the battle, braving rattlesnakes which, upon acquaintance, failed to live up to their reputation for aggressiveness. City women incased their still-white hands in huge gloves and, with a repugnance no extremity could completely erase, endured the first few weeks somehow. The music teacher wore gloves to the very last.

The first winter always brought the most squeamish to a proper appreciation of this cheap and practical solution to the heating problem.

We forgot that we could not saw down a tree if our fuel ran short in midwinter, and after only two months of moderately cold weather our house was so frigid that we wore old coats in the kitchen and the baby was swathed like an Eskimo. The winter was unusually open and warm, as some wag said everyone's first winter in a new country always is. The cattle that were to pay off the $1,700 mortgage coming due in the fall had survived fairly well on nothing except a bit of corn fodder and range. Now the faint green of spring was on the hills. The last day of April brought a warm rain; it turned to snow by night.

"Three foot of snow by morning," Father predicted, voicing a standing exaggeration joke of the hills, but one just a bit too near the truth for unadulterated humor. The next morning Mother tunneled out of the door with the fire shovel and followed the yard fence to the windmill, as invisible in the flying snow as if it were in the Antarctic instead of fifteen yards from the house. The wind screeched and howled. Mother didn't return. Had she taken the wrong fence from the tank, the one that led off into the pasture? Just when I was mustering the courage to awaken the family, she came back, white, snow-covered from head to foot, her eyelashes grizzled with ice.

"The cattle are gone!" she announced, exploding her bomb with characteristic abruptness. She had been to the shed and they had evidently drifted with the storm, to stumble into snowbanks, to chill into pneumonia, to smother, to freeze. With them went our home on the Niobrara, our start in cattle in the hills, even our team, successors to the buckskins, mortgaged for the interest.

That May Day was a gloomy one. We foraged along the fence, tearing out alternate posts to chop up on the kitchen floor with the hatchet. No one was permitted out of the door without being tied to a rope. The lamp burned all day.

The next morning, long before daylight, Mother awakened Young Jules and me. The wind was dead; the stars were out; and the shed was empty of everything except Blackie and Brownie, nickering for feed. They were saddle-broken and on them we were to trace our cattle, dig out and save what we could. After gulping a hot breakfast we were bundled into most of the clothing the family possessed. Mother wrapped an endless fascinator about my tender head. Climbing upon the old horses, we set out, equipped with a spade and a hammer.

Daylight stalked cold and gray over the knolls as we crunched into the frozen snow. About two hundred yards from the house we found a cow, up to her neck in a drift, her eyes already white—mad. Mother waved us on. She would salvage that one. From the top of a wind-cleared knoll, we looked across the valley, lightening into a pure sheet of white. Not quite pure, for here and there were dark heads, moving or still, along the dim snow trail. With true horse sense, Brownie smelled out the drifts that held her up. If she or Blackie broke through into the bottomless drifts, there was nothing to do but scoop a path to a knoll or another crusted drift. The first few "critters" we reached were range cattle—Herefords, evidently from the Spring-lake herd that had drifted past our shed and tolled our cows away.

By the time we were on the hill half a mile from home, the sun shimmered on the endless field of spotless white. Mother had dug the cow out; her blackish hulk lay free in the glare. Over the ridge of hills toward the south the trail was blown clearer; here and there a track was visible, the crusted snow carved into fantastic sculpture or trail-ing white behind the soapweeds. We found several range cows, thin and exhausted, lying flat, and one of our calves, only his starred fore-head out of a drift, dead.

The sun began to burn our faces. Perspiration, aroused by the shoveling, chilled us when we stopped on a hilltop to plan. There must be a trail for the return of whatever we might save.

The Strasburger homestead was scarcely discernible, house and barn little more than hummocks of snow. At least three hours gone to travel a mile and a half! In the next valley we found one of our cows up to her neck in snow and "on the prod" as the sandhiller would say. We dug her out, changing off on the spade and keeping a sharp eye out for the long horns. The snow was softening. We were wet to our hips. And when the cow was free and could stumble about a little on her frost-numbed legs, she rushed headlong at Jules and was stuck again. In disgust we left her and rode on.

The next one we found was dead. And still we climbed on and off our horses, digging, sweating, our feet clumpy and wooden with cold. Noon came. My face burned; my lips were blistering in the unpro-tecting fascinator. I wished vaguely for the smoked glasses at home in Mother's trunk. Jules, more protected by natural skin tone and a huge cap, was hungry. But there was little time for physical discom-forts. A neighbor who was digging out a saddle horse caught in a draw shouted to us.

"You kids better get for home!" He said more but it was lost in the snow echo. We couldn't stop. Cattle that stayed in the snow much longer would be hopelessly chilled, probably be dead by morning. So we whipped the tired, sore-kneed horses on; threw snow left and right when the need arose. Our shoulders were numb now. They had ceased aching long ago.

About four o'clock, in a choppy range, we found the cattle. First three head, then five, other small bunches, jammed together by high drifts, unable to move. They bawled as we approached. At last, about six o'clock, we had them all free and had lost only the two cows along the way and the dead calf. The animals were gaunt; their skins jerked like palsied hands from cold, but they could walk, which was more than most of the range cattle could do.

Slowly we started homeward, not daring to push the cows for fear of their plunging into drifts or slipping and being unable to rise. I carried a new little calf, still damp and curly, across my saddle. Thanks to our day of pain, the trip home was short. Darkness came on gradually and there was joy in our yard when the bawling string trailed, single file, up to the shed. But we were beyond praise. We literally fell from our horses and were taken into the house with a solicitude entirely new to us. My head ached; we were starved, chilled; and the house was dark.

"Why don't you light the lamp?" I demanded.

Mother made a funny, gurgling noise. "Ah-h," her voice choked. "The lamp is lit. You are blind!"

Before morning I was delirious with pain and sunburn fever. Scorching pinwheels whirled in my head. Father gave me a small dose of morphine to quiet my screams, and when that wore off, another. But he dared not give me any more. My eyes burned like seething, bubbling lead. My head seemed tremendously large, bursting. My face itched. I tore at my skin, so burned that it peeled off in strips like tissue paper. I could not eat nor sleep. And when the pain began to die down into a dull, monotonous ache, I, who was never still without a book, was a most impossible patient. The few people who found time to come in suggested all sorts of neglected precautions. I should have worn a black veil or smudged my cheekbones with soot. They talked of crippling cattle losses. Whole herds scattered like ours had died because they became chilled. One rancher lost over two hundred head piled into draws and smothered. Another lost five hundred head of stock in one lake. We, evidently, were fortunate.

At last I could find my way about to peel potatoes, carry water from the well, and do odd jobs about the house. The slightest infiltration of light under my bandage maddened me with pain. And when I finally took my bandage off, I found I could aim a gun without closing my left eye. It was blind.

The settlers suffered little from the late blizzard. Few of them had the money to stock their sections; they leased their land to the ranchers. Father tried to get them to farm. He argued that where sunflowers grow man-high, corn will also grow; that land which grows well-rooted sod only five to fifteen feet above ground-water with no intervening rock strata will grow alfalfa; that the northern slopes covered with chokecherries and wild plum thickets would grow tame fruit. Rye and corn proved reasonably successful. Crops brought better homes, more space, deep window seats with red geraniums, and perhaps tinted walls to suit the fancy of the girls becoming educated through the mail order catalogues, the Kinkaiders' "bible." But the homes like music boxes remained as they were, for the $100 annual rent permitted no luxuries.

Prosperity, unless it becomes too great, brings neighborliness. Where once each little shack curled pungent blue smoke from its stovepipe, now wagons, buggies, and saddle horses were grouped about a home on Sundays for a community dinner. Pure democracy excluded only the fat old widows who were afraid of horses and could not "hoof it." The music teacher was always remembered by someone who "could just as well swing 'round that way."

Out of the growing prosperity came the cattlemen's decision that these people actually intended to stay. No one seemed to starve. Father had a fifty-acre field of Turkistan alfalfa, and his orchard was doggedly growing in the white sand. The rising price of grass-fed stock on the Omaha market brought an offer for a good hay flat here and there. The offers became general. Kinkaiders who had never seen so much money before took their thousand dollars and wrote glowing letters to us. The grass grew wonderfully green in Cotter's Corners or in Hutton's Bottoms. Here and there a music box stood empty, the ruffly curtains gone, the owner glad, for the moment, that she was no longer compelled to live by herself. But our music teacher was loyal. With an old organ bought at Rushville, she gave music lessons. Her house should not be moved to a ranch for a tool shed! Boldly Father withstood the buyer when he came with an offer remarkably generous then, but not so generous now when I can appreciate the significance of his experiments. Yet our hearts beat just a little faster at the wonderful stories the letters told.

Then came the Bad Winter; unrivaled, old-timers told us, by any ever seen in the hills. On Election Day the first white flakes began to fall, fell every day until Thanksgiving, until Christmas. Disappointed children were told that Santa Claus was snowbound, but that Easter would be green and lovely and perhaps the Easter rabbit. . . . By Easter there was desperation in many homes. The usual January thaw, with frozen roads for coal hauling, did not materialize. Old hay burners were dug up and smoked the tinted walls, the oatmeal paper. Starving cattle bawled and then were still. No horse could plow far through the valleys. Illness, caused by long confinement, restricted diet, and discouragement over mortgaged cattle dying, was present in almost every home.

The first week in May brought the sun and summer winds. Snow water filled the valleys and the cellars, drowning out the alfalfa. This was the buyer's opportune moment. The music teacher, weak from a severe cold, was one of the first to sell. The shrewder, the more courageous, sensed the promise of the latent hills and mortgaged their claims to buy out their neighbors. Sod walls gaped open to the sun, making good rubbing places for the cattle, lousy from lowered vitality. But we scarcely noticed the Kinkaiders go, so busy were we with the extra work of Father's new orchard. To us it was not a general movement, an exodus; only the Wests, the Tuckers, and the Wyants went. I missed them, especially the music teacher. I missed her books. She had cried, just a little, the day she went away.

"But it's four miles to the Zimmers'—and six to the next neighbor's—and I—" she choked a sob into a fine old lace handkerchief. "It's no use—I'm afraid of dying alone."

Quickly she put her arms about my shoulders, kissed my unaccustomed cheek, and then climbed into the mail wagon.

The years piled up and I went away too, and now, after ten years of absence, there are only the weeds and the stove. As the mail truck moved on, we passed old cylinder holes, almost filled, often with a piece of galvanized pipe still sticking up. All that is left of an optimistic venture. Long grayish streaks, grassed over, show where corn, rye, and alfalfa once grew and will grow again. For there is Father's orchard, the most talked-about spot in the State, to show the skeptic what can be done.

And there are the prosperous ones who stayed, ranchers now, their range deeded, safe from homesteaders and fence-cutting troops. Where once each valley held its own peculiar little home, now ten, fifteen miles reveal nothing except fat cattle, windmills, and haystack-dotted meadows. There are few fences and the truck does not stop for these, bumping over pipe and cement contraptions called "corduroy bridges." Families who started twenty years ago in dugouts today have huge homes of fifteen rooms, high-powered family cars,

Fords for hack driving, and radios. Sons and daughters are home from college, or abroad for the summer. Their parents can choose between Florida and California for wintering. The terrors of stalking man and beast, of cold and of loneliness, are gone—for those who stayed. Who can say how those who are gone have fared?

Each year finds the old home sites more nearly obliterated. The next storm will tear down from the rusty nail the little teacher's sign with its brave legend. It will fall into the sand and become a part of the hills, as will also the memory of the dear woman who so carefully lettered it, wherever she may be.

II

Musky

This piece, which develops an episode mentioned in "The Kinkaider Comes and Goes," was written three years later, in 1932. It first appeared in *Nature*, November 1933.

WHEN FATHER drove his buckskin ponies out of the valley and left us alone on his new homestead, twenty-five miles from the rest, I kicked a loose sod as nonchalantly as I could. My brother James spit into the dust. Father was a frontiersman, a locator and trapper. Staying alone in the wilderness of sandhills and rattlesnakes meant nothing to him. But I was only thirteen, James younger. Before Father was out of sight we ran to the shack for the twenty-two rifle and climbed to the top of the south hill to look around.

During the hot days of August we saw scarcely a cowboy. Mostly just meadow larks, grouse, perhaps a dun coyote against the morning hillside. There were no near neighbors, so we spent our time hunting in the hills and the drying swamp of the valley over the hill north, or watering the few scrawny cabbages in the lower corner of the ragged breaking about our shack. Now and then we saw a rattlesnake under a tilted sod, found coiling tracks about our shallow-dug well, or caught the faint smell of dead things that clings to the haunts of the diamondback. I knew about rattlers. I had been in the hills once before, alone with Father, the time he was struck on the back of the hand by one. I still dreamed about that day, especially here in the pitch-piny shack with holes for windows and the door, sleeping on the ground, in the center of the breaking.

One night I awoke in a cold sweat, the blood pounding in my ears. Something scaly and cold moved slowly across my neck. I had to let it, and every moment I expected the punctures of fangs from a flat, arrow-shaped head.

I listened. There was not a sound. Even James, rolled in a blanket a few feet away, seemed not to breathe, as though already dead. And somewhere in the dark was the cold body, the poised head. The blackness of the room began to shimmer in fiery spots, pressing down, choking me. At last I had to breathe, and with the sound of a rip-saw through the stillness. There was no movement anywhere. Nothing except the faint smell of dead things.

Two feet away was the lantern, and matches, and along my arm lay the warm barrel of the rifle. But these things were as nothing—for somewhere, near my face, near my eyes, perhaps, was the cold scaly body of a snake. A move and there would be a whirr, a strike. Suddenly the darkness went spotty again. I was already bitten. My arm was numb, cold. It was spreading.

Then something cold touched my cheek, not piercingly, as with poisoned needles, but daintily, as the lick of a black tongue.

From there on I don't remember much, except that I lay tense and unmoving for as long as it took to build up all the layers of the earth under me. Gradually I became conscious of someone whispering.

"Mari, Mari—" very softly.

It was James, but I dared not answer. For the thing that had touched me had not moved away. When my brother's whispers veered from fright to horror, I answered, out of the far corner of my mouth. So we lay, listening, our eardrums almost splitting. But there was nothing to hear except the faint sound of quarreling water birds in the swamp, the occasional deep call of the thunder-pumper, the sudden sharp howl of a coyote on the knoll. At that there was a faint swishing sound at my ear and then nothing more.

Daylight came at last and the familiar things took form—the stove, the homemade table, the bench, finally the ridges in the dirt floor and James' drawn, frightened face. Cautiously I lifted my blanket. Nothing. But there, between us, were many tracks as of a finger drawn back and forth in graceful curves on the rough ground.

We slipped into our shoes and before dressing looked about the shack, even upsetting the cowchips from the fuel box. At last we settled down to breakfast.

Suddenly James made the queerest noise, dropped his fork, and ran to the corner where our old broom stood. A black, flattish tail and a brown, furry bunch showed on one side of it and on the other side a bit of dark nose and whiskers. James jerked the broom away. Cowering in the corner was a muskrat, two-thirds grown, pulled together in a shaking lump of frightened brown fur. So that was the cold tail that trailed over my neck; his whiskers, not a snake's tongue, had touched my cheek. We leaned against each other in foolish relief and laughed until the little fellow scurried away under the wall, where he had probably been all the time we were looking for him. But he was soon back behind the broom.

By dinner time we had Musky, as we called him, eating before us, nibbling with his bright yellow teeth at the thick roots we dug for him in the swamp. When we spoke to him he stood up tall and sniffed but returned to his food.

By evening we had put up a sod pen about three feet high, with the top link of our stove-pipe, which kept blowing off anyway, buried in the ground for a burrow and a nest from a rat house in the swamp in the far end. We built a little pond lined with alkali mud and fringed it with rushes, cattails, and arrow-heads. But Musky ran back and forth, trying to get out.

"Let's let him go," I suggested, half-heartedly, because our backs ached and our hands were blistered.

About dark he let James push him into the stove-pipe with the spade handle, but only a little way. After all, we couldn't tamp him into his hole as you would soil about a post.

Before we rolled up in our blankets we took the lantern out but couldn't find Musky. The next morning he was gone; nothing left of him but a hole between the sods. We were suddenly very lonely and a little angry too at his lack of appreciation. James walked through the browning marsh grass to our dried water-hole, calling, "Musky, Musky." I fried pancakes.

And then while we ate he came out from behind the broom. Our enthusiastic reception frightened him into a lope through the doorway but we headed him and drove him back into the house. Once more he settled behind the broom, his bright eyes watching. After an hour or two of apparent neglect he sallied forth to smell the bit of pancake we dropped for him.

Musky was curious and liked to explore the legs of the table, the stove, the chip-box, standing up and reaching as high as he could with his queer handlike forefeet. Once he stuck his nose against the hot ash-pan I lifted from the stove. He gave a sharp little squeak and loped away to his broom, wriggling his nose. There he rubbed it with his paw and looked at me from hurt eyes. The next morning he was gone.

"You went and let him burn himself!" James complained.

"Aw—can't he learn to keep out of the way?" I demanded in sisterly resentment. But I spent several hours searching for tracks like the insertion on my Sunday petticoat, a strip of graceful curving like ribbon in the center. That was his tail. The regular, dainty little spots on each side were the tracks of his feet. But the wind had rippled the surface of the sandpass leading to the swamp. I gave it up and went home to put the shack in order. We were expecting Father. James took the twenty-two and went out alone, pretending to look for game.

And then all at once Musky was in the doorway, wrinkling his nose in the air. Satisfied that he was welcome, he slid in and plodded to his corner. He was round as a ball, his sides sticking out like a bloated cow's. For the first time he let me pick him up. He even snuggled down in my arms and went to sleep. There was a scabby place on his shoulder, with a little dried pus, probably an old battle wound. From this came that dead smell I caught the night he trailed his tail over my neck and pushed his whiskers gently in my face. I sopped the scab with a solution of carbolic acid and let him sleep curled up in the corner.

That evening Father came, with Jule, our eldest brother. We tried to coax Musky out to nibble crumbs but he was shy and aloof. Probably not hungry. Anyway he took one look at the newcomers and scurried to the door.

"Head him off!" Father ordered, but Musky slipped between my awkward feet.

"Oh, now you let him get away. His hide is green yet but he'd bring fifteen, twenty cents."

James and I looked at each other. Of course our trapper father would look at it like that. Jule took the lantern out but came back alone.

"We'll set a trap for him. He may come back," Father said over his pipe.

There wasn't much we could do. Remonstrances were out of order in our family, but a little subterfuge was not. When the rest were in bed I slipped out and listened. It was September, chilly, and the rattlesnakes were holed up for the night. So I slipped through the breaking. Down at the lower edge of the garden plot I heard a soft gnawing that stopped every time I moved. Probably Musky in the cabbages. I sat down and called softly. The noise stopped completely and after a long time I felt something like fluff along my stocking and a cold nose against my hand. He let me carry him to the house and put him into an empty nail keg. There he was, a round, brown ball, when I crossed the frosty yard the first thing the next morning.

By the next evening we got permission to snap the number one steel trap set along the door. Father decided he might as well wait until the fur was prime.

That day he tacked in the windows and hung the door. Jule tried to make friends with Musky but the little chap's affections couldn't be forced. When our impatient brother tried to make him nibble at a root as he did for us, Musky bared his yellow teeth and snapped them on Jule's finger. He almost died for his daring. James rescued him and ran away, the frightened little head buried under his arm. When we were alone again he learned to trust us almost as before. He still slept behind the broom and foraged about the room at night, his long digger nails making a loud noise on our new floor. On cold nights he snuggled in at James' feet. Sometimes he tried trailing along when we went hunting but he couldn't understand this climbing the towering sandhills and after the first pitch he usually gave up and plodded back to the cabbages and the sod corn or waited outside the door until we came to open it.

Musky made few noises with his mouth. Once or twice when I stepped too close to him he gave the funny cry of the day he sniffed the hot ash-pan. And once when a coyote howled daringly close to the house he cried like that outside the door and scratched frantically until we let him in to be safe in our companionship.

He was less and less interested in the roots we brought from the swamp, preferring to chew on the loose nubbins from our corn fodder or on a bit of cabbage. Snow fell. Musky's fur got thick and close and grayer, but still a little shaggy, not glossy as that of his kind in the cold swamp. He got fatter and softer, too, and when Mother came down with the household goods and the babies she found him in the cowchip box behind the stove.

"Out you go!" she commanded. "No, I won't have animals like that in my house. Couldn't you catch a badger or maybe a skunk or two?" She chased Musky out into the dark with the old broom that had sheltered him so often. It was sad.

But the next day we found that he had made a nest behind an anchor post of the windmill set up on the new well that took the place of the old spade-dug hole, now covered with a few boards and hay so the children wouldn't fall into it. Musky seldom came to the house after that but he got his cabbage hearts and corn, and he drank at the chicken trough. And often I was scolded for spending my time scratching his jolly soft sides and pulling his fat cheeks when I should have been minding babies. Sadly I gave up my free ways of the last few months. My *Wanderjahr* was over.

But James was loyal and even Jule fed Musky now and then. Father scratched his beard and laughed as he told us, prophetically, how much he would get for the hide.

When winter was upon us we carried home sacks of hay and, with manure over it to generate heat, made a house for Musky. He trotted out to the chicken coop to eat and drink and, while the rooster was suspicious, the hens ignored him. But somehow he seemed a little neglected and sad now. I hoped he would make the break and run away, not to the north swamp, however, for Father was chopping into the freezing rat houses and setting traps.

Then one day as I poured steaming water into the frozen chicken trough, Musky didn't come. I hadn't noticed him for several days. Neither had the boys.

"Now you let him get away," Father said, but even he didn't seem to be so very sorry.

The winter was cold but short and February brought a fine thaw with snow-water running. It washed away the hay from the old well and Mother decided it must be filled. Something floated about on the surface. We dipped a bucket under it. Musky. The call to water had become too strong for him.

His hair was slipping and so we buried him in the dead cabbage patch. James almost cried for this foolish little Musky who deserted his fine swamp and his gay fellows for a corner behind the old broom, some cabbage hearts, and two stupid children. And I didn't share James' boyish fear of shedding honest tears.

III

The Son

In regard to the origin of my social consciousness, the members of my father's family were followers of Pedro Waldo in his pre-Reformation rebellion against the tyranny and corruption of the church. When the executions and recantations began, our family fled from Lombardy to France, and when the religious persecutions became too intense there, they crossed over into Switzerland, where a branch of our family participated actively in the progressive legislation that made Switzerland, at the end of the nineteenth century, a model for new nations.

The members of my mother's family were from the Canton of Schwyz and took an active role in the formation of the original confederation of Uri, Schwyz, and Unterwalden in 1291, from which emerged the Confederation of Switzerland.

My own liberalism came from this fertile past as well as from a childhood of living in the midst of poverty. A continual caravan of the world's disinherited passed by our house in quest of free lands which my father helped them to find. Among them there was also the constant recognition of the exploitation of the Western states by the loan-bankers of the East. All of this we heard talked about in our childhood as well as the history of rapacious empires—of the expansion of Rome to all Europe, the expansion of Spain in the New World, the expansion of England all over the globe—and the expansion of the United States, which already at that time resembled England in its use of military power and financial capital.

Thus, having at an early age become aware of the long struggle to obtain and defend a small and decent portion of individual liberty, and of the recent pressures against this liberty—as society became more and more complex—the development of my social consciousness was logically inevitable. Moreover, there was another determining factor in my childhood: the daily presence of an expropriated race, the American Indian. I was attracted to them very much, as children are always attracted by men of grand bearing, graciousness, and wisdom. One of the greatest of these, old He Dog, brother chieftain of the great Crazy Horse, called me his granddaughter until he died around 1937. From him and others like him, I developed a feeling of the brotherhood with all the things on earth which is the essence of the ancient philosophy of the Sioux, and the foundation of the deep sense of responsibility which each Sioux feels for each member of his community (63).

. . . My two Indian books, a biography of the Sioux war leader, Crazy Horse, and one on the Cheyennes, involved, along with the research, much renewed contact with the Indians. As recently as the fall of 1949 I went to live on the Cheyenne Reservation at Lame Deer, Montana. More and more I have become convinced that the American Indian as I knew him had much to teach us about rearing the young to live free, useful, and happy lives. And they did it under what seems to me much more difficult circumstances than ours (62).

ONE MORNING the summer I was eight a small playmate from the Indian camp across the road came to tap shyly at our kitchen door, motioning to me.

"Ahh! I have a brother too now!" she whispered, her dark eyes on the baby astride of my hip. "He is just born. Come see!"

I pushed the oatmeal to the back of the stove and hurried out as fast as I could, holding my brother close as I ran. He laughed and shouted, bobbing heavily on my hip, already so big that we seemed like some wobbling, double-headed creature. But I slowed up at the smoky old canvas tipi, shy too, now, as I looked into the dusky interior where an Indian woman bent over the new baby on her lap.

At the noise of our excitement, the tiny red-brown face began to pucker up tighter. But the mother caught the little nose gently between her thumb and forefinger, and with her palm over the mouth, stopped the cry soundlessly. When the baby began to twist for breath she let go a little, but only a little, and at the first sign of another cry, she shut the air off again, crooning a soft little song to the child as she did this, a Cheyenne growing song to make the son straight-limbed, and strong of body and of heart.

I watched the mother enviously. Although our baby was a year old and able to run if I had the time to play with him, he rode my hip most of his waking hours, except when he was fed or when our mother was home from the field or the orchard and could sit down a moment. Otherwise he howled, and our father was not the man to tolerate a crying baby.

I already knew why none of my small Indian friends made more than a whimper at the greatest hurt. An old grandmother had told me that Indian mothers always shut off the first cry of the new-born, and as often after that as necessary to teach this first, this greatest lesson out of the old Indian life: No one can be permitted to endanger the people; no cry must guide a skulking enemy to the village or spoil a hunt that might mean the winter's meat for a whole tribe.

But I knew too that never, in the natural events of this small boy's life, would he be touched by a punishing hand. Somehow he would be made equal to the demands of his expanding world without any physical restriction beyond the confines of the cradleboard, and no physical punishment. I remember the stern, distant faces of the Sioux when, in the swift heat of his temper, our father whipped us. These Indians still consider the whites a brutal people who treat their children like enemies—playthings, too, coddling them like pampered pets or fragile toys, but underneath always like enemies, enemies that must be restrained, bribed, spied upon, and punished. They believe that children so treated will grow up as dependent and immature as pets and toys, and as angry and dangerous as enemies within the family circle, to be appeased and fought. They point to the increasing lawlessness and violence of our young people, so often against their elders, a thing unheard of among these Indians.

Our brown-skinned neighbors had a traditional set of precautions against such immaturities and resentments. They tried to avoid any overprotection of the young, particularly the mother's favoritism for the eldest son as we saw it all around us, a favoritism that aroused our own father's anger, and not assuaged by our mother's long practice of hurrying the first-born son away from any punishment. Even so it was better in our home than in most because our father took his sons hunting, trapping, and on surveying trips. He let them have guns and traps almost from infancy, showed them how to use these well and safely. He let the eldest drive the wild team while he sat on the seat beside him and talked of the early days as to another adult.

Yet even so there was enough anger between the father and his first-born son to drive the boy away to his uncle at fourteen, not to return for four years, and then as a towering, laughing young man who could make light of his mother's coddling anxieties and his father's resentments.

Our Indian friends, out of their long years in the close confines of skin lodges, winter and summer, understood these natural conflicts. A continent people, they usually spaced their children so no woman was encumbered with more than one child too small to run if they must flee from an enemy or a buffalo stampede. Yet a prolonged infancy was recognized as fatal to a proper maturing and a good orientation into the life of the community, particularly for the eldest son, who was derisively called "the little husband" if he tagged at his mother's moccasins. The Indians understood the resentment that could grow up in the most tolerant, fortitudinous man if he saw his wife's affection and attention turned to his son, and they appreciated too a badly reared boy's jealousy of his mother.

So, by custom, the eldest son was provided with a second father, usually a man with a warmhearted wife at whose fireside the boy would spend a great deal of time and whom he could treat with less formality than his own mother. The second father selected for the boy born across the road from our house was an uncle, and the man's white teeth flashed in the sunshine with as much happy pride as the actual father. If later the boy should show some special bent, he might select still another man, one fitted to guide these new interests. Once it was perhaps a fine warrior, a hunter, arrowmaker, holy man, or an artist and band historian. Now it would perhaps be a good farmer, a cattleman, rodeo rider, mechanic, office worker, athlete, artist, engineer, or perhaps a doctor, from a long line of healers.

The young Indian's relationship to his mother-in-law was even more carefully circumscribed. Unless already an important chief, the new groom left his people for his wife's, sometimes to live within the close confines of the same skin lodge with the girl's mother, or a one-room reservation shack. To avoid the tensions and conflicts, respectful conduct required that both the husband and the mother-in-law address each other only through a third person, never directly. Even if they sat across the table from each other three times a day it was the ultimate in disrespect to let their eyes meet. I recall a gay, gregarious young Sioux who liked to visit with the family of his girl friend as much as he liked taking her to dances. But the marriage stopped his pleasant gossipy visits with her mother, until he maneuvered his new wife into a divorce. The next day he had returned to her mother's kitchen, chair tilted back, passing the time.

I have never known a case of mother-in-law trouble among the Cheyennes or even the Sioux, whose women are a little more assertive than some, perhaps because they recall the days, not so distant, when the lodge belonged to the woman and if her husband displeased her too much she might throw his regalia out into the village circle and all he could do was pick it up shamefacedly, and lug it to his mother's lodge.

My youngest brother was born with a hernia that might be aggravated by crying. At six weeks it was completely healed but the damage was done. He was rotten spoiled. I knew that an Indian mother would probably have controlled his crying without danger, considering the Indians' expert management of hernia, and so I looked with increasing envy from the boy on my hip to the new baby across the road, sleeping so quietly and sweetly in his cradleboard. With him handy at her elbow, the mother went about her work, perhaps beading moccasins or belts and bags for the white-man stores along the railroad. But the boy must be free to try his legs and to get his discipline in the natural way, through experience and from his peers, as he must be free to take his ideals and aspirations from the precepts and examples of his elders. So the dark-eyed little Indian was out of the cradleboard for long hours, lying contentedly on a blanket while the other children of the camp played around him and someone tended the little sweetgrass smudge to keep the flies and mosquitoes away.

Here the boy heard the shouts and laughing of the children, the talk of the camp, of the formal evening smoke, and the counciling. But he heard no quarrels. Repeated dissension within the village circle brought ostracism among both the Sioux and the Cheyennes, and only too much white-man whisky will make an Indian break this old, old taboo today. Nor would the new baby hear loud voices in his mother's dwelling, and as a good son he would never speak loudly or rudely in her presence. But early he would learn the power of chastising laughter, whether at the quiet fireside, on the playground, or against those in the highest position. Even great war leaders have bowed in humiliation before concerted public laughter.

When the Indian boy began to crawl no one would cry, "No, no!" and drag him back from the enticing red of the fire. Instead, his mother or anyone near would watch only that he did not burn up. "One must learn from the bite of the flame to let it alone," he would be told as he jerked his hand back, whimpering a little, and with tear-wet face brought his burnt finger to whoever was near for soothing. The boy's eyes would turn in anger not toward his mother or any grownup who might have frustrated his desire, but towards the pretty coals, the source of his pain. He would creep back another time, but slower, warily, and soon know where warmth became burning.

By the time he was six weeks old he had learned about water. "He must go into the river before he forgets the swimming," the mother told me, an ability she was certain was given to the young of all creatures alike: the pup, the colt, the buffalo calf, the child. The boy swam well before he could walk, and so it was safe to let him play around the placid river when they came visiting again the next summer. If he fell in he could paddle and grab at the grass of the bank. He had learned to walk stalking up and down on the belly of one or the other of his fathers, the man flat on his back, holding the boy up with his hands and laughing at the sturdy thrust of the young legs. He fell into cactus and rosebrush and learned to pull the thorns out or hobble to the other children for help.

I watched this year-old Indian boy who could look after himself as a puppy would, or a colt, and then upon the brother who still clung to my hip, two years old, and heavy as stone. I set him down and when he howled I whipped him until my hand stung, and every time that our parents were away I repeated this, until he learned to look around before he opened his mouth, grinning sheepishly at me if we were alone, and then impishly, good-natured. It was hoeing time, a busy time, and in two, three weeks he was well along to a cure, but there was a day or two when I had trouble sitting down.

The boy across the road was learning too that there are acceptable patterns of conduct and some that are not, perhaps from the long heroic tales told at every fireside, and from the example of his elders, but surely from the sting of laughter or another boy's fist in his face. Gradually he discovered how to avoid some of the laughing and blows, or to fend them off. One of his grandfathers had been a wrestler and was very useful in the fending. Mostly, however, the boy learned from those a few years older, as later he passed on what he knew. The Indians believed that discipline from those who are young too comes as from the earth, and is accepted as naturally as hunger and weariness and the bite of winter cold, without the resentment aroused by commands from grownups, from the big and the overpowering. True, the laughter, the rule of his peers was at times unjust. It was an unjust world in which the boy must live, a world where lightning strikes the good man as well as the bad, where sickness respects no virtue, and luck flits from this one to that as vagrantly as the spring butterfly. The realization that injustice exists and must be met with resistance where possible, tolerated where necessary, comes with less bitterness to the very young.

The boy from across the road learned about sex in the natural way too, early enough so the meaning came to him gradually as out of a misted morning, without morbid curiosity or shock. The Indians understood the pattern of development that the young male follows, whether colt, young buffalo, or boy. First the unsteady legs struggled after the mother, then the young were gradually drawn together, until the males began to show a preference for their own kind. So the pre-puberty Indian boys raced and hunted in troops, in gangs, explored and played war together. In the old days the fathers and the holy men watched these boys, planning the time for the puberty fastings and rites. The warrior societies looked them over for prospective recruits, as did the relatives of young girls, the girls before whom the boys would soon be showing off, as the young Indian does now around the dances, the little pole corrals where the wild reservation horses are ridden, or in sports. Remnants of the old-time warrior societies, with their stress upon courage, fortitude, a straight tongue, and responsibility for the peace and the protection of the people still survive. Some of these ideals are carrying over into the Indian version of such groups as the 4-H Clubs and the Boy Scouts. A young Cheyenne who wrote me from Korea that he spent his eighteenth birthday in a foxhole had some of his preparation from the last of the Dog Soldier society, whose duty was never to leave a position until the last straggler of the village was safely away, and thereby won themselves the reputation as the most stubborn and reckless fighters of the Plains.

Even with all the precautions, an occasional youth failed to make his way to complete maturity; perhaps through some early sickness or injury he never quite got away from his mother's moccasin tracks into manhood. He, like all members of Indian society somehow set apart, as the blind, the crippled, or those whose medicine dreams forbade killing, was looked upon as possessing some special gift for the preservation of the people. He was considered of special sensitivity, particularly outside of the realm of fact and reality, and so became an agency intriguer, as he once would have been a spy and a diviner of future encounters with the enemy, particularly for formal war parties going into battle. Sometimes a black hood to cover all the head was part of his diviner's regalia, designed to isolate him from all sight and sound, to complete his release from actuality.

Normally the young Indian's attitude toward girls was established early. "See how the boy is with the women of his lodge and you can know how the young man will be with your daughter—" was an old saying among the Cheyennes, where virtue in a woman was most highly prized. Overfamiliarity has been discouraged since the days in the skin lodges, when perhaps seven or more lived about a winter fire, the father in the place of honor at the back, the youths and boys to his left, the women and girls to the right, with an old woman at the lodge opening as keeper of the entrance, seeing all who came and went. Such close living demanded an iron paternal hand, unknown among these Indians, or a well-established pattern of conduct if there was to be order and peace all those confining months.

From about his seventh year a boy stopped addressing his sisters and his adopted sisters directly, speaking to them only through a third person, even in the persistent joking of the Sioux.

"Fat Boy seems to like watching the sun go down over our pigpen," I once heard a young Indian say, as though to the mouth harp he was pounding against his knee. His pretty sister did not reply but went about her supper preparations. She could not have defended her plumpish suitor any more than she would have noticed him those first few times that he stopped his old car as though only to smoke a cigarette with the men folks in the yard. "Our spotted colt will make a good one for the rodeos," she said. "He has already thrown the big rider of our family—" not looking at the skinned face of her brother, but laughing softly.

Something of even the stricter formalities has survived.

The Indian boy also sees the religion of his people all about him from the date of his birth. The older, more important men of his family probably still offer the first puff of the council pipe, the first bite of food each meal, to the sky, the earth, and the four great directions, which together are the Great Powers in whom every man, every creature, every rock and cloud and tree are united in brotherhood. In such a philosophy hatred can never be honestly harbored, not even hatred of an enemy. During the protracted if sporadic intertribal conflicts of the buffalo days, war prisoners sometimes became wives of head chiefs and returned to visit their people with their husbands. Captured men and boys too might be taken into the tribe. Sitting Bull's adopted brother was a war captive and honored all his lifetime by the Sioux. Imagine the alarm if our President adopted a young Communist war prisoner as his brother, brought him to live at the White House, had him at his elbow in all the councils of strategy as Sitting Bull did.

The Indians have added much of this concept and the rituals of the Great Powers to their notion of Christian beliefs and symbols, and with the peyote trances from the southwest, have formed the Native American Church, which, judged good or bad, is their own. But even those who joined the churches of the white man have clung to some of their basic beliefs. One Sunday morning, while camped along an agency trail, I went out for wash water from the creek. As I stooped to dip it up, I heard low Indian singing and the swish of water below me. A young Sioux knelt among the gray-green willows of the bank washing a blue shirt. He lifted it high from the water towards the sky and then dipped it towards the earth and all around, as the pipe and food are offered. Silently I slipped away, and a couple of hours later the young man came riding by, wearing the clean blue shirt. He raised his hand in greeting, palm out, in the old, old gesture of friendship, the left hand because it is nearest the heart and has shed no man's blood. He was on his way to Mass at the Mission, where his father and grandfather had joined when they came in from the buffalo ranges—going in a shirt offered in the old way to the Powers of the world, and the recognition of his brotherhood in them.

The realization of death too comes early and naturally to the young Sioux and Cheyenne. There was no demonology among these peoples, no evil being or spirit to be appeased or circumvented. If things did not go well it was not due to supernatural anger but because the people and their leaders were out of tune with the Great Powers. To discover what must be done men went to fast on high places, hoping for guidance in their dreaming, or endured mutilating humiliation of the flesh to bring a higher sensitivity to the spirit, a greater discernment and understanding and humility.

These Indians still do not take Satan and hell-fire very seriously, or the concept of an avenging God. The whole idea of building up fear is very alien to their philosophy, their ideal of personal discipline, their notion of the good life, and their conception of death. There was no fear of the dead and no uneasiness about them. The body of a warrior who fell in enemy country was rescued immediately if possible, or by a later party sent out with the skin sack painted red for the honorable return. Often relatives and friends went to sit at a burial scaffold, now the cemetery, as they would have gone to the fireside of the departed one. Children saw the sickness, the dying, the burial, and often went along to visit the burial place and listen to the story of the duties and responsibilities left behind. Sometimes there was a song or two, or a few ceremonial dance steps. Once, on my way home with a bundle of wood, I ran into an old Indian dancing gravely by himself on a little knoll. The man was a stranger but curiosity drew me closer and closer, and when he noticed me I started to run, guilty because I had spied on a grownup.

But the old Indian called me back with the one word, "Granddaughter—" Gravely, with pictures in the dust and his sign talk, which I understood very imperfectly, he told me the story of the old woman who lived in the moon that was just rising full out of the east. He showed me the burden of wood she had hurriedly gathered before the storm that always followed the moon's first waning. Then he talked of other things, why he had come here, where over fifty years ago a great man of his people had been left on a scaffold, to return to the grass that fed the buffalo, who would, in his turn, feed the Indian.

I left the man there, filling his feathered stone pipe, the last of the evening sun on his wrinkled face and his neat, fur-wrapped braids. He was a scarred old warrior come to the burial place of a chief killed by white soldiers. Yet he could call a barefoot child of these whites, a stranger, "granddaughter," and tell her a story to dignify the detested task of wood bearing.

This Indian use of the words *grandson* and *granddaughter* contains, I think, the essence of their attitude towards the young. The first lesson of the new-born child teaches him that in matters of public safety, public good, the individual must subordinate himself to the group. But in return he senses from the first that all his community has an equal responsibility towards him. Every fire will welcome him, every pot will have a little extra for a hungry boy, and every ear is open to his griefs, his joys, and aspirations. And as his world expands he finds himself growing with it, into a society that needs no locks against him, no paper to record his word, and no threat of ostracism. He is a free man because he has learned to discipline himself, and a happy one because he can discharge his duties and responsibilities to others and to himself as an oriented, an intrinsic part of his community, a partner in a wide, encompassing brotherhood.

IV

The Neighbor

Although written in 1945 at the same time as "Martha of the Yellow Braids" which follows, "The Neighbor" was not published until eleven years later. It appeared in the Winter 1956 issue of the University of Nebraska's literary quarterly *Prairie Schooner*, on the occasion of the retirement of its founder and first editor, Lowry C. Wimberly. Thirty years before, a story signed with the pen name Marie Macumber had been Professor Wimberly's choice as the opening piece in Volume I, Number 1 of the *Schooner*. See "The Vine," page 117.

CHARLEY SEARS CAME TO OUR REGION, the upper Niobrara River country, sometime in the 1880's as a youth with his landseeking family. Later he bought a small place one mile east of us. Another Irishman had owned it, until he marketed a good wheat crop and started home with the money in his pocket and a jug of whisky under the wagon seat for comfort on the lonely night road. Next day the team was found grazing beside the trail, Pat dead in the wagon box. He had fallen forward with his throat across the dashboard and choked to death. Before that, lightning had struck Pat's place a dozen times. Once it knocked out all four corners of his house and left him unconscious. The place was a hoodoo, a jinx, Pat said, and after he died some agreed.

But although Charley Sears knew a lot of fine ghost stories, he was not the man for such nonsense as jinxes and hoodoos. Perhaps it was his sensible Scotch-Irish ancestry coming out and whatever infusions were picked up in the migration from early Pennsylvania through Kentucky to western Nebraska. Although I was a small girl then, I recall when he moved in. One afternoon a big wagon drew ponderously up the sandy pitch from the Niobrara River—a bundle rack loaded with beds, dresser, kitchen stove, cupboards, and other household goods. The three, four milk cows plodding behind the wagon were driven by a horsebacker, a fine straight figure in the saddle. I watched as I often did along our road, crouched down in the green forest of our asparagus patch where I could see the travelers headed toward the free-land region east of us: freighters, cowboys, occasional herds of cattle and sheep trailing in from Wyoming, and always the home-seekers from far places.

When the horsebacker with his cows seemed well past, I stood up, hanging to the baby brother astride my hip, but the man must have seen me as he rode by for he turned in the saddle, lifted a hand in the western greeting, and smiled to me. It was an amused smile for a peaked-faced, spying little girl, and more friendly than from the ranch hands, more restrained than from the usual settlers—probably men that my father had located on new homes. I was desperately shy and withdrawn then, and so, embarrassed and ashamed, I dropped back down into the feathery green of the asparagus. The sharp dusty smell comes back to me now, and the warmth and friendliness of the man, perhaps because I met that same greeting, those same teasing, smiling eyes several times a week for most of the remaining years of my childhood.

It was some time before I discovered that this man was Charley Sears, our new neighbor, or noticed him any more than a child would where people drift through like tumbleweeds on the vagrant wind. Besides, there was the antagonism left for Pat, his dead predecessor, with whom my father had sustained a rifle-carrying feud that nat-urally never came to any actual shooting, and had certainly terrified Pat considerably less than it had me.

Although Charley Sears took no sides in the quarrels common to a new region, and those sprouted by my father's need for drama, he was soon established as our good neighbor. Like many new settlers, he was a bachelor but not a bunch quitter, no loner. If necessary Charley could fiddle and call a good square-dance set. He was willing and handy at branding, butchering, threshing, house or barn raising, and in time of flood or prairie fire. He sat up with the sick and the dead and knew how to comfort the sorrowful, the alarmed. He had helped gather the settlers to the sod blockhouse on his uncle's place back in the Ghost Dance Indian scare, and had ridden out of its pro-tection to find a lost puppy that one of the children cried for at night.

Charley had known my father, Jules Sandoz, in the early days and understood something of this Swiss visionary who had the patience to develop an orchard where no tame fruit had ever grown, and who was crippled for life through a practical joke that exploited his extreme excitability. Charley had seen Old Jules work to protect the early settlers, and when the new courts wouldn't act against a man who was burning them out, one after the other, and shooting at the women through the windows, the youth Charley Sears joined the vigilante group my father raised. He was along when they hanged the pyromaniac but with incredible good luck were saved from murder by the toughness of the man's neck. They let him down, and he had them all arrested.

After that there had been little contact between Old Jules and the Sears family. They had their own problems, but they managed to stay on through the nineties when drouth and hard times shook loose many settlers with hardier taproots. Charley knew that Father had been arrested several times for apparently shooting at his neighbors, and also that he would go to his worst enemy in a blizzard to deliver a new baby. Everybody knew he would be out on a hill looking if one of his children was a few minutes late coming home, and limping anxiously up and down if one of them had even a trifling fever, but he whipped one of them at six weeks until his arm was weary and his anger spent because the infant cried in the night.

Without apparent uneasiness our new neighbor set up a mailbox next to ours on the daily route a mile west of us, and whoever went for the mail first brought it all as far as our place; so, one way or the other, we saw Charley almost every day. He could understand a lot of the German-Swiss dialect spoken in our house, and admired Mother's energetic efforts to keep her family fed and covered, while ignoring her cry of calamity at every turn, and her pride in telling everyone the baldest truth about himself.

The first night the new neighbor stopped by he spied me back in the shadows of the lamp with the sleeping baby across my knees. Afterward he took a remote but unfailing notice of me, not as an occasionally diligent child, a "good little mother," or "a little old grandmother," as I often heard myself described, or even as the child of a man who helped the landless. Charley showed an amused tolerance of me as myself despite my old-womanish ways and my curiously aged face that so often brought exclamations from strangers. Looking back, I can guess how disturbing we children must have been to such a thoughtful man, isolated as we were from anyone of our own age, speaking almost no English, and growing up in that immoderate, even volcanic household. I think Charley worked on me particularly, and perhaps properly, as the eldest. With Father crippled and an intellectual, most of the field and orchard work fell to Mother, and so most of

the care of the other children was left to me. Because Father must
never be disturbed into a temper by a crying baby again, each new
one was put into my bed at around the third week and from then on
was mine to feed and diaper and comfort, and to amuse as well as to
teach.

From the first Charley Sears liked to tease me a little, but gently,
about the two-headed shadow creature that followed me and the baby
on my hip wherever I went. He entranced my brothers by making pennies disappear from their palms, to be found in their pockets or behind
their ears. Once, after their cries of joy and my usual silence, although
I had edged a bit closer, he looked over to me and demanded, "Cat
got your tongue?" But his eyes were so gay and laughing that for once
I didn't try to hide when made aware of myself. I did back away a
little, but I recall that my brothers clung to the man's legs, begging for
more tricks, begging him not to go home.

And once, after a rain, he surprised me while I was busily patting
sand over my bare feet to make foot houses for my baby brother. We
were laughing over them together when suddenly our neighbor was
there on his horse, saying something about how this Miss Sobersides
could giggle. I started to gather the baby up and run, but he leaned
over and said, very softly, "You can't run away—" and suddenly I
couldn't. After that he made many occasions for laughter, until he had
to caution me now and then: "Little ladies don't show their gums
when they laugh," saying it as he once said, "Ladies don't swing their
arms, and they do their walking from below their hips."

Charley Sears was as straight as Father's Sioux friends, tall and well
built, with gray-blue eyes and a dark bearding that was always clean
shaven except for the moderate mustache. His brown hair lay in a lazy
curl from the exceptionally neat part, a threading of gray creeping
toward it from the temples. I recall thinking of him as around twenty-
five, which seemed to me about the last stop before senility. Yet he
must certainly have been older. The veining at his nose I knew came
from a little steady dragging at the bottle although we never smelled
more than a slight odor of spice about him, or found any change in
his usual thoughtful, courteous way. He seldom drank publicly. In
very cold weather he might have a bit with Father from the winter's
bottle of Ilers Malt Whisky—barefoot as he called it, meaning neat.

Very early my mother let him know that winning my allegiance
wasn't much of a conquest. She told him that by the time I was a year
old I had been trailing after any man my short legs could keep
in sight. Charley laughed, not to my mother but to me, and for the

first time the story didn't seem a shameful and embarrassing thing.

Gradually this new neighbor drifted closer to our family, appearing Sundays at the edge of the casual, uninvited group that usually gathered at our place. He seldom stayed to dinner, although it couldn't have been because we were so hard up. It is true ours was a home-grown table, but a hearty one. "Plates enough to need the horse trough for the washing as 'tis," he might reply to Mother's invitation to stay for Sunday dinner. But usually his horse was tied to the fence again later in the afternoon, with Charley sitting at the wall somewhere, offering a complimentary word or two for the old country songs Mother started for us all while we washed the stacks of dishes, or perhaps while I peeled potatoes or picked wild ducks for the next meal.

Mother couldn't prevent bad language from Old Jules or even from herself in her moments of high emotion, but she would have none of it from us. Yet Charley Sears went a little farther than that with us. He protested that many of the first words of English we were learning were really slang or worse. He believed in poise and moderation in speech as well as in conduct. "All buzz and no barley," he would say when my impulsiveness or my temper carried me to silly extremes. He knew many amusing little poems that I learned later had morals tacked on—the kind of verses found in the public speakers of his youth. He taught some of them to me, laughing at my guttural German-Swiss pronunciation. He knew many folk songs and sometimes brought a yellowed old composition book to read me the words in faded pencil for, say, "The Gypsy Maiden," "Jimmy, Go Ile the Cairs," or "Mary across the Wild Moors" or songs he got from the Texas trail drivers on the ranches around us, "Red River," and "Streets of Laredo," and so on. Some he wouldn't read to me because they were not for a nice girl to know.

I remember that so very clearly now. Nobody had ever implied that I could possibly be a nice girl. Mother considered praise of her children as suspect as self-praise would be, and Father never spoke well of anyone who might make his words an excuse for less prompt jumping when he commanded. This included his wife and children, although later we discovered that he bragged on us all when far away, if he happened to recall our existence.

From the start Father said that Charley Sears had no get-up. He had come into the region early enough to get the cream of the free land and got not an acre of it. Even when he bought Pat's place he could have gone ten miles farther east and taken up a homestead free, much better land too, not the gravelly knobs that were a fine carpet of white and purple and magenta of loco bloom in summer, but with only a little strip of sandy farm ground. Perhaps Charley would have felt guilty doing his scratchy tilling on good earth. The house was a small story and a half set in a shallow pocket where lightning tended to strike, as even the unsuperstitious admitted. Perhaps there was a concentration of the rusty hematitic nodules common to our sandy deposits, enough of the iron to attract electricity, or, as some suggested, a deep dyke of wet earth reaching up through the dry. Anyway, horses, cattle, and the windmill had been destroyed in Pat's day, and the house struck repeatedly, in addition to the time the corners were blown out and Pat stretched out for dead—enough to drive any man to the jug. Of course the lightning kept right on striking there after Charley bought the place, but he put up rods, grounded his fences, and disconnected his telephone line at the first close roar of thunder.

Women often disliked homesteading far beyond the promise of school and neighbors, but bachelors usually didn't mind. Charley apparently liked close and noisy neighbors. His mother had been sickly and as a boy he learned to keep a spotless house for the family, his floor always white as sanded wood, his bread so fragrant it tolled the far traveler in off the prairie. Yet somehow he never made lesser housekeepers uncomfortable, although he used his Irish sayings now and then to inculcate a little tidiness into my housekeeping. "Where cobwebs grow, beaus don't go," he would say, but even at six I knew that when girls were scarce as in our region beaus went wherever they could.

We were five miles from the school in our district and Mother was too proud to have her children get out in public barefoot, whatever the distance. Father said American teachers were ignorant and that his children could learn more from him, which was possible. By my ninth year I had learned the multiplication table through the twenty-fives, understood such terms as *spiral nebulae* and *spontaneous generation* from Father's long discussions with visiting scientists. I could even write a passable hand in the old copy book that Charley Sears brought me, but nobody had bothered to show me that words were made of the alphabet, with some relation to the sounds of the letters, or that a certain word always looked the same. My inability to read disturbed our neighbor. Along in the summer he said that I must start

to school in the fall. I answered in my broken English that it would
not be permitted, and that I had not the shoes.

Charley laughed. "The shoes your mother will manage as she does
other things." Later it turned out that somebody reported my age to
the county superintendent and my parents were compelled to send me
and my brother Jules to school in the adjoining district, only three
miles away. I was almost delirious with joy, and embarrassed that
other children my age were at least in the third grade.

Charley Sears had usually been most careful not to go against the
teachings of our parents, but as soon as I could read a little he ignored one of Father's pet notions. Fiction to Old Jules was for the
hired man and hired girl, if you had them, but never for a Sandoz.
Gradually Charley let me discover that he had something worth all
the world to me then: a tall bookcase full of books, varying from Hawthorne, *Nicholas Nickleby*, and Bill Nye to Mary J. Holmes and *From
Ballroom to Hell*. He also had a lot of old magazines, including at
least ten years of a woman's periodical that left its sentimental mark
on the attitudes and face and figure of a generation of village and
country womanhood—*The Comfort*. Charley started to sneak these
down for me, and because the attic where I slept with whoever was
the baby had outside stairs, I could slip the books up to my bed and
hide them in the straw tick. But even so there was never enough reading matter and I started to write stories for myself, very bad ones.
Still, the first one was printed in the junior page of the Omaha *Daily
News* and brought me a whipping and a short time in our cellar. As
soon as Father's anger cooled he took me out quail hunting. Charley
Sears approved of my writing but not of the product. "Still a tongue-
tied Dutchman," he wrote on the margin of the story in the newspaper. Years later, when I sneaked away to take teachers' examination, Charley was a bit more encouraging. "Sticking feathers on a
buzzard's neck won't make an eagle out of him," he told me, and then
added, laughing, "but maybe you can fool 'em—"

Although I still had a baby on my hip at ten, a sister now, Mother
began to think of my posture. "Walk straight as a princess even if your
feet are dirty," she said. I tried, but I was very thin and small and
there were, in addition to the baby, water to draw from the deep well,
grain and flour to carry into the attic, and a hundred other heavy burdens that Mother was too busy or too tiny to manage. This, added to
the stooped shoulders characteristic of Father's family, bent me round
as a drawn Sioux bow. But Charley Sears brought a sawed-off broom-

handle and showed me tricks with it. A substantial six-footer himself, he could grasp the stick with both hands, swing it back over his head, and crawl through it as smoothly as a garter snake going through a fence. I worked for months to do it as easily, and, for a time, became almost as straight as he. "Ah, ha!" Mother told him. "She still is tagging at a man's heels!" But for once she let me see she was pleased.

Long before this Charley had begun to work on my native tactlessness, emphasizing the need for special thought and gentleness. I could see that it worked for him. He was welcome anywhere in the region, particularly where there were young ladies. He always did his share to make the new schoolma'am welcome in the fall, paying her polite court until she was well acquainted and had a suitable beau. One of my teachers could have trapped this wily bachelor if she had been so minded. For a while I hoped there would be a piece of wedding cake for my pillow, to make me dream of my future beloved. But when I dared ask Charley about the wedding date, he was brusque and stiff. He wouldn't ask *me* such a personal question, ten, fifteen years from now, and embarrass me, he said. The next fall he was gallantly calling on another pretty teacher, but this time I tried to be tactful, although nobody else in my family ever worried about tact. Mother would say anything if she thought it would serve to set someone right. She generally felt it her duty to tell you that so-and-so was talking about you behind your back. She always told the truth, the last bitter drop of it.

"Carrying tar only dirties the hands," Charley once protested mildly to Mother, and I recalled a story told about him, about an early affair with a woman who still lived in the community and who still hinted that one of her sons was his. But this bit of tar not even Mother would ever carry to him.

By this time our father had bought a phonograph that we could not afford, and a lot of records; so there was music as well as good talk to draw visitors. Much as he liked our Irish records, Charley usually observed the custom of the West and didn't get off his horse if Father was away. But the night a burglar shot a lock of hair from my head, Charley came as soon as we got the cut telephone line repaired. Even then he brought a neighbor along, more for propriety than for help. If Father was home Charley generally settled somewhere against the wall in our smoky kitchen–living room, on a bench perhaps, or a box, listening. He usually took no part in Father's talk. Limited in education, he lacked the arrogance of the ignorant and was hungry for talk of ancient history, horticulture, the possible origins of the Niobrara River fossil beds, and so on. But he was gone the minute the talk turned to topics that aroused Father to his violent speeches on his injustices, real or fancied, or to complaints against the politicians, the mail service, cattlemen, or women. Somehow Charley was never pressed to side with Father in these tirades as almost anyone else would have been: that was Charley's tact, I suppose, tact and diplomacy.

Perhaps Charley Sears was really lonesome, a lonesome man even after his sister came to live with him. Perhaps he liked the occasional drink he got at our place, usually from a pitcher of wild-grape wine, with Mother's good smoked sausage and heavy bread of macaroni wheat set out on the cutting board. He was an accommodating old-time Westerner, to whom any request for help immediately became a cow in the well. He went to endless trouble to carry out errands in town for us, knowing that Old Jules' women folk didn't get to town even once a year. He let us hook a telephone to his little fence line, which was the top strand of the barbed-wire fence and efficient enough in dry weather, when no breachy animal had broken it down. Occasionally communication to the outside was possible through a very erratic central at the house of one of Father's enemies, but very useful in time of local calamity, say a prairie fire, mad-dog scare, or a child lost in a blizzard, although then the line was generally grounded by drifting snow. Charley let everybody know when bank robbers were fleeing our way, when an incapacitated settler's corn needed husking, or a shivaree was due. Not that any of us ever went to any social events. I had seldom spent two continuous hours away from home except at school.

Pioneer life is never free from emergencies very long and in our community the man who usually arrived first upon bad news was Charley Sears. He came the time my father's brother was shot by the hired killer of a ranch near by—shot down while milking a cow, right before his wife and seven children, and dying. Father was away in the sandhills, locating settlers in the cattle country and in much greater danger than his brother, or so it suddenly seemed to us. The sheriff was slow and the killer still loose.

That night was a very long one for us. Charley came down right after supper, as though for his mail, but calling out a loud greeting before he rode into the yard to let us know it wasn't the killer. He blinked in the lamp-lighted kitchen and sat down quietly but out of range of the windows, as Father always did in those dangerous years

of cattleman-settler troubles. Several times during the evening men
rode up looking for Old Jules to lead them against the ranch where the
killer had worked, find him, drag him out to a telephone pole somewhere, burn the whole damn outfit to the ground. When Mother told
them in her excited, melodramatic way that Father was away, off
alone in the hills, they looked serious, perhaps even spoke darkly of
bullets from behind some soapweed. While my brothers and I drew
closer together in alarm, Charley remained quiet. "Jules will look out
for himself," he said several times, perhaps remembering that Father
was a crack shot, or thinking of the time he led the vigilantes to hang
a tough-necked man, almost twenty years before.

Nobody except the babies went to bed. Young Jules and Jim stayed
up near Charley while Mother tried to busy herself patching their
worn overalls, but up at every sound, her faded blue eyes rolled dra-
matically toward me in a warning that this, *this* time it was the news of
our uncle's death, or of Father's. Or perhaps the killer was at the door.
Several times Charley went out to look after his stomping horse and
came back to tell more stories of squirrels and hornets' nests back in
Kentucky, and of berryings and play parties, hoop snakes and sting
tailers. He asked us riddles and casually pulled string tricks from his
pockets; he made a dinner knife stand out straight from the edge
of the table, got water up into an inverted glass without touching it,
pulled matches from his pocket, and said, "Can you take two from
twenty-two and leave only four?"

Midnight passed and the deep-toned old-country clock tocked the
hours on. Once Mother's face was turned bleak as winter from the
telephone. Men had ridden the sandhills since yesterday and now it
was dawning and nobody had found any sign of Father or his wagon.
Charley glanced from his coffee cup to the rounded stack of loaded
guns always standing in the corner behind our door. "Nobody'll get
close to Jules—they know it ain't healthy."

"But from far—"

Charley smiled, and looked to my concerned face and laid his
matches out in five neat squares. "Remove three, and leave three
whole squares," he said in the same teasing way that, eight hours
earlier, he had said to my brothers, "Take a card—any card" from the
spread deck he held out to them.

Somehow we lived through that time. Our uncle died, Father came
home, and was ready in the doorway with his Winchester up when
the killer rode around the corner of the house. No man worth his pay
as range protection would go against a Winchester with a revolver,

and from a faunching horse at that, but I can still see the white faces of my mother and brothers behind Father until the sneering man finally set his spurs and was gone.

It was years before I realized what that tragic time, particularly the night of waiting, after Uncle Emile was shot, might have meant to us without Charley Sears. Who can measure the effect it might have had on us children if there had been only the high-pitched lamentations of our singularly courageous but singularly excitable mother and the dark-faced, armed men riding in with their short, violent words, their warnings of the killer's probable coming? Not a tear was shed all that night, although Charley's eyes seemed to water a little as he swung into his saddle in the morning sunlight and looked down upon the barefoot little girl holding out a jar of plum jelly from the cellar.

Then there was the time my father was bitten by the rattlesnake. We got him home by sundown, nine, ten hours later. There the horses dropped in exhaustion in the harness, and once more our telephone was dead.

"Run for the doctor!" Mother cried, and helped lift Father from the buggy.

I ran for Charley Sears, a mile away, mostly uphill. Afterward I realized I could have run to a couple of other places, nearer, and with direct telephone line to a doctor, but I had let my feet lead me.

Soon after this we moved into the sandhills, and we seldom saw Charley any more. Three, four times he wrote me stiff, formal little letters, but evoking all the sense of wholeness and well-being many of us felt when around him, reawakening the affection and trust and respect that must have been planted that day he first rode past a little girl with a baby on her hip. Charley lived to be an old man, and when he died a clipping of his funeral was sent to me in New York. Suddenly I was confronted by a deep and disturbing loss. This man had tried to lead a peaked-faced, shy, and ashamed little girl down on the Niobrara to see that she could learn to be a person in her own right, a person outside of the comfort and security she might be for her small siblings. He made her see that perhaps she could live without too much embarrassment and shame over her shortcomings, no matter how barefooted she might have to remain. Perhaps she could learn to use a little of the tireless energy, the bald out-spokenness of her mother and yet restrain the excitability, the gloom and fault-finding that were also her inheritance. He showed her that the swift, almost murderous temper of her father need not be uncontrolled in her, even while she nursed a little of Old Jules' fierce intellectual independence and any bit of his creative builder's vision that, with luck, he might have bred in her.

But perhaps most of all Charley Sears feared the sense of persecution that destroyed so much of my father's fine talent. "No use trying to blame things on other people," he once said to me at a time when I needed the reproof particularly. "If you got a bellyache it's you that's been eating the green apples."

But even that he said with the old teasing smile, this good neighbor of ours.

V

Martha of the Yellow Braids

When it appeared in the *Prairie Schooner* in 1947, this piece carried the subtitle "A Recollection." "'Martha,'" the author wrote in an accompanying note to the editor, "is a piece from my autobiographical files, one of those bits of irrelevant matter that crystallize out of my memory in the heat and pressure of getting a long book together. Some day I shall select enough for a volume, if I decide that the contrast to my more purposeful writing is not too great."

THE DAY MARTHA CAME the sun was warm as May on the midwinter drifts, and I ran most of the two miles home from school in my hurry to see her. I had never been around girls much. In a frontier community they are usually scarce; besides, my father was so often embroiled in some spectacular battle for human rights or perhaps sitting out his fines in jail—a background apparently not considered the best by the local mothers of growing girls. So my few playmates were boys, often Polish boys, perhaps because they didn't seem to mind that I was spindly as a rake handle, with my hair roached close to save Mother the combing time, and that I usually had a baby astride my hip. Besides, there were always my brothers.

But the winter I was going on ten Martha came. My father was a locator, and one of his Bohemian settlers brought his family to live with us until he could plow the spring earth for the sod needed to build his house. This was common enough, except that there had never been a girl near my age before. Now there was Martha, eleven, and all the things my mother always wanted me to be: plump, white-skinned, a good bread-baker, a young lady with nice young-lady manners. Martha had grown up in town around her mother's series of boarding houses and showed no deplorable tendency to sneak off for an hour's fishing or sledding, particularly not with rude little Polaks, as she immediately labeled my playmates. Disloyally I tolerated this insult to my friends, for Martha was not only what my mother wanted me to be but all that I wanted too. She was a big girl, free of babies, and she had pale yellow braids thick as pile-driver rope to hang below her knees or to wind in a crown about her head above her garnet earrings from Vienna.

There were other things about Martha that attracted me: her father's teasing pinches at her tight, pink cheek, her mother's goodnight kiss—incredible as a storybook existence to me. But I still think it was the braids that made me desert my Polanders; the pale yellow braids and Martha's way of whispering secrets as she walked beside me with an arm chummily around my shoulders, almost as though we were two of the pretty young Hollanders from over on the Flats, or maybe even American girls.

There must have been the usual difficulties in our family that spring: snow, cold, cattle dying, bills unpaid, and surely Father's temper and his affinity for trouble. Mother must have been as impatient with him as always, and with me too, for I was certainly even less skillful at my work around the facile-handed Martha, and certainly no prettier than before. But I remember nothing much of those three months except a vague, cloudy sort of happiness in my discovery that I could have a friend like the other girls in school. There was the usual housework to be done, with Father away hunting or locating settlers, and Mother busy with the stock and the feeding, the fences to be repaired, the trees to be planted before the leaves came. Martha and I told each other stories as I did the cleaning and fed the baby—not any of those I had written myself, printed in the junior page of our daily paper. It wasn't that I didn't trust her to keep the secret of my writing from my folks; I was ashamed of the stories. Although I usually dismissed fairy tales as plain lying, I even listened to them from Martha because I couldn't bear to see the hurt that would come into her blue eyes if I said so. And one night, after her mother allowed me to brush the long, yellow hair, I cried hours of envious tears—I who had surely put such childish things behind me long ago.

April came, with tight little clumps of Easter daisies on the greening hillsides, and finally the new sodhouse on the homestead was begun. When the swallows were back with us to skim the morning air, I stood in our yard and waved my baby sister's hand to Martha in the wagon that was taking her into the sandhills. Of course we wrote letters, long ones, every week; then shorter and not so often, for Martha's mother was down at the railroad somewhere running another boarding place, and Martha kept house for her father. Her letters were less of childish stories and more about such things as washing greasy overalls, churning, or singing for the Sunday school that a walking sky pilot had organized among the settlers. By this time there was another baby coming to our house, and while I still got away for an hour now and then, Mother needed my help more and made as much fun of the Polish boys as Martha ever did. Finally one of my brothers and I were sent to the hills to live alone on Father's new homestead, only a few miles from Martha. But I had never been allowed to go visiting and so it didn't occur to me to walk over to see her. Months later, when Mother had moved down too, Martha came for some wolf poison. A coyote was getting her turkeys. By now her skirts were to her shoetops and her talk was all of woman things to Mother. When she got into a young bachelor's top buggy in our yard I knew that I had been left years behind.

Of course we were still friendly, and in a couple of years I got my hair coaxed out into braids long enough to cross at the back. With pins in it and the hems of my faded calico dresses let down, I felt as old as anybody. By that time we had a school district organized, the teacher boarding at our house, and Father giving occasional dances in the barn. Martha came, usually with her folks, and while her mother talked about good matches for the girl, her father pulled the accordion for our dancing. Calmly, easily, Martha would put her hand on the arms of the older men, some at least twenty-five, while I stumbled around the floor with boys of my age, bickering with them about who was to lead, or perhaps talking about bronco busting or pulling a skunk from his winter hole with barbed wire. We were still known as the two good friends and sometimes Martha left the woman bench and came over to whisper giggling secrets into my ear about who was asking her to eat supper or perhaps warning me against this man or that one who had to be watched.

"He'll hold you so tight you can't breathe, if you permit him—" using grown-up words about grown-up things that I pretended to understand.

By the time I had hair enough to cover a rat I managed to have as many dances left over when daylight came as Martha, but still not with the same crowd, for hers were with bachelors who had homesteads, cookstoves, and bedsteads waiting for their wives, while mine were mostly with fuzzy-faced young ranch hands, outsiders visiting relatives in the hills, or Eastern schoolboys working in the hay camps. I was handy at picking up new steps and I had discovered that a ready foot and a glib tongue would do much to discount what

I saw when I stood before the looking-glass of Mother's dresser.

"Ah, you are always wasting your time with those silly boys—" Martha would try to warn me, using words from her mother's mouth against me.

The spring she was sixteen Martha came over on her flea-bitten old mare instead of sitting easy in some red-wheeled buggy. She had news, and a ring on her finger. Of course the diamond was small, she admitted before I could say it, but the setting was white gold, very stylish. Very expensive too, and much better than a big stone in cheap, old-style yellow tiffany. By then I had learned some young-lady ways too, and so I pretended that I liked the ring, although I wouldn't have been interested in a diamond the size of a boulder set in a ring of platinum the size of a wagon tire, for I was secretly planning to be a schoolteacher and have fine clothes and many beaus for years and years, maybe even write some more of my stories, but for grownups. Although certainly no romantic, I wasn't prepared for Martha's further admission—that she had never seen the man. It was all right, though, she assured me. His people and hers were friends back in the old country, and he was known as a good provider, strong, healthy, and twenty-two, right in the prime of life. Evidently Martha wasn't satisfied with what I managed to say, for she told me crossly that she hadn't expected me to appreciate a good man, not with my nose in a book all the time and without the sense to see that a girl had to do the best she could for herself while she was young.

The wedding was a year later, in June. Martha's father took them up to Rushville to be married. Although I didn't get to go along, I was supposed to pretend that I was the bridesmaid for the dinner. Mother let me cut a dress from a bolt of eleven-cent organdy on the shelf of our country store. Even with a bertha, said to be softening, the unrelieved white was so unbecoming that I dyed an old scarf for a sash. It turned out a dirty lavender, the best I could do with Father's red and blue inks. If I could have found even a stub of indelible pencil, the sash would have been a pungent but vivid purple. I tried the dress on, and while I looked no worse than I had all my sixteen years, somehow it seemed much worse. I even wondered why I had never tried holding my breath long enough to die. Of course there was the wolf poison on the top shelf of the shop, but that was a little drastic.

For the wedding present Mother cut ten yards off the family bolt of white outing flannel, and tied it up with a red ribbon from one of the candy boxes the hay waddies brought me. I came near crying

over this baby bundle, which I considered most insulting and sug-
gestive. But no one was interested in my opinion, and, besides, I
had to take something. Fortunately Father's peonies were particularly fine that year, and the only clumps in all the sandhills. He let
me cut a whole armful, half of them deep wine-red and the rest white.
I rolled these in a newspaper twist and tied them to one side of my
saddle, the outing flannel in a flour sack to the other. With my white
dress rolled up around my waist over my khaki riding skirt, I rode
to Martha's for the wedding dinner. She came running into the yard
to meet me, holding her veil and her embroidered new dress up out
of the dry manure dust with her farm-girl hands in elbow-length
white silk gloves. I was overwhelmed by her strangeness, and couldn't
do anything except push the peonies at her. Of course she couldn't
take them, not with her gloves, and so I carried the flowers to the
house and arranged them in a blue crock with Martha giving the advice. This helped us both through the embarrassment of the outing-
flannel present and into the dinner, which was delayed by a discussion about the gloves. Should the bride eat with them on or might she
take them off? By this time the groom got to making enough noise
so that I had to notice him.

"Off!" was his firm verdict about the gloves. No use having to wash
them right away. They would last a long time, years, if Martha took
care of them as his sisters did theirs—laid them away in blue paper
to keep out the light. As the talk went around the table I looked the
man over. He was that bleak age which the twenties are to the middle
teens. His hair was clipped far above his ears in a highwater cut, as we
called it, his knobby head showing blue around the back. The collar
propping up his cleft chin was real linen, but the suit looked wooly
as Grandfather's old wedding broadcloth in our trunk at home. Yet
Martha seemed to like her man very much, with all his talk of "the
little flat I got feathered for my little bird—" which I considered sick-
eningly mushy. Nor did I think he came up to any of my dancing
partners, not even the one who always puffed so in the schottisches
because a horse fell on him when he was small and smashed something inside.

After everybody was full of dinner and there was nothing more
to do, things got particularly bad for me, with all the old-country
wedding jokes and horseplay. So I managed to slip out to the clearer
air of the porch. After a while Martha found me and with an arm
around my back as in the old days, she looked into the yard where
her flea-bitten pony stomped at the flies. And as in the old days she

whispered a secret into my ear. It was about her mother. With only one daughter to be married off, she wouldn't let Martha have the dinner she wanted, with both bride's cake and *kolaches*.

"My one big day—" Martha said, blinking at the bank of tears in her blue eyes.

I tried to tell her that it didn't matter, not out here in the hills, but all I could think about was this unknown woman beside me, talking about such foolish things as bride's cake and *kolaches*, making an important secret of them. She saw my silence for something else and suddenly the kindness that was the Martha I knew broke through all the grown-up woman air of the dress and the day. Laughing out loud as when she was eleven, she said that we must make a charm to bring us together again some day. She would leave me a piece of her hair that I used to love so much. Before I had to say anything she gathered up her veil over her arm and was gone to get the scissors.

But I didn't have to take the hair, for Martha's new husband followed her out and standing between us, an arm around each, reminded us that he must now be asked about everything. Maybe I'd better give him a kiss too, just to make sure he would say yes. I pulled away but no one was watching me, particularly not the old people inside the house, who were laughing, taking sides, the women encouraging Martha.

"Go ahead, cut it off. Right at the start you have to show him—" they called to her. But the men shouted them down, slapping their knees in approval at the new husband's firm stand. By golly, you could see who would rule that roost—

So the newlyweds argued a little, pouted and kissed, and then went into the house to sit on the bench along the wall while a pitcher of wine was passed around and the father played the accordion. As soon as I could I said something about going home.

"You know how the folks are about me being off the doorstep a second—"

Martha knew. It was a wonder they had let me come at all, the very first time I ever managed to get away without some special errand to be done for my father. So I shook hands awkwardly all around and went to put on my riding skirt. I hated walking through the room with it hanging out below my white dress, but there was no back door. When I finally got to my horse Martha came running through the yard, her veil flying loose behind.

"Oh, I hate to go—to leave everything!" she cried, her gentle eyes swimming.

At last I got away, and as my shaggy little buckskin carried me across the wide meadow, I thought of that fine springtime on the old Niobrara when we used to lie awake nights in the attic, telling stories, Martha's always of beautiful maidens, and princes who were bewitched into frogs or cold wet stones; whispering the stories carefully so the baby wouldn't waken or Mother hear us from downstairs. But that was when I was little, a long time ago, and today the sun was shining and the first prairie roses were pink and fragrant on the upland side of the road. On the marshy side mallard ducks and their young chattered in the rushes, or dove in the open water, busy with their feeding.

And at the fence beyond the first rise a top buggy was waiting, one of the red-wheeled ones from Martha's old crowd.

"Maybe you think I got to have an automobile—?" the serious young German settler complained when I wouldn't ride in the buggy with him, although I did let my horse idle alongside while I teased the man a little for being such a slow-poke, letting an outsider come in and take Martha away.

At the next dance I ate supper with one of my hay waddies as usual —an art student from Chicago who brought me *Lord Jim* to read and had no cookstove for a bride, no place of his own at all, not even a saddlehorse. But he was teaching me a new kind of fox trot, and anyway I knew that I could have those other things if I wanted them, for now I was really grown-up, with a bachelor in a red-wheeled buggy waiting for me along the road.

Of course I still didn't have thick yellow braids to hang as far as my knees, but that hadn't mattered for a long time.

VI

Marlizzie

In the winter of 1934, while working on her novel *Slogum House*, Mari Sandoz also wrote "Pioneer Women," a paper commissioned for a minute fee by a women's club. The author illustrated her points with passages from *Old Jules*—which at that time had still to find a publisher—and from Willa Cather's *My Antonia*, and "The Windfighters," a story by Keene Abbott which appeared in *Outlook* in 1916 (67). Excerpts from "Pioneer Women" follow:

This paper had its origins in an old assigned topic: "Women in Pioneer Literature," but unfortunately I found that the earlier and more exciting portions of pioneer literature have little reference to women outside of dance-hall girls, Indians, and breeds, or those mere bits of icing added for romantic interest in later rehashings of early tales. . . .

The early accounts of the white man's penetration up the Missouri, the Platte, the Republican, and the Niobrara sometimes mention women, usually referred to as the wife or the squaw of so-and-so, seldom the narrator's—and almost always Indians and breeds. Later came the dance-hall girls of the Wild West stories, the Calamity Janes, the Poker Alices, the Silver Nells. No pioneer women in the common sense of the term. These came later when actual settlement began. However, in the Panhandle of the state those days are not far behind us. . . . [The date of Old Jules' arrival in western Nebraska—March 1884—was] in the transitional period between the footloose frontiersman and the early pioneer, an important period in the taming of any land.

As soon as the romantic days of the long rifle, the beaver trap, the bull boat, and the whisky wagon began to fade and the frontiersman was compelled to settle down and make a living, his thoughts turned eastward to women of his own kind. But after her arrival the wife found that her husband seldom mentioned her in his letters or manuscripts save in connection with calamity. She sickened and left her work undone and so the pioneer could not plow or build or hunt. If his luck was exceeding bad, she died and left him and his home without a housekeeper until she could be replaced. At first this seems a calloused, even a brutal attitude, but it was not so intended. The tamer of the wilderness was a doer, a man of deed, a man who had lost the ability to taste the everyday things through satiation with the sharper spices of frontier life. Only accident or sickness or death were worth mentioning at all. . . .

The fine thing, it seems to me, is that the early pioneer woman made

59

the best of the situation, and usually without complaint, if one can trust the few letters available. Although her place in literature of the time is negligible, we know that nothing happened after she arrived that did not vitally touch her. Particularly important was her place in accident or sickness, with doctors so few and far between. . . .

If the man of the place fell into a well or got caught in a runaway, it was usually the woman of the place who managed his rescue, cared for him, carried on his work. When drouth and hail and wind came, it was the housewife who set as good a table as possible from what remained and sustained the morale of her family. . . .

If hardships came, with hunger and sickness, the man could escape, at least temporarily, into the fields, the woods, or perhaps to the nearest saloon where there was warmth and companionship. The woman faced it at home. The results are tersely told by the items in the newspapers of the day. Only sheriff sales seem to have been more numerous than the items telling of trips to the insane asylum. . . .

No account of pioneer women is complete without the conflict of man with man. In our region it was with the settlers and the cattlemen. In our home, as in those around us, children grew up in the fear of expulsion or extermination by the Winchester . . . (13).

The author concluded with the observation that the story of the pioneer woman had yet to be written.

Out of this paper grew the following article, which appeared for the first time in 1936 under the title "The New Frontier Woman." It was a portrait sketched from life—for Marlizzie was, in fact, Mary Elizabeth Fehr Sandoz, the author's mother.

THE AMERICAN FRONTIER IS GONE, we like to say, a little sadly. And with it went the frontier woman who followed her man along the dusty trail of the buffalo into the land of the hostile Indian. Never again will there be a woman like the wife of Marcus Whitman, who, exactly a hundred years ago, looked out upon a thousand miles of empty West from the bows of a wagon rolling up the Platte toward Oregon.

But there was a later, a less spectacular, and a much more persistent frontier in America, a frontier of prairie fire, drouth, and blizzard, a frontier of land fights and sickness and death far from a doctor, yet with all the characteristic gaiety, deep friendships, and that personal freedom so completely incomprehensible to the uninitiated.

Among my acquaintances are many women who walked the virgin soil of such a frontier and made good lives for themselves and those about them. And when they could they did not turn their backs upon the land they struggled to conquer. They stayed, refusing to be told that they occupy the last fringes of a retreating civilization, knowing that life there can be good and bountiful.

One of these frontierswomen is Marlizzie, living more than thirty miles from a railroad, over towering sandhills and through valleys that deepen and broaden to hayflats, with scarcely a house and not a tree the whole way.

No matter when you may come, you will find her away somewhere: chasing a turkey hen, looking after the cattle, repairing fence with stretchers and staples, trimming trees in the orchard, or perhaps piling cow chips for winter fuel. A blow or two on the old steel trap spring that hangs in place of a dinner bell at the gate will bring her— running, it seems to strangers, but really only at her usual gait, a gait that none of the six children towering over her can equal.

She comes smiling and curious, shading her faded blue eyes to see who you may be, and eager to welcome you in any event. And as she approaches, you see her wonderful wiry slightness, notice that her forearms, always bare, are like steel with twisted cables under dark leather—with hands that are beautiful in the knotted vigor that has gripped the hoe and the pitchfork until the fingers can never be straightened, fingers that still mix the ingredients for the world's most divine concoction—Swiss plum pie.

And while you talk in the long kitchen–living room, she listens eagerly, demanding news of far places—the Rhineland, not so far from the place of her birth; Africa, and the political games in the Far East. Apologetically she explains that the mail is slow and uncertain here. Her daily papers come a sackful at a time, and there is no telephone. Besides, the decayed old stock station thirty miles away is little more than a post office and shipping pens. News still travels in the frontier manner, by word of mouth.

And while Marlizzie listens, perhaps she will make you a pie or two or even three—for one piece, she is certain, would be an aggravation. Gently she tests the plums between her fingers, choosing only the firmest, to halve and pit and lay in ring after ring like little saucers into crust-lined tins. Then sugar and enough of the custard, her own recipe, to cover the plums to dark submerged circles. She dots the top with thick sweet cream, dusts it with nutmeg, or if you insist—but it is a serious sacrilege—with cinnamon, and slips them into her Nile-green range, gleaming as a rare piece of porcelain and heated to the exact degree with corncobs. And as she works, her hair, that she had so carefully smoothed with water before she began the pies, has come up in a halo of curls, still with a bright, glinting brown in it for all her sixty-nine years.

It is a little difficult to see in this Marlizzie, so like a timberline tree but stanchly erect, the woman of forty years ago, delicate of skin with white hands, and what was known as "style" in the days of the leg-o'-mutton sleeve, the basque, and the shirred taffeta front. She came hopefully to Western Nebraska with eight new dresses of cashmeres and twills and figured French serges in navy, brown, gray, and green. One had a yard and a half in each sleeve, and one—a very fine light navy—had two yards of changeable gold-and-blue taffeta pleated into the front of the basque. Marlizzie got so many because she suspected that it might be difficult to find good tailoring, with good style and cloth, right at the first in this wilderness. It was, and still is; but she found no occasion for the clothes she brought, or the renewal of her wardrobe with anything except calico or denim. Gradually the fine dresses were cut up for her children.

Within three months of the day that she struggled with her absurd rosetted little hat in the wind that swept the border town and all the long road to her home in the jolting lumber wagon, Marlizzie had ceased for all time to be a city woman. She had learned to decoy the wily team of Indian ponies and had converted, without a sewing machine, a fashionable gray walking skirt and cape into a pair of trousers and a cap for her new husband.

Ten years later her children found the tape loops once used to hold the trailing widths of the skirt from the dust of the street. When they asked what the loops were for, she told them and laughed a little as she buttoned her denim jacket to go out and feed the cattle. She had married an idealist, a visionary who dreamed mightily of a Utopia and worked incessantly to establish his dream and forgot that cattle must be fed to stand the white cold of thirty-below-zero weather.

By the time the calluses of her hands were as horn, her arms gnarling, and she had somehow fed every hungry wayfarer that came to her door, she had learned many things—among them that on the frontier democracy was an actuality and that, despite the hardships, there was a wonderful plenitude of laughter and singing, often with dancing until the cows bawled for their morning milking, or winter-long storytelling around the heater red with cow chips.

The six children of Marlizzie were brought into the world and into maturity whole and sound without a doctor in the house. Though sugar was a luxury and bread often made from grain she ground in

a hand mill, they were fed. Despite the constant menace of rattlesnakes to bare feet, and range cattle and wild horses and the dare-
deviltry the frontier engenders in its young, not one of the children
lost so much as a little finger.

Marlizzie learned the arts of the frontier: butchering, meat care,
soapmaking, and the science of the badger-oil lamp, with its under-
wear wick speared on a hairpin. Stores were remote, even had there
been money. Not for twenty-five years, not until she was subpoenaed
on a murder case, was she on a train. Finally in 1926 she was in town
long enough to see her first moving picture. She stayed in the dark
little opera house all the afternoon and the evening to see it over
and over, and talked of it as she talked so long ago about the wonders
of *Faust*.

During those years Marlizzie saw many spring suns rise upon the
hills as she ran through the wet grass for the team, or stopped to
gather a handful of wild sweet peas for her daughter, who was tied
to the babies and had little time for play. Often before the fall dawn-
ings Marlizzie stripped the milk from her cow. It was far to the field,
and she and her husband must put in long days to husk the little
corn before the snow came.

In those forty years Marlizzie saw large herds of range cattle driven
into the country, their horns like a tangled thicket over a flowing
dusty blanket of brown. She saw them give way to the white-faced
Hereford, and the thick-skinned black cattle that crawled through
all her fences. She saw the hard times of the East push the settler
westward and the cattleman arm against the invasion. She helped
mold bullets for the settlers' defense or listened silently, her knitting
needles flying, to the latest account of a settler shot down between
the plow handles or off his windmill before the eyes of his wife and
children.

She knitted only a little more rapidly when it was her own man
that was threatened, her brother-in-law that was shot. And always
there was patching to be done when her husband was away for weeks
on settler business and she could not sleep. In the earlier days, when
there was no money for shoes, she made the slippers for the little
ones from old overalls on these nights, making a double agony of it.
Nothing hurt her pride more than the badly shod feet of her children.

She dug fence-post holes along lines of virgin land, hoed corn,
fought prairie fires. She saw three waves of population, thousands
of families, come into the free-land region, saw two-thirds of them
turn back the next day and more dribble back as fast as they could

get money from the folks back home, until only a handful remained.

Marlizzie still lives on the old homestead. With a hired hand—a simple, smiling boy—she runs the place that she helped build through the long years with those gnarled hands. Now that her husband has planned his last ideal community, even the larger decisions are hers to make: the time for the haying, the branding and vaccinating of the cattle, the replacing of trees in her orchards. As the frontier women before her, she looks to the sky and the earth, and their signs do not fail her.

The last time I saw Marlizzie at her home she was on a high ladder, painting the new barn built from the lumber of the old one that the wind destroyed. Winter was coming, but in her vegetable pit was enough produce for herself and her neighbors until spring, with jellies and vegetables and fruit and even roast turkey in glass jars. And in the barn, swathed in a clean old sheet, hung a yearling beef that she and the hired hand had killed and dressed.

Tomorrow she was going to town, a 120-mile trip in a son's truck, to the nearest town large enough to carry husking mittens and the things she needed for Christmas. Then there must be the special bits for the Thanksgiving dinner, such as dates, nuts, and cranberries and a few candies and other goodies.

Most of the dinner will be of her own growing. Always she roasts the largest young tom turkey from her noisy flock. The turkey is eked out with perhaps a couple of pheasants or capons and some catfish dipped from the barrel of running water where she has been fattening them all fall. And toward noon on Thanksgiving day the uninvited guests will begin to come, and come most of the afternoon, until every dish has been washed several times and the last comer fed in true frontier fashion.

And then they will all gather around the old organ, played by one of the daughters of Marlizzie. They will go through the old song books until they are all weary and sentimental and very sad and happy. Toward evening someone will surely come running. Perhaps a gate has been left open; the cattle have broken into the stackyards or a horse is sick. And Marlizzie will tuck up her skirts and fly to the emergency, much as she did the time a three-hundred-pound neighbor came down with a burst appendix and there was nothing better than the sheet-covered kitchen table for the emergency operation, with Marlizzie to stand by the doctor.

Or she will fly to the help of the new frontier woman. Economic stringency has always given the more sparsely settled regions the miraginal aspects of a refuge. During the past five years remote habitations have sprung up on deserted or isolated tracts of land that lay unclaimed.

This newer woman of the frontier lives in a log house, a soddy, a dugout, or even a haystack, much as her predecessors. Thrust from a factory, office, or from the bridge table, she comes alone or with a husband also the victim of the times. Often strong from tennis or swimming she can lay sod, hew a log, or dig a dugout, day in and out, beside most men. She learns to cook over an open fire or in a dutch oven, and, if necessary, to make an oil lamp with a wick from her husband's sock, cut round and round, and speared on an unbent hairpin across a sardine can.

I saw one of these new homemakers in the south sandhills of Nebraska not so long ago. Twenty miles from the nearest boxcar depot, an old Model T without a top, fender, or windshield drew out of the rutted trail to let us pass. In place of an engine the motive power was an old fleabitten mare, the single-tree slack against her hoary fetlocks. The car body was rounded into a neatly tiered mound of cow chips, the native coal of the sandhills. In front, his feet reaching down to brace against the dash, sat the driver, a young man in frayed-bottom trousers. In the back was a young woman in overalls and an orange felt hat that still carried a hint of the jauntiness of a good shop. Beside her was the battered old washtub used to gather the fuel.

As we passed, they acknowledged our greeting with the salute of the hills, hand in air, palm out. A mile farther on, in a half-acre pocket, was the home of the new settlers: a low structure of Russian thistles and bunch grass tamped between layers of old chicken wire for the walls, held up by posts. There was one glassless window and a door, and through the thatch of brush on the roof rose an old stove-pipe chimney with screen tied over it. Against the north side of the little house hung the pelts of a litter of half-grown coyotes, and drying from the clothesline were wreaths of green beans, covered with the skirt of a wash-faded voile dress. In a low plot spaded from the tough sod grew beans and late turnips and rutabagas and Chinese winter radishes. In a square pen shaded with an armful of weeds across a corner, a fine red shoat slept.

I felt a glow of recognition as we passed. These people were already my people. From Marlizzie and her kind they were learning all the tricks of wresting a living, even a good life, from this last frontier.

For amusement the young woman in the orange hat will go to the sandhill dances with others of her kind, perhaps in an outmoded party dress, but most likely in a mail-order print, perhaps made by hand or on the sewing machine of Marlizzie. Their men will be in overalls, turned up jauntily at the cuffs, with open shirt necks and loose ties.

The women will sit on planks over boxes along the wall as their grandmothers did. Now and then the older women, like Marlizzie, will dance to the same fiddle and accordion of forty, fifty years ago. And at midnight there will be cake and sandwiches and coffee.

And toward morning the crowd will scatter, on horseback, in wagons, and in a few old cars that cough and sputter in the sand. The women go to their homes, the straw ticks and cottonwood-leaf mattresses, and to refreshing sleep.

They are not so different from Marlizzie or even the wife of Marcus Whitman. They, too, will learn to look to the sky for the time of planting and harvest, to the earth for the wisdom and the strength she yields to those who walk her freshly turned sod.

VII

Sandhill Sundays

In this sketch, written in 1930 about a year after "The Kinkaider Comes and Goes," the author no longer confines herself to an autobiographical frame of reference. Here recollection of tales told, research, observation, and firsthand experience are combined to evoke a half-century of Sandhills history in a series of action pictures.

OUT OF THE EAST AND THE SOUTH, God's country, came the movers, pounding their crowbait ponies or their logy plow critters on to the open range of Northwest Nebraska. They exchanged green grass, trees, and summer night rains for dun-colored sandhills crowding upon each other far into the horizon, wind singing in the red bunch grass or howling over the snow-whipped knobs of December, and the heat devils of July dancing over the hard land west of the hills. No Indian wars, few gun fights with bad men or wild animals—mostly it was just standing off the cold and scratching for grub. And lonesome! Dog owls, a few nesters in dugouts or soddies, dusty cow waddies loping over the hills, and time dragging at the heels—every day Monday.

Then came big doings. Cow towns with tent and false-front saloons; draw played Sunday afternoons in the dust of the trail between the shacks; cowboys tearing past the little sod churches, shooting the air full of holes while the sky pilots inside prayed hell and damnation on them; settlers cleaned of their shirts by cardsharpers whilst their women picked cow chips barefooted and corn leaves rattled dry in the wind.

When the settlers got clear down in the mouth, the sky pilots showed up among them. The meeting-point of the revivals was most generally Alkali Lake, on the Flats. All Sunday morning moving wagons, horsebackers, hoofers, and a buggy or two from town collected along the bare bank. Almost every dugout or claim shack for twenty, thirty miles around was deserted. Everybody turned out to hear the walking parson.

From the back end of a buggy, fortified by a beard cut like that of Christ in holy pictures, the sky pilot lined out the crowd hunched over on wagon tongues, stretched on horse blankets or on the ground, hot with the glaring sun.

"You see them heat waves out there on the prairie? Them's the fires of hell, licking round your feet, burning your feet, burning your faces red as raw meat, drying up your crops, drawing the water out of your wells! You see them thunderheads, shining like mansions in the sky but spurting fire and shaking the ground under your feet? God is mad, mad as hell!"

Somewhere a woman began to moan and cry. The crowd was up like a herd of longhorns at the smell of fire. A swarthy ground-scratcher from down on the Breaks began to sing "Nearer My God to Thee," couldn't remember the words, and broke out crying, too. Others took up songs. "Beulah Land." Somebody broke into the popular parody and hid his face. "Washed in the Blood of the Lamb."

Two whiskered grangers helped the parson off the buggy. "Come to Jesus! Come to Jesus!" he sang as he waded into the already cooling water of the lake. The moaning woman was ducked first and came up sputtering and coughing. The crowd pushed forward, to the bank, into the water.

And when the sun slipped away and the cool wind carried the smell to stale water weed over the prairie, almost everybody was saved. Mrs. Schmidt, with eight children and a husband usually laid out in the saloon at Hay Springs, sang all the way home she was so happy. The next week they sent her to the insane asylum. The youngest Frahm girl took pneumonia from the ten-mile trip behind plow critters and died. The lone Bohemian who scratched the thin ground on the Breaks strung himself up.

Talk of the big revival drifted back into the hills. "I wisht I coulda gone; it'd-a been a lot of comfort to me," Mrs. Endow mumbled when she heard about it. But one of their horses had died of botts and her only chance of getting out now was in a pine box.

II

The nesters, well versed in drainage, were helpless against the drouth. Each spring there was less money for seed, and Sundays were more and more taken up with the one problem, irrigation. Everybody threw in together here, the Iowa farmer, the New England school-teacher afraid of his horses, and the worn-out desert rat, the European intellectual, and the Southern poor white. There was no place for women at these meetings and so they stayed at home, wrangling the old hen and chickens and watering the dry sticks of hollyhock.

Ten years later the drouth, the cold, and too much buying on pump had driven out the shallow-rooted nesters and the sky pilots. A few hilltop churches took care of those who still believed in a benevolent God. The stickers took up dry farming, pailed cows, and ran cattle. But farming and milking meant long hours; ranching called for large pastures and consequent isolation. Night entertainment grew more common. First came literaries, with windy debates on Popular Election of Our Presidents and the British Colonial Policy, followed by spelldowns and a program—songs: "Love Is Such a Funny, Funny Thing," "Oh, Bury Me Not on the Lone Prairie"; dialogues; pieces: "The Deacon's Courtship" and "The Face on the Barroom Floor"; food. Then the long trails across the hills, dangerous at night, particularly along the gullies and river bluffs.

Eventually most of the communities settled upon dancing as the most conducive to all-night entertainment. Everybody went. If Old John was running the floor at the dance, there'd be a shapping match if he had to cuss out every cowhand or bean-eater there. He'd begin to look the crowd over while he was calling the square dances:

> Gents bow out and ladies bow under,
> Hug 'em up tight and swing like thunder

—up on an old tub or bench, stomping his boots to hurry the fiddlers until the girls' feet left the floor and skirts flew. At midnight he'd help carry in the wash boiler full of coffee, dip a tin cup among the floating sacks of grounds, and pour it back through the steam.

"Looks like your coffee fell in a crick coming over," he always bawled out. Nobody except Mrs. Beal, Old Man Beal's mail-order wife, ever minded.

With his cud of Battle Ax stowed away in a little rawhide sack he carried, Old John would sink his freed jaws into a thick slab of boiled ham and bread as he helped pass the dishpans full of sandwiches and cake to couples lining the walls, sitting on boards laid between chairs. The remains in the pans he'd distribute among the stags sitting on horse blankets, like flies gathered about drops of sorghum on the floor. And afterward, while he swept the dust and bread rinds into little piles, he'd egg on the shapping match.

"Times ain't like they was," he'd complain, looking the crowd over. "There ain't a feller here with spunk 'nuff to take a leatherin' to git a purty girl."

Somebody who didn't bring a girl but would like to take one home finally grinned and stood up, his neck getting red when the prettier girls, those that might be chosen, giggled. And somebody who was afraid of losing his girl, or had a general prod on, got up too, and the bargain was made.

A horsebacker's leather shaps are brought in and unlaced so the two legs fall apart. Each shapper takes half and the crowd follows them to the middle of the floor, Old John passing out advice impartially between trips to the door to spit.

Coats, if any, are jerked off, collars unbuttoned. Norm and Al, the two shappers, sit on the floor, facing, their legs dove-tailed, each with half a shap. Everybody crowds up, the dancers first, then the older folks, and around the edge the boys and dogs.

They draw straws from Old John's fist and the unlucky one, Norm, lies on his back and snaps his legs up over him. He takes the horse-hide across his rump with all the sting Al can spread on it. Al's legs are up now; Norm gets his lick in on saddle-hardened muscles. The crowd yells. The *whack-whack* of the shaps settles down into a steady clockwork business, the legs going up and down like windmill rods. After a while Al jerks his head and Old John drags him out. He sits up, his face red and streaked as a homesick school-ma'am's, only his is sweating.

"Norm's got two pairs of pants on."

The accused is taken out and fetched back. "Only one pair," says Old John. The whacking starts again. Girls giggle nervously, their men hanging to them. The crowd is taking sides. Two sprouts near the edge take a lam at each other. Old John separates them. On the floor the whacking is slowing up. He drags Al away again, the puncher's head lolling, his face gray as window putty.

The crowd shies back. A pail of water is brought in. Al's face is wet down with a towel. He grunts and turns over on his belly, the sign that Norm's won. Who'll he pick? There's no hurry. He can't dance any more tonight and it's a long time until "Home, Sweet Home."

Everybody is talking. The fiddlers start:

> Honor your partner and don't be afraid
> To swing corner lady in a waltz promenade.

Sunday was spent getting home and sleeping.

III

As the nesters pulled out, sheepmen bought in along the fringe of the hills. Here and there a settler who couldn't make a go of the newer farming or cattle took up woolie culture too, and then the coyote, up to now a raider of hen coops and scrub calves, developed into a killer. Wolf hunts were organized. The regular hour for a hunt was about nine in the morning. A relay of shots started the horsebackers off on a fifteen-mile front, from Mirage Flats to Keplinger's Bridge. Yelling, whistling, running any coyote that tried to break the line, they headed for Jackson's towards a big V made of hog wire, chicken fencing, and lath corncribbing with a wire trap in the point.

Broad-handed women unpacked baskets of grub in the big barn now for the dinner.

"Time they was rounding up a few coyotes," Mrs. Putney says, as she uncovers a roaster full of browned chickens. "Henry lost twenty-five sheep last week, just killed and let lay."

"They been having three, four hunts a year since '84 and all they does is make the critters harder to catch. They nearly never gets none," Mary Bowen, an old settler, commented as she measured out the ground coffee. "Dogs or poison, that fixes the sneaking devils that gets my turkeys."

"But where's the fun in that?" asked one of the girls climbing into the mow, late, but not dressed for work, anyway.

By one o'clock black specks are running over the Flats like bugs. Yells, commands, a cloud of dust. Horses tromping on each other's heels. A few shots. That's all.

Four rabbits, one badger, and two coyotes for two hundred hunters.

"Got sight of a couple of more, but they musta snuck outa the lines. Not many-a the Pine Creek bunch showed up."

Now the dinner, dished up on long boards over barrels in the mow. Windy fellows talking about long-ago hunts, when there were real wolves, too smart for a mob. Cigars were passed by the local candidate for the legislature; an invitation to a hunt at Rushville two weeks come Sunday was read, and the hunt was over.

IV

But the grass in the loose soil died under the sharp hoofs and close cropping of the woolies. The ranchers hated sheep and made it as

hot for the woolie nurses as they could. At last most of the sheepmen
pulled their freight. But just as the country was going back to cows,
the Kinkaid Act was passed. The land rush put a shack on every
section of land—Easterners mostly, who established Sunday schools,
with ladies' aids to meet Sunday afternoons because the horses must
work on weekdays. Many of the newcomers objected to dancing and
had play-parties instead. The soddies were small and the Kinkaider
chose his games accordingly. Charades, guessing games, or

> Tin-tin,
> Come in,
> Want to buy some tin?

Perhaps

> Pleased or displeased?
> Displeased.
> What can I do to please you?

Foot races, pussy wants a corner, drop the handkerchief, or all outs
in free on moonlit summer evenings. And endless songs, many of
them parodies on popular tunes:

> Al Reneau was a ranchman's name,
> Skinning Kinkaiders was his game,
> First mortgages only, at a high percent,
> Jew you down on your cattle to the last red cent.

But no matter how much truck the Kinkaider grew, he couldn't
turn it into cash profitably unless it could walk the thirty, forty miles
to a shipping point. They must have a railroad. Once more the women
stayed at home while the men gathered at the local post office,
chewed tobacco, talked, wrote letters, signed petitions, and bought
more machinery on pump, on the hope of a railroad that never came.
Once more the shallow-rooted left and the rest turned into combina-
tion farmers and stockmen. Sundays became ranch days, with a new
crop of cowpunchers to show off before the native daughters at
scratching matches.

The crowd is perched on the top planks, on the up-wind side of the
corral. Here Monkey Ward cowboys strut about in bat wings and
loud shirts. Riders that are riders sit on their haunches in the sun,
dressed in worn shaps and blue shirts. In the corral several green
hands are running a handful of wild-eyed colts around, trying for a
black gelding. They snag an old sorrel mare, have to throw her to
get the rope, try again.

"Why don't y'u do y'ur practisin' on y'ur bucket calves to home?"
an old-timer laughs, nudging his straw-chewing neighbor. Dust,

mix-up of horses and booted cowboys. They have the gelding, snub him short. Now for the blind and the leather. Red climbs on the last horse, the drawing card of the Sunday afternoon.

"Let 'er go!"

The corral gate flies back. The blind's jerked away. The black shakes, gathers into a hump, pushing Red up into the sky.

"Rip him open!"

The spurs rowel a red arc on the black hide. The horse goes up, turns, hits the dust headed north, and it's over. Red's still going south.

A hazer snags the horse, not head-shy, and brings him in. The fence hoots when Red gets up, dusts off his new hat, and walks away to himself. Not even hurt.

Lefty is prodded off the fence, not so keen now as he was a minute before Red lit. He climbs on. The black, instead of going up, spraddles out, sinking his smoke belly to the ground.

"Scratch him!" an old-timer shouts. Lefty does. The horse is off across the prairie, bucking and running in a straight line. That's nothing. But he stops short, all four feet together. Lefty comes near going on.

"Fan him!" a tenderfoot shouts. An old rider spits. His guess is correct. There isn't time for fanning. The black leaves the ground, swaps ends, runs, swaps again. Lefty hangs on as best he can but the turns come too fast. He's down on his shoulder, just missing the double kick the black lets out before he quits the country. Lefty picks himself up, his arm hanging funny.

"Collarbone's busted."

A couple of girls in overalls slide off the fence and fuss over Lefty. Any rider's a good rider while he's hurt.

"That horse belongs in a rodeo string," they comfort him.

The fence is deserted. "See you all at my place tonight!" Madge Miller shouts. The young people scatter down the valley in little knots and couples. Some shag it over the chophills, hurrying home to do the chores so they can go to the party at Madge's.

"Next scratching match at the Bar M week come Sunday," someone reminds the riders.

"Hi!"

V

The country is scarcely grown up and people are already building a tradition, a background. Old settlers and their children are suddenly superior to newer settlers and entitled to an annual barbecue as befits the honor. An old-time roundup dust hangs over Peck's

Grove. Horses shy and snort at the smell of fire and frying meat.
Cars are lined up by the signal stick of Mike Curran, who once
prodded cows through the branding chute. Cowboys tear up, leading
wild horses for the bucking contest.

"Hi! Gonna ride that snaky bronc? Betcha two bits you can't
even sit my old broomtail!"

Women hurry about, lugging heavy baskets, picking a shady place
for the old settlers' table. The men look over the race track, the horses,
the new cars.

"Well, you son of a sand turtle! Step down and look at your saddle!"

Logan-Pomroy grins and gets out of his imported car. He shakes
the hand of Old Amos, champion muskrat trapper, for this one day a
year forgetting that he is the owner of a ranch and three banks and
that Amos is in dirty overalls, with gunny sack and baling wire for
shoes. Today they are old cronies, the two oldest settlers.

"How's the meat hole coming?" Logan-Pomroy demands, and
leads the way to the barbecue pit. Two sweating ranch cooks are
turning quarters of browning beef with pitchforks or basting the meat
carefully with a mixture of water, vinegar, salt, and pepper. The
drippings sizzle and smoke in the red bed of ash-wood coals in the
pit under the barbecuing racks.

"Come and git it!" a fat woman calls after what seems hours.

The men trail over to a table made of salt barrels and planks covered with white cloths. At the head Logan-Pomroy and Amos sit,
with later settlers down the sides. Old settlers' daughters wait on
them, passing huge platters of beef, mutton, and pork, followed by
unlimited vegetables, salads, pies, cake, fruit, and several rounds of
the coffeepot.

After the dinner there'll be contests. Fat men's, sack, three-legged,
potato, and peanut races. For the women there is that old rip-snorter,
a wagon race. Each contestant draws two horses, a wagon, and enough
harness. First to drive around the track wins. The young cowboys
with hair on their chests will show their guts in the bucking-bronco
contest, twisting the broncs in approved style, and take part in the
wild cow, wild mule, and surcingle races. But before that there are
cigars and speeches and songs. Old Amos adds his rumblings to the
"Nebraska Land":

> I've reached the land of drouth and heat,
> Where nothing grows for man to eat.
> For wind that blows with burning heat,
> Nebraska Land is hard to beat.

About sundown the crowd scatters. Logan-Pomroy's motor roars up the hill. Without a good-bye Old Amos shuffles away through the brush down the river. The big day is over.

VI

But the sandhiller lives in the present also. The young folks take long car trips to dances that break up at midnight, by command of the law, and endeavor to spend most of the time until Sunday morning getting home. Sunday is a good day for those who need it to sleep off bad liquor. The more prosperous ranchers escape the cold by going south, the heat by going to the lakes. Some of these are old settlers noted for forty years of unfailing hospitality. They still entertain, when they are home, in comfortable ranch houses with refrigerators and radios. Once their invitations, usually printed in the local items of the community paper, read something like this:

NOTICE

Party and dance at Bud Jennet's, April 2.

Dinner from one to seven.

Beds and breakfast for all.

Everybody welcome.

Seventy, eighty people would come in those days, some of them forty miles in wagons or on horseback. Next day the men slept between suggans in the haymow, the women all over the house. But that was when Yvette was a baby. Now she is home from college and with formal bids, as she calls them, they rounded up twenty guests for about four hours of housewarming in their new home. Some of them came a hundred miles, and it was worth the trip. There is an orchestra in the music room, with flowers from Alliance, and candles, Japanese prints framed in Chinese red, and tapestry panels.

"Such a beautiful home!" the guests exclaim to Mrs. Jennet.

And in three hours the maid has the muss all cleared away.

There is no disputing the fact that the Jennets did well in cattle and potash. The callers were all prosperous and charming. Not like the Jennets' guests once were, when all who read the notice were welcome. Today nobody ate with starvation appetite. Nobody had to be thawed out at the hay-burner before he could sing "The Little Old Sod Shanty on the Claim" or play "There'll Be a Hot Time" on the fiddle or the accordion. Nobody let habitual curses slip and surely none of the guests today would ever think of stomping and singing:

> Just plant me in a stretch of west,
> Where coyotes mourn their kin.
> Let hawses paw and tromp the mound
> But don't you fence it in.

These people believe in sealed copper coffins in vaults, and they are decidedly not planted but laid to rest. And not one of them forgot himself so far as to ask about Bud Jennet, knowing that he must be in Alliance with his new lady friend, seeing that he wasn't to the housewarming.

INDIAN STUDIES

*I long ago took to heart the saying of one of my
old teachers: The historian should have no memory—
write it down (46).*

THE GREATEST DIFFICULTY encountered when working with frontier material is the dearth of sources written close to the date of observation—close enough to be fairly free from the tricks memory plays and written by an observer capable of evaluating what he sees. The frontier is usually occupied by nonwriters—sometimes illiterates, sometimes refugees from justice who have no desire to leave records, and always by men of action. The occasional visitor leaves letters, manuscripts, and books behind, but his observation is often faulty or completely misleading and valueless because he just isn't "posted," as one man said of Parkman's discussion of Indians in his *Oregon Trail*. The deeper you get into your problem, the more cautious you become. The temptation is to research all your life, and never write anything down (57).

While gathering material about Crazy Horse I camped on the Pine Ridge Reservation in 1930–1931, but the first year,while I could find out almost anything else, any mention of the Custer fight was met with stony silence. At last Oliver Jumping Eagle, head of the Indian police, told me what was wrong. The Sioux at that time had a $700,000,000.00 suit pending in the Court of Claims and the story had got around that if it was awarded $1000.00 would be deducted from the allotment of every family that had a member engaged in the Custer battle—and I was supposed to be seeking them out! Nothing takes the place of documentation, however, and I sought out the old army records, then piled up helter-skelter above the Department of Interior garage. For days on end I waited before they would let me in. When I did get in, I found many things—some by accident. . . .

I long ago took to heart the saying of one of my old teachers: The historian should have no memory—write it down. But the last word in history is never in. When we read in Nebraska's archives the complaints of Dodge's dragoons about mud they had to drag through up the Platte, and a few years later the Oregon Trailers writing of the terrible ordeal of dust storms, we thought they were exaggerating their difficulties. We had all seen dust storms and they were not too hard to live through. Then, almost a century later, came the dust storms of 1934. And then we knew what they were talking about (46).

VIII

Some Oddities of the American Indian

This paper was outlined by the author at the September 1954 meeting of the Denver Posse of the Westerners, a national organization of people interested in the Old West. During the course of her talk she remarked that

It is interesting how different these oddities that struck our early white men so forcibly seem to us now, after a later and closer second look. I had the need for such a second look impressed upon me very early. Hunters often came to our place on the Niobrara River of western Nebraska, particularly if they were having bad luck getting game. There was always good hunting at Old Jules'. I recall one night a buggy came driving in through a fall thunderstorm. It was a hunter friend of our father's from Alliance, with Buffalo Bill Cody along. I was about five and the noise of getting Cody in the house awoke me and I peered out. There, in the light of our kitchen lamp, stood the handsomest man of my life, tall, in beaded buckskin, and with long white curls falling over his shoulders.

The next morning Mother sent me to call Mr. Cody to breakfast. There was no reply to my knock and finally I pushed the door open a crack. Evidently Bill had gone duck hunting with my father, for the bed was empty, but on the bed post hung that handsome head of curling hair. In that one moment I learned something of disillusionment and something of the need for a second look, always a careful second look.

Now, even after a manuscript is in early draft, I find I have to go over my notes and sources once more and, if possible, take the manuscript back to the actual locale. I carried both of my Indian books from site to site. I took *Crazy Horse* to the icy ridge where Fetterman died, and to the Tongue River winter camps. With *Cheyenne Autumn* in my brief case, I retraced the September flight of those people north from Indian Territory, and through October to Fort Robinson and the sandhills, examining every important site on the way, and finally on to the Tongue, considering every Indian idea once more as I went (45).

MOST OF THE ODDITIES of any society only seem so to the newcomer, the outsider. Because the life of the new world broke with great abruptness upon the civilized world, few societies have ever seemed stranger than that of the American Indian to the early explorers. This was partly because these Europeans were generally untrained in anthropology or any social observation, mostly because they had little interest beyond the mercenary and the missionary. Both of these classifications are notoriously intolerant of other ways, no matter how successfully these ways seem to fit the man and his environment. For instance, there was the common disgust over the Indian's habit of eating every part of the animal, say the buffalo. In shocked glee the early accounts of Indian hunts report seeing the women strip the small intestines of their contents, put a droplet of bile on each for seasoning, and give them to the young children to munch like sweetmeats. Only very occasionally does anyone note how well the young savages seemed to thrive on such revolting diet.

Then there was the perpetual complaint about nakedness, which probably seldom reached the bareness of our present-day Bikinied bather, and the general misconception of woman's place in Indian society. Plainly, too, the Indian's scriptural benightedness gave the early observers much real satisfaction, and justification for some inhuman treatment of this red savage who had never heard of Christ. Even the frequent bathing of the Indian was viewed as somehow corrupt by the suspicious Europeans, probably pretty gamy individuals to the Indian, who perspires little and considers even the bathing white man as often a stinker.

To the early settlers, from Plymouth to Oregon, the commonest oddity, the one that brought fear for property and for life, must have been the Indian's way of peering in at the window, say out of the darkness into a lighted room. Most settlers never discovered that to the redskin it was very good manners to look in on his neighbor. The Indian's commonest protest of neglect was, "You never lift my lodge flap to see how it is with me." Even rudimentary manners demanded this attention, specially to newcomers. The window was a convenient lodge opening and the peering Indian was being friendly and polite in addition to satisfying his curiosity and perhaps later his hunger. If he really wanted to kill and burn he would not expose himself in a lighted window frame.

Back in the dangerous days of spear and arrow it was necessary for the Indian women to carry the burdens. A man always had to have both hands free to fight off any enemies that might spring out upon him and his people, or for any game that might flush if his hungry ones were to be fed. Most Indian society within our nation was matrilinear: the man, unless already a powerful and well-established chief, left his people, his tribe, for his wife's, and the children belonged to her people. So a Zuni became a Santa Clara, a Ute a Shoshoni. The Cheyenne Young Chief Little Wolf was a chief among his people and then become one among the people of his Sioux wife.

The notion that brides were sold came out of a general misunderstanding of this matrilinear pattern. The bride's family accepted the new husband as son, brother, and uncle, and as a sort of second father to the wife's nephews and nieces. He had every right to the affection, the assistance, and the protection of such a relative, and to profit from the family prestige and following. In return he was expected to contribute certain ordinary assets to the family: a good name, honorable and agreeable deportment, and the honors and coups that testified to a passable achievement in the hunt and in war. Since the horse herds were more or less community family property and his to use when he wished, it was considered only right that he make a reasonable contribution here. Besides, his ability as stealer and catcher of horses was proof of his command over one of the chief items of Indian commerce, an index to his ability to make a living for his family. To the European who welcomed a dowry with his bride, this custom of the man bringing the dowry seemed very odd and somehow degrading, but, curiously, degrading *to the woman.*

Among our Indians courtship was by fairly fixed pattern, as it is in most tight little societies. Yet the presence of an old woman in every lodge with a young girl should have pleased the observers if they had bothered to understand her position. Most of the courtship was under the watchful eyes of this Old One. She slept just inside the lodge door, on the left, the woman's side. She knew all who entered or departed. She was usually nearby during all the waking hours, perhaps working skins or making moccasins with the other old women, or gambling with the plum pits.

The young buck waited along the evening water path for the girl, to exchange a few bantering words with her and her friends, perhaps play an Indian trick or two. He met her at dances, where by custom she drew the youth into the dance, the choice always hers. More formal court was at the evening lodge door, the youth waiting patiently, hoping the girl might come out to stand inside his blanket for a few moments, for a little talk, a little joking. But if the girl was popular there might be half a dozen others waiting too, all taking their chances at a public slight. Later the youth might tie a fine horse outside of the girl's lodge, and if it was led away and added to the family herd, he knew his suit found some favor. From then on the settlement was through some old member of the band, often an old woman, who trotted back and forth in great busyness. Sometimes this took years. Perhaps the youth had to make a greater name for himself as hunter, warrior. Perhaps he had to catch more and better horses so his bride could make a great showing in the ceremonials, on a horse fit to set off her beaded saddle trappings, her dress of good red flannel, perhaps decorated with some elk teeth, with more to come later, perhaps as many as a thousand, as was fitting for the wife of a really important man. But for the early days a few would do, and some ribbons and beads, perhaps rings and bracelets too—all this except the horses and the elk teeth to be obtained by trade of horses, robes, and furs, or taken from enemy Indians.

Before the whisky days, a man usually spent all his married life with the people of his first wife, and any position of importance came to him there. Divorce, however, was always easy, for no one could be held to anything that was repugnant. It was particularly easy for the wife. The tipi or lodge was hers and any time she was dissatisfied with the husband she was free to throw his accoutrements and goods out into the village circle as public notice of the divorce, and all he could do was pick up his belongings and take them to his mother, or, if from elsewhere, to the warrior lodge or a temporary wickiup. He could get a go-between to attempt a reconciliation; or at least he might get part of his dowry back.

If things went well and his importance grew he might take a second wife or even a third, particularly on the Plains. A nomadic hunting and warrior life was dangerous. Many men died young and yet every woman must have a hunter, so the women doubled up. Usually the second wife was a sister or cousin to the first, for there must be peace in the lodge. The good husband consulted his wife before he took a second. Often the wife made the first suggestion. With the man's growing importance there were more guests to feed and provide with presents and the children to care for. No one was a servant in Plains society, and so the chief had to have two wives or more. As the soldiers decimated the warrior ranks, often he had three or even four.

Plains Indian life was very confined during the long winters, with perhaps ten or twelve adults and some children jammed into one habitation, skin or earth, all the snowy months. Quarreling and dissension, tabooed in the village, could not be tolerated at all in the lodge. To keep a good peace, very formal rules of etiquette had grown up. After around seven years of age no boy ever addressed his sisters or his mother directly but spoke through a third person, and he never raised his voice in his mother's lodge. Out of mutual respect the mother and her son-in-law never spoke directly to each other, never looked squarely into each others' faces, although they might live in the same lodge for fifty years. Some of this mother-in-law custom still held among the Sioux in my childhood. I recall a young Oglala who spent a great deal of time visiting at a neighbor's. He finally married the daughter of the household. But it didn't last and once when he was at our house he explained why. "I couldn't go sit around and visit with my mother-in-law no more. So I gets split up an' now I can go back there and talk to her all the time."

Of course a man could throw away his wife too, but there was a little more to it, for, with perhaps some of the horses to be returned and the implied criticism on all the family, the woman's male relatives might resent the breakup. Often they took quick action if a woman relative was mistreated by her husband. Among the Cheyennes any-one who shed the blood of a tribesman, even by accident, suffered ostracism, and yet when the sister of two prominent Cheyennes was struck by her husband of Sioux blood, they killed him. This was toler-ated because, although he was a Cheyenne by marriage, the moment he died he was no longer married and so was only a bad Sioux. A nice bit of legal sophistry worthy of a Philadelphia lawyer.

This brings me to the general handling of lawlessness among In-dians. A people without jails can tolerate no lawlessness; without locks they can tolerate no thief, and without paper for records, no liar. Perhaps this was why one of the great oddities the Indian found in the white man was his casualness about the unkept promise and the outright falsehood, even on a governmental level.

There was some difference between the large tribes and the small on the matter of intratribal bloodshed. Minority peoples are usually firmer about such killing and in this the Cheyennes were particularly severe. As I said before, any spilling of Cheyenne blood by a tribes-man brought ostracism, usually for four years. With enemies all about him this could easily be a death sentence. Often the ostracized, man or woman, drew enough followers to provide some security. Perhaps the expelled one went to another band, if they would accept him, or to allies, Sioux or Arapaho, or even to enemies. Plains intertribal wars were never total. There was always some visiting back and forth and any Indian was safe as a guest in an enemy camp, once he got in. He was entertained, given the usual guest presents, and on his way home escorted safely beyond the outlying scouts. Carl Raswan, of *Black Tents of Arabia*, told me that he found this same custom among the Bedouin Arabs. Perhaps sparse population makes even the enemy visitor welcome.

Among the Sioux, the majority people of the Plains, the rare killings were usually settled between the relatives and friends of each side, with the enforced counsel of disinterested men. Usually the killer was sent away from the band for a cooling-off period all around. Sometimes he went out on a war party or on a long hunt or a visit, perhaps with his wife, if there was one, and she cared to go. In some instances his lodge was destroyed, but more often it was marked by the usual crossed brush at the doorway to indicate the owner's absence. If, however, the man killed was a prominent one, there could be tragic consequences for the band or tribe. Under the influence of trader whisky, young Red Cloud killed Chief Bull Bear and thereby split the Oglalas apart "as a rock is broken," the Indians said. The rift was not healed for twenty-nine years; not until, in 1870, Little Wound was appointed to Bull Bear's place. As late as 1931 there was still a rift between Little Wound's Cut-Offs and Red Cloud's Bad Faces on Pine Ridge reservation.

For a minor offence the Indian was usually given a talking-to by some of the wiser members of the band, and if he persisted he was deprived of certain privileges. Repeated lawbreaking and trouble-making in the lodge or the camp got the culprit bow-whipped by whichever warrior society had been selected for the policing of the village. If still unreformed, the trouble-maker could be ostracized.

Indians have always complained that the white man never understood their system of chieftainships, and it is clear that much trouble did rise from such misunderstanding. No Plains tribe and perhaps few others ever had one head chief. The Sioux and the Cheyennes had councils of chiefs, usually with four head or Old Man Chiefs; as, for instance, the four Shirtwearers of the Oglala Sioux. The Cheyennes had a council of forty-four chiefs, made up of four from each of the ten bands and four Old Man Chiefs. Of course none of these positions were hereditary, and while the selection was usually for around four to ten years, any chief could be "thrown from his place" at any time that the people and the council thought he had failed to keep his oath of office, which always included the promise to put the good of the people first. The most stringent oaths were those required of the four Oglala Shirtwearers and the Cheyenne Bearer of the Sacred Bundle. The latter, always one of the four Old Man

Chiefs, had no more power than the other three but he had a greater responsibility for the purity of his motives. Failure of the other chiefs to abide by their duties brought no loss of attunement with the Great Powers which were a composite of the earth, the sky, the four directions, and all the things between. If the Bundle Bearer acted from any but wise and unselfish motives, both he and his people lost the mystic guidance and power of the Sacred Bundle with which he was entrusted.

The failure of the whites to understand that no one man could speak for the whole tribe brought death to several good chiefs. The Government settled on Conquering Bear in the treaty-making of 1851, when no other man would let himself be set up as head of all the Teton, the western, Sioux. The Bear had been reluctant to accept this position but when the whites insisted, he took the job, and the goodly presents too, of course. But three years later he was shot down by the white man Grattan. As the chief was dying he selected Man Afraid of His Horse as his successor, but the Man firmly refused the offer. Incidentally, the spot where the scaffold for Conquering Bear's body was placed later became part of our orchard on the Niobrara. In my childhood an occasional old Sioux used to come to dance a few solemn steps there, and then smoke a pipe in the evening sun, as though communing with the old days, when the Sioux were a free people, the great tribe of the Plains.

Perhaps here is the place to mention another white-man oddity in the eyes of the Indian. A paleface who did wrong was always treated as an individual criminal, but if an Indian was guilty of wrongdoing the whole tribe was the criminal and any part, or the whole, that could be caught was shot down. This complaint was made when Wild Bill Hickok killed the peace chief Whistler. The Sioux were finally given permission to capture Hickok but they must bring him in to the whites for trial, and they must harm no other white man. Yet when any whites were killed, or even horses stolen, all the Indians were pursued, and if they didn't move very fast, were destroyed.

An important aspect of the Indian that the white man never understood was the redman's notion of property; and the other way around. To the Plains Indian nothing that was made less by division could be inherited. A good name, art and craft designs, as the arrows and feather bonnets of the men, the women's patterns for beading and paint, were passed on to the heirs, the men's things to the men, the women's things down the women's line. Everything else was distributed in a Giveaway Dance after the owner's death. Some special items went to friends, but most of the divisible property went to the needy and the sad and unlucky who must be made glad.

To the Indian, personal ownership of land was impossible to conceive. Food, arms, clothing, livestock could be owned, given, sold, or destroyed. The tribe could give a man the temporary right to tell a particular story, to sing a certain sacred song, or carry and guard a ceremonial object, such as the Oglala Lances or the Medicine Arrows, the Buffalo Hat and the Sacred Bundle of the Cheyennes. A man could even sell or bestow his place in a warrior society, subject to the approval of the membership. This was also true of some women's societies, but not the Only One society, made up of those who had had only one man, nor of the secret bead and handicraft society, in which each woman worked on her inherited designs with such modifications as she developed. The right to use these designs could only be passed on down the woman's line, never sold or given, but the articles adorned with these designs could become cherished gifts.

But land was something no one could ever own. It was held for the tribe, for its lifetime use and for posterity. Sale of land could never be more than temporary; so when Indians, from Plymouth Rock to Oregon, sold land, they thought of the sale as a temporary arrangement. The moment that the payment ceased to come the land returned to the tribe; or so they thought as long as they could. To the Indian, land, the earth, was revered as the mother from whom all things came, all such things as the rock, the tree, the cloud, the man. This reverence was expressed at the beginning of every smoke, and with the first bite of every meal. Nothing could ever be done to diminish the land, nothing to make it less for all those whose moccasins walked upon it, and for all those whose tracks were still to come.

IX

The Lost Sitting Bull

This study originally was published with the title "There Were Two Sitting Bulls." Concerning its genesis, the author wrote: "The public, and frontier historians too, had made one man of the two diametrically opposed individuals. One was the great friendly Oglala chief, Sitting Bull the Good, who, among a dozen other good exploits, had saved the whites at Red Cloud Agency up near the later Fort Robinson from massacre twice and was given a 'gold'-mounted and inscribed presentation rifle by President Grant in May 1875, only to have this presentation used as evidence of the treacherous nature of the Hunkpapa Sitting Bull, because *he* was in the Custer fight in June 1876, little more than a year later. The Oglala Sitting Bull [was] entirely lost in the personality of the other to newspapermen.

"For years I tried to explain this to researchers and historians, but it always required long letters to cite the endless documents that proved two men instead of one. When I discovered the presentation rifle in the Museum of the American Indian, I finally blew up, wrote the salient points into an article, and had it published where outdoor men would see it, in *Blue Book*. Unfortunately, my map and much of the explanatory matter establishing the presence of the two men at entirely different places at a dozen given historically important dates wasn't used by *Blue Book*" (70).

HISTORY IS THE MEMORY of the race and, like the individual's memory, it plays odd tricks. Not the least of these was the almost total disappearance, within eighty years, of one of the nation's real friends, and the transfer of his achievements and rewards to another, where they served as the final evidence of a treacherous nature.

For over ninety years the name of Sitting Bull has been well known, first as a leader of the warlike Sioux and then as the principal Indian attraction with Buffalo Bill Cody's Wild West Show. Over America and Europe he was a picturesque figure in a feather headdress selling his photograph to small boys. Sometimes he even put the painful scrawl that was his name in the white man's language upon pieces of paper.

Yet in the summer of 1876, after the shocking news of General Custer's annihilation by a lot of supposedly naked, whooping, blood-thirsty savages, an army officer said ruefully, "It must be true that Sitting Bull is a West Point graduate."

Whether this salved the army's wounds or not, the military pursuit of the Indians after the Custer fight was energetic, and with the buffalo very scarce, Sitting Bull decided to lead his starving Hunk-papa Sioux out of their hunting grounds of the Yellowstone and the Upper Missouri country north into Canada. Soon a newspaper man was circulating a spurious interview with the Hunkpapa leader, claiming that Sitting Bull was an alumnus of St. John's College. Others produced other schools, and listed the Bull as a student of French history particularly enamored of Napoleon. Some called him a linguist, and finally R. D. Clarke came up with the real coup. In a pamphlet called "The Works of Sitting Bull," he presented the old buffalo-hunting Sioux as a writer of Sapphic verse in Latin.

But there were angry charges too, claiming that all the years Sitting Bull was fighting the government, costing the nation millions of dollars and hundreds of lives, he was listed on the rolls of an Indian agency, drawing the regular annuities and rations, and, worse, ammunition for war. Accounts of such reliable and unsensational papers as the New York *Tribune* proved that Sitting Bull had visited Washington as a friend of the whites several times and, the spring of 1875, received a handsomely engraved repeating rifle from the President of the United States. Yet a year later he was in the fight that left Custer and his men dead on the ridge overlooking the timber-lined Little Big Horn. Six months after the battle the presentation rifle was back in white-man hands, picked up outside of General Miles cantonment on the Yellowstone, the brass mounting still bright as gold to the Indians, the inscription untarnished:

> Sitting Bull, from The President
> for Bravery & True Friendship

There was no denying the rifle; millions had seen the story. Many, including army officers, reported they had seen Sitting Bull study the campaigns of Napoleon and knew that he liked to look through any newspapers he managed to save from his trips to the Overland Trail stations or the army posts, and that he carried them along even

while out fighting the whites from the Smoky Hill of Kansas to the
Bozeman Trail of upper Wyoming. Further, it was easy to prove
that his name stood on the agency rolls from the settling of the Bozeman war in 1868 until long after the death of Custer. Here was the
treachery of the redskin, plain to see.

Or it would have been treachery if this man on the agency rolls,
this recipient of the gift rifle, had been the leader of the Hunkpapas.
But he wasn't. This man was of the Oglala division of the Sioux,
whose hunting grounds were from the Powder River into Kansas,
and he was not only called Sitting Bull, but Sitting Bull the Good.

The two men were born about ten years apart, the Hunkpapa in
1831, the Oglala around 1841, when the traders' whisky was whipping
the villages into such violence that his own grandfather, the head
chief of the Cut-Off band of the Oglalas, was shot down in a drunken
brawl by Red Cloud, who was already a great warrior then, and
later was named the government's chief of all the Oglala Sioux.

Early in his youth the southern Sitting Bull,* called Drum Packer
then, had found the white man full of curious and interesting ways.
When the transcontinental telegraph line went through along the
Overland Trail in 1861, Oscar Collister came to operate the station
at Deer Creek, up above Fort Laramie. Because the Indian agent
located there, and several traders, Deer Creek became a center of
much pleasant loafing during those peaceful years before the war
of 1864. The Oglalas grew very fond of the little white man who
often let them try his talking wires. One of the most eager was young
Drum Packer, whose name as warrior against Indian enemies was
already Sitting Bull. In his letters Collister wrote of teaching him
to use the tap-tap machine, and to speak and read English. This
must have been a very elementary knowledge, and yet fairly striking
in the company of young Sitting Bull's contemporaries. Travelers
and army men, including Lieut. Caspar Collins, often mentioned the
Sitting Bull of the Platte, amused by this son of the fighting Sioux,
with his broad, bland baby-face bent over a book. Often it was
Napoleon's *Campaigns,* borrowed from the post library at Fort Laramie for him.

When this Sitting Bull was away with his village he sent in by
Bissonnette, the village trader married into the tribe, for the newspapers, perhaps writing his order with a lead bullet on a strip torn

* Often interpreted as Slow Bull, perhaps a term of ease and familiarity. When
the old buffalo-hunting Indians spoke of either Sitting Bull by one name it was
usually Slow, and in any amusing situation always Slow Bull.

from a margin: "Want the black and white papers," and signed with the outline of a man's head, a buffalo on his haunches, a sitting bull, floating above it—his Indian picture signature. In an interview published in the *Annals of Wyoming* almost seventy years later, Collister still recalled this, but now in his old age he, or perhaps his interviewer, mixed up the two Sitting Bulls and made one man of the two. But back in the early sixties Collister's letters from the upper Platte show that he knew the man squatting at the fire in the telegraph station the winter of 1862–1863, braids falling over the maps in the *Campaigns*, was the head soldier of Little Wound's Cut-Off Oglalas. This band was a serious, individualistic lot who used to hold the southeast fringe of Sioux country, roughly across the middle of Nebraska, north and south, against the Pawnees, raiding their earthen villages, matching their own few guns and stone-age weapons against the best mounts and arms that the white man could furnish the Pawnees, his early trade allies.

In the meantime the Hunkpapa Sitting Bull was pretty busy in his own country. His father had died in battle and was left on a scaffold up on Cedar Creek, a tributary of the Cannonball, in the present North Dakota. Little Crow, fleeing west from Minnesota the fall of 1862 after the New Ulm uprising, found Sitting Bull around up there, a good three hundred fifty, four hundred travois miles from Collister at Deer Creek Station.

According to the Sioux accounts, the friendship of the southern Sitting Bull, the Oglala, for the whites lasted to the so-called Indian War of 1864, in which the Sioux raids closed the Overland Trail, and which ended in the massacre of the friendly Cheyennes at Sand Creek in Colorado that fall. Sitting Bull was visiting up in the Powder River camps at the time and, packing his medicine bag and shield, he rode down with the warriors under Crazy Horse in answer to the Cheyenne war pipe sent out in a call for help. On the way they stopped to look over the winter prairie around the Blue Water, where eight years earlier Crazy Horse had come upon the smoking camp of Little Thunder after General Harney had struck it. Women and children were scattered all around, torn by cannon shells, their clothing still smoldering, some not yet dead. Several of Sitting Bull's Oglala relatives had been visiting in the camp then, and died there, and yet he had remained a peace man. Now the two men talked of the sorrow of that day, and of this recent attack that had come to the Cheyennes. Always it was the friendlies who were struck, the peace-lovers staying in near the troops as the Great Father asked.

Now at last the remedy seemed plain even to the peace man Sitting Bull, the long-time white-man-lover. They must all fight, everybody be ready.

For the next four years, until his uncle, Little Wound, signed the treaty of 1868 that was to withdraw all the whites and their forts from the Indian country so long as grass shall grow and water flow, only Indian accounts can tell of Sitting Bull, the Oglala, for no white man saw much of him except his flying bullets. And none could know these, for bullets do not carry a man's mark as his arrows did, but they killed just the same.

The first killing was around Julesburg, Colorado, January 1865. From there the great camp of Sioux, Cheyenne, and Arapahoes, out to avenge the Sand Creek massacre, moved north toward the Powder River, destroying ranches and Overland Trail stations, burning a strip a hundred miles wide clean of every white man. With the women and children, the pony herds, and all the goods and the warriors of the Indians usually remaining south of the Platte—they marched north through deepest winter, spreading death and fire and alarm all the way.

The following summer the Oglala Sitting Bull was with the three thousand warriors who attacked the Platte Bridge near the present Casper, Wyoming, named for Lieut. Caspar Collins, who had written so enthusiastically about his visits to the camps of the Oglalas, and of his friend Sitting Bull who liked to study the maps of Napoleon. Chance put the young officer at the Bridge station that one day. The attacking Oglalas recognized him in the fight and cried, "Go back, friend! Go back!" parting to let him through. But he had a wild horse that bolted on into the Cheyenne warriors over the hill, and they knew only that he was one of the hated blue coats who had killed their women and children. When Sitting Bull and the others found out about this, their hearts were so bad over their friend that they had to kill ten more whites.

The rest of the summer of 1865 the Oglalas and their allies harried the Overland Trail from eastern Nebraska to South Pass. Only large, troop-escorted wagon trains willing and able to fight their way through were allowed to try it.

Up in the Hunkpapa country there was action too. The summer of 1864 General Sully had struck at some of the Minnesota Sioux near Killdeer Mountain, far up in what is now North Dakota. Sitting Bull, camped nearby, was drawn into the fight but with small loss to the Hunkpapas. Angered by this and other, larger grievances, Sitting Bull timed his attack on Fort Rice with the Platte Bridge fight the summer of 1865, and then chased the soldiers still marching around north of the Black Hills, and attacked the gold seekers headed for Idaho. The Oglalas found miners too, heading up through Wyoming, on the Bozeman Trail, and then the 4,000 troops of the Powder River Expedition spreading northward from the Overland Trail to punish the Indians for their attacks in the Platte country. But the best the soldiers could do was fight off the warriors they had come to attack, until finally they were glad to start back to Fort Laramie, barefoot, eating their starving horses as they fled before the taunting Indians.

The next year brought new forts like Buford far up the Missouri, where Sitting Bull the Hunkpapa kept up a casual sort of siege. Three new posts strung northward through Wyoming started the Bozeman Trail War, and now Sitting Bull the Oglala found himself drawn up across the Platte to follow Red Cloud, the man who had killed his grandfather, back in the bad, drunken times of whisky wagons in every camp. Now Red Cloud was the man to follow in a very strong fight against the enemy soldiers pushing into the treaty-guaranteed Sioux country. Under the leadership of Red Cloud, the powerful young warrior force developed by the fighting of the last two years harassed the Bozeman Trail and kept Fort Phil Kearny under siege until on December 21, 1866, they wiped out Fetterman and all his men.

By 1868 the fight against the encroaching soldiers was won, the Bozeman forts were dismantled, and a new treaty signed. It was a victory over the white man, and Sitting Bull, the Oglala, saw its glories, but he also saw that the buffalo was vanishing. Soon everybody must live on reservations, on the little islands in the rising sea of whites. To prepare for this some of the strong fighting men must go there right from the start to watch, to protect the women and children. So Sitting Bull, the Oglala, decided to go to an agency even though the head chief was Red Cloud. By 1870, although only twenty-nine years old, he had become so influential with both the white man and the Indians that he was selected as one of the twenty Oglalas to represent them well in Washington. His dignity and his face, still broad and almost as bland as a baby's, surprised everybody who heard his name, particularly the newspapermen. But the government was not confused. They knew about the Hunkpapa Sitting Bull too. He had grown vastly in power, as a medicine man, a diviner, a dreamer, as well as a leader in war and in the council of the Hunkpapas. He had turned down the gift of tobacco sent to coax him to Washington. He would hear no talk about settling on a reservation.

Although the Hunkpapas were busy thrusting the Crows back from the shrinking buffalo ranges the spring and summer of 1872, there was another problem. Troops were escorting the Northern Pacific railroad survey up the Yellowstone, right through the Indian country against all the Indian treaties. They hit the country of Sitting Bull, the Hunkpapa, first and he sent for help. Crazy Horse took his hostile Oglalas up, joining in the attack on Colonel Baker near the mouth of Arrow Creek on August 14. The soldiers got a good look at the Hunkpapa leader, recognizing his limp as he walked out between the battle lines and settled himself with a few of the more courageous followers to smoke a pipe, with bullets spurting up the dust all around. In the meantime the other Sitting Bull was in the midst of Red Cloud's fight against the proposed move of his agency from the Platte up to White River. April 14, 1872, the Oglala agent, Daniels, reported anger and threats of war from the excited Indians. But Sitting Bull arose, quietly pointed out that they had already agreed to go and now they wanted the guns and ammunition they had been promised—which they got. October 25 Daniels made another report on his Sitting Bull. A couple of Indians had been found dead along the Platte, perhaps killed by whites or breeds. Immediately warriors came streaming in upon the agency, armed, painted, whooping, singing war songs.

"Our hearts are bad!" they cried. "It will take white blood to make them good!"

The white men barricaded themselves inside the stockade, thirty men against five hundred mounted warriors, while in the camps the skin lodges began to fall, the women and children hurrying into the sandhills out of range of any flying bullets, while the warriors circled the stockade, firing into the air, lifting arrows to fall inside. Haranguers on the roofs of the buildings roared for burning and for slaughter.

But fifteen young friendlies, guns pointed outward, planted themselves at the stockade gates. Leading them was Sitting Bull, high up now in the Head Band society—warrior sons of noted Oglala chieftains. Through the calm and influence of these men the attack was held off until General Smith's troops arrived from Laramie the next morning. Then the agent made a cracker and molasses feast.

Things were no quieter a year later after the agency was moved to White River in northwest Nebraska, far from an army post, up under the breaks of Pine Ridge that covered the approach from the hostile camps up north. The new agent, Saville, complained to Washington that the Crazy Horse hostiles were slipping in, although getting them to surrender was a major part of his job. Arrogantly, these wild Sioux pushed forward for a share in the annuities and demanded the right to trade for powder and guns, intimidating both the whites and the agency Indians. Many of the young men had been in the attack on Custer, August 1873, on the Yellowstone with Crazy Horse and the Hunkpapa Sitting Bull. They talked big, particularly some Cheyennes who had lost their families to Custer down on the Washita.

"This time, if the cannons had not come hurrying up, he would have been the one wiped out!"

So they bragged, and raced their good horses taken from the whites. The new stockade had no gates, and often before going out on raids along the settlements of the Platte they rode around the inside, four abreast, painted, singing war songs, shooting into the windows while the whites cowered on the floor. Saville finally got carpenters to finish the stockade gates, but a northern Sioux whose brother had been killed came in with his heart bad. At night he dragged loose lumber up to the wall, climbed over, and shot Frank Appleton, the acting agent.

He got away, but by morning thousands of warriors rode whooping around the stockade, fearing for their people in the camps scattered out over the valley, showing their readiness to fight any vengeance. The chiefs came in, admitting they could do nothing with their young men. So the half dozen whites, even those intermarried with the Indians, hid in the cupola at one corner of the stockade, built up high to look out over the White River plain from Crow Butte to the bluffs standing along the north. They had one gun among them, the Winchester the butcher used to kill beef for the old and helpless at issue time. With a keg of water, and sacks of flour for barricading, they stayed up in the cupola four days, the Indians milling around below like a herd of longhorns smelling blood. While the chiefs counciled and Agent Saville was held as hostage, the whites thought about the bull train that was overdue and with the usual kegs of whisky surely hidden under the goods. If the warriors got to that it would be a massacre.

But outside Sitting Bull the Oglala was urging peace upon the young men. If they burned the agency, soldiers would certainly come to shoot the women and children. Even those who got away would have no lodges or robes or meat and with winter upon them. He kept talking, hour after hour, and as the Indians cooled he planted his followers around the agency supplies and cupola while a squaw man living out from the agency whipped his pony for Fort Laramie and the soldiers, with no assurance that he would get through.

Finally there were mirror signals and new excitement among the warriors. The bull train or the military?

It was the military—both horse and walking soldiers and a train of army supplies moving dark on the Laramie trail. Immediately the Indians broke into factions, some wanting to burn the agency and go north, others hurrying the women and children into the breaks before the soldiers arrived and found there was a dead white man to be avenged. The rest charged the friendlies who had held them off until it was too late. But Sitting Bull's following stood fast and it turned out that General Smith was not anxious for bloodshed. Once more presents were made and a feast, with some of the wildest of the hostiles slipping away north afterward. Not Sitting Bull. He went to sleep. When he awoke he found that the soldiers had started a post there, called Camp Robinson, and knew they would never go away again.

The next summer brought more provocation for trouble. Custer marched into the Black Hills, where, by the treaty of 1868, no white man was ever to go. But the Northern Pacific railroad was in financial difficulties and locating the gold known to be in the Hills would promote investment. Custer obliged; he reported gold at the grass roots, and made a starvation march back to the Missouri through country burned black by the northern Sitting Bull's Hunkpapas and their allies. The newspapers carried the stories of Custer and the Hunkpapa leader and nobody bothered to point out that there was another man of the name who was saving the Red Cloud beef herd from the wild Indians so there would be meat for the agency hungry. Nor was there any action on the Indian complaints about issue pants and blankets that proved to be poor as dark blotting paper in water, the sugar half sand, the flour coarse and moldy and often double-sacked, so the outer ones could be removed and the flour stamped and counted a second time. Cattle, too, were double-tallied, cattle that were mostly hoofs and horns to these Indians who had been fed on the finest fat young buffalo cows.

Understandably, the agent's life as Little Father of the Oglalas wasn't too peaceful. Even the friendlies were arrogant and demand-

ing day or night, as one can be with a father. Along in October he
announced that the chiefs and the agency employees should all have
a rest on Sundays. To let the Indians know which was the day, he
would raise a pole and run up a flag. So the agent, a political ap-
pointee innocent of any understanding of his Indians, brought on
an incident that is still disputed among the Sioux. The one point of
agreement was the expressed gratitude of both the military and the
Indian Bureau to Sitting Bull, now called The Good.

It seems that the first objection to the flagpole came from the soured
band of old Conquering Bear, who had been set up as chief over
all the Sioux by the government back in 1851, and then killed in the
Grattan fight of 1854 over a Mormon cow. When some long pine
poles were dragged in from the canyons back of the agency, these
Indians stopped their usual horse racing and pushed into the stockade. With their war clubs they chopped the poles to pieces.

"We will not have a flag on our agency! A flag means war!"

As usual, Red Cloud and his headmen were around, this time sitting on a pile of lumber inside the stockade. By now Old Red had
six years experience as an ally of the white man. He filled his pipe,
saying neither yes or no—waiting.

But the little agent recalled his nephew shot not long ago. He had
the stockade gates slammed and sent a runner to the new Camp
Robinson. That meant soldiers coming. The Indians, both friendly
and hostile, came charging in from all directions, kicking up dust,
roaring that soldiers must not come to their agency. Just then a pitiful little handful of troopers appeared, with angry, painted warriors
racing along both sides, whooping, waving war clubs, shooting off
their guns, while between them and the soldiers rode Sitting Bull
and Young Man Afraid of His Horse and their friendlies, first one
and then the other charging out against the wild Indians, pushing
them back, Sitting Bull swinging his three-bladed knife long as a
scythe against them as the troopers' hurried advance became a flight
to the comparative safety of the stockade. The gates banged behind
them but Lieutenant Crawford ordered them opened. Dismounting
his men he faced the howling warriors. It was a brave thing, and
stopped the Indians a moment. But the soldiers were mostly green
eastern recruits, and so excited that Crawford had to whip them into
something like a line with the flat of his sword. The whooping warriors crowded harder, but Sitting Bull and Young Man Afraid and
another brave man called Three Bears stood against them—three
against almost a thousand now.

"Burn! Burn the whites out!" the surging mass chanted, a few roaring back, "Burn! And kill the white-man-lovers!"

Now it looked like a real battle, and a few sons of the agency chiefs saw how it could end, with only Sitting Bull and the two others making the stand. They joined on their side, fighting anywhere they stood. One of them clubbed young Conquering Bear, son of the dead chief, from his horse. Instantly two Red Cloud followers were off and, laying a bow across the Bear's throat, stood on the two ends.

"You are all troublemakers!" one of them said to their struggling victim. "If your father had given up the Indian who killed the Mormon cow long ago, there would never have been a war with the whites. No soldiers here among us at all!"

But as the man on the ground stopped his struggling and began to turn black as a hanged one, the word of it spread back through the wild mass, and a dark, dangerous silence followed it. The Cut-Offs and Red Cloud men separated from the crowd of warriors and moved together, guns cocked ready for the first blood as the man on the ground seemed to die. And now even some of the wild northern Indians backed their horses out of the way of this brother-war.

Then Sitting Bull came pushing his horse through. He knocked the men choking Conquering Bear aside, and, turning upon the silent stand of warriors, he swung his great three-bladed war club before him.

"Think what you do, my friends! Would you shed your brother's blood here today? You are all small-braves—fighting each other in your own village, on your own agency!" he roared.

"Hah! Hear the small-brave talk!" a hostile of Red Cloud's family challenged. "He is the one who was too weak to wash out the blood of his grandfather when he was left dead on the ground by our man in there smoking. Would you stop before such a grandson as this Sitting Bull?"

So now it was finally coming out—a blood avenging between the Cut-Offs and Red Cloud's band—long, much too long deferred.

But this must not be, and Sitting Bull roared out against it, his warning lost in the "*Hoka hey!*" of the Red Cloud warriors who charged him from all sides, their horses thrusting against his, their clubs striking at him. Then it came, the first bullet for him. It went past his braid, but before the man could reload Sitting Bull had knocked him into the dust. Then he sat back on his horse, his arms down, quiet in the fury upon him, and now the warriors faltered, drawing their plunging horses back before the set stoniness of the broad face that the whites thought looked bland as a baby's.

But one warrior was undaunted. He rode his horse straight up to Sitting Bull. "You are flesh like the rest and bullets will go through you too!" he shouted as he brought his rifle down against the scarred, dust-caked breast.

Sitting Bull sat motionless, his big club still unraised. "Yes, I am flesh," he said, "and bullets have gone through me—Pawnee bullets and from the Crows and the whites up around the Piney Fort, but you are not the man to put one there—" and as the Indian hesitated a moment, finger on trigger, one of the Head Band warriors grabbed him from behind and jerked him from the horse, the rifle booming into the sky.

Without glancing down upon the man, Sitting Bull pushed his horse out through the mass of Indians and the dust to a little rise. Then a Red Cloud man rode out to stop his horse alongside The Good's. Next two Cut-Off's followed, and many others, even some of the wild ones from the Crazy Horse camps, for it seemed that even a good friend of the whites could still be a brave man.

Slowly the alignments of agency bands broke, began to move around, mixing in with the hostiles, who seemed to be drifting away, the poor handful of soldiers in the stockade gate almost forgotten in what had so nearly happened.

With signs to his followers, Sitting Bull rode down to make a double line for the soldiers to ride out between. They went swiftly and afraid between the two silent walls of Indians who watched with their guns across their horses. When the troops were gone the warriors wiped the paint from their faces and hurried into line for the inevitable feast. Later forty fine blankets were distributed to the chiefs.

The trouble was reported to Washington by both Agent Saville and the military. The report from Camp Robinson, Nebraska, briefed to the essentials, said:

At the agent's call for help Lieutenant Crawford and 22 men started to the agency with the available men of the 3rd Cavalry. . . . At his arrival he informed me by courier that 200 Indians, mounted and armed, approached. Through efforts of Sitting Bull and other Oglalas, the Minneconjous were prevented from attack. . . .

The agent knew erection of the flagstaff would cause trouble . . . and should have waited until I had a stronger force (two companies from Spotted Tail, etc.). . . . Indians sent runners to all camps, thinking, of course, they were to be attacked. They were determined to fight. Had the

Lieutenant's party been massacred, the agent and the person who held up two companies at Sheridan [Camp Sheridan, at Spotted Tail's agency 40 miles away, M. S.] would have been responsible. . . .

Sitting Bull and his band saved the agency and should be rewarded. . . . Red Cloud was passive inside the stockade during the troubles. Either he has no control of the Indians or he was afraid to do anything.

Although the troublesome warriors were underestimated in number, and dismissed as Minneconjous instead of mostly Oglala followers of Crazy Horse and disgruntled agency young men, ten days later it was admitted that there were three thousand wild Indians camped out on White River when Professor Marsh of Yale requested guides and protection for his scientific expedition into the Badlands. The wild Indians called him a gold thief, but the professor was good at listening to Red Cloud's complaints against his agent, so he got permission to go in if Sitting Bull the Good and an Indian escort went along. But the expedition came with a company of infantry to protect the wagons. Immediately a thousand angry warriors streamed in from the hills and with rifles and Colt revolvers cocked they surrounded the party. Once more women and children ran, lodges fell, and the agent ordered Marsh to get his infantry up to the fort before he provoked a massacre. The little column went, followed by whooping, shooting Indians all the way. Marsh made the usual feast but doubled it, and got appreciative pats on their stomachs from the Indians, and demands that he start back to the Platte tomorrow. So he made a night start for the Badlands, and, with the Sioux aversion to night fighting from the time when dew softened the bowstring, they let him go.

Once more the newspapers played up the story, denouncing the powerful Sitting Bull who made trouble all the way from the upper Missouri to the Platte River. And denouncing the government for feeding and arming this treacherous savage at taxpapers' expense. Both the military and Saville protested to Washington against such misinformation. An excerpt from the agent's letter of November 13, 1874, shows the tone of it.

Regarding quelling of disturbance at the agency—Sitting Bull is not the Uncpapa but an Oglala, the nephew of Little Wound, chief of the Kiosces, noted among the Indians for his courage and daring. During the late war he was a bitter enemy of the whites. Since the treaty he has been friendly and a warm friend since I have been on the agency. He is head soldier of the Head Bands, of which Young Man Afraid of His Horse is chief. I have made him leader of the soldiers whom I have armed with permission of the Department.

Once more, January 11, 1875, Saville wrote suggesting some reward
for those who helped in the flagpole incident. It would help dispel
the notion that only the bad the Indian does is reported, never the
good, and that only the troublemakers are rewarded, adding:

A present in the name of the President would give satisfaction and prestige.
The favorite present is a nice gun.

The winter was a hard one for the friends of the white man. The
promised rations didn't come and the starving Indians moved in
close to the agency to call attention to their misery and finally up
to Fort Robinson, leaving the stripped bones of their butchered
ponies under the eyes of the commander. Sitting Bull and his police
tried their best by cooperation and by anger to get the rations for
the people but none came. The buffalo had disappeared, even all the
small game, with so many hungry Indians around. Cold Indians, too,
with only one thin blanket for every three people, and wood very
scarce, the buffalo chips gone even if the ground weren't covered
with snow.

In the north the hostiles were cold too this snowblind winter, but
they managed to send some robes down to their relatives at Red
Cloud, and fought the gold seekers willing to risk freezing to death.
With spring the gold rush to the Black Hills was like snow water
roaring in the gullies, and there was news in the papers that the
Great Father wanted the chiefs to come to Washington to sell the
Hills.

"One does not sell the earth upon which the people walk," Crazy
Horse told the messengers come to draw him to Red Cloud and
another of the white papers that he would never sign. Up north Sitting
Bull the Hunkpapa was as strong in his refusal.

But the Oglala Sitting Bull went to Washington as the right-hand
man to Red Cloud, who insisted he was only going to tell the Great
Father about the thieving whites who starved his people. At Omaha
they stopped and were feasted and given fine clothes and had their
pictures taken. In Washington they found their agent still being in-
vestigated through the kindly intercession of Professor Marsh. Nothing came of that, although there was plenty proof of graft and
thievery. Only nobody seemed to be doing it.

Nothing came of the Black Hills sale either. The southern Sitting
Bull sat quietly with the Oglala delegation at Washington and kept
out of the squabbling of Red Cloud and Spotted Tail, both between
themselves and with the whites. After futile weeks the Commissioner

of Indian Affairs got the whole unhappy delegation together and, according to the New York *Tribune,* June 7, 1875, said he was sorry nothing had been done. He scolded the old chiefs for it, and then turned to the younger men:

Now, I want to say a word to Sitting Bull. I have heard from your agent and from the military officers at the agency of the great service you have rendered the government. You have proved yourself to be a very brave man—a friend of your own people and to the whites. Your good conduct has been reported to the President, and I am instructed to give you a token of his regard.

This turned out to be a fine rifle in a leather case, the *Tribune* reported, with a brass mounting that gleamed so the Indians called it gold, and engraved to Sitting Bull.

It was a very busy spring and summer for the Hunkpapas. Enough miners were getting killed up there so there was some fine victory dancing among the northern Sioux. Among the whites there were loud and urgent demands that the miners be given military protection in the Black Hills instead of being summarily expelled by General Crook's troops. A commission was sent out to buy the Black Hills, prepared, it was rumored, to go as high as seven million dollars, if necessary. Such figures brought a swarm of hungry contractors like a plague of Mormon crickets moving up the trail to Red Cloud Agency. The Hunkpapa Sitting Bull refused to come to the conference, but a lot of Crazy Horse's hostile Oglalas went down to watch Red Cloud and Spotted Tail and their jealous maneuverings and to warn them of their duty and the bullets that would enforce it. There was enough galloping, whooping, rifle fire, and prairie burning in the night to scare away the white women who came to the conference for a little amused sightseeing. At the Lone Tree council ground it was the same. While the circle of chiefs under the spreading cottonwood delayed and delayed, the little group of commissioners—senators, generals, a missionary, and so on—waited under the canvas flies that shielded them from the sun. At first the handful of soldiers close behind them seemed good protection, but gradually they realized that the soldiers too were walled in by the Indians, who stood eight, ten deep all around, mostly wild, painted warriors, their guns cocked. Beyond, a dozen haranguers for war rode up and down, shouting, singing. "It is a good day to die! A very good day to die!" All that was needed now was one wild shot that hit—

On a little rise Sitting Bull sat his horse quietly, his hand ready

on the bright breech of his gift rifle, his face still bland and emotion-
less. For a long while it seemed that none would ever dare rise to
speak in this council because the first word might bring a bullet,
many, many bullets. Then Young Man Afraid got up from the circle
of chiefs and stood, his blanket drawn about him, a bold, steady
target for all to see. When no one fired, he gave a signal and Sitting
Bull ordered his warriors to clear the grounds. Now the whites held
their breath, and the Indians too, the chiefs squatting on the ground
motionless as stone, knowing it could be the end of every one of
them, with both the Indian and the trooper guns turned their way.
No hostile moved to leave. Swaggering and threatening, they waited.
Here and there a shot was fired, but still into the air.

On his knoll Sitting Bull waited without one motion, the September sun warm on his dusty braids. Without shifting an eye he saw
the sickness of the white-man faces, the soldier guns nervous, the
warriors seeing this too, and pushing in, hot for the start.

Once more he gave the harsh command. "Back! Back, my friends!"
saying it angrily, his lip curling in the deep scorn of the Sioux.

This time the hostiles drew back, one, then another, more, and
through their thinning the commission was rushed into the ambu-
lances and hurried off to the agency stockade. To both sides of them
the slopes were dark with watching Indians who knew that once more
the Black Hills had been saved.

"Wholesale Massacre of Commission Barely Averted!" the newspapers screamed out across the nation.

The year 1876 was the high point in the career of the Hunkpapa
Sitting Bull, but it was the tragic year for the one called The Good.
While his Oglala relatives with Crazy Horse helped whip Crook on
the Rosebud and then, a week later, wiped out Custer, there was a
commensurate tightening at the agency. The usual buffalo hunt was
canceled, and when the Cheyennes went out anyway, they were
whipped back to the starvation of the agency, the women who remembered Sand Creek scuttling in terror before the soldiers.

By September another commission came to buy the Black Hills.
This time there was no such foolishness as an open conference. It
was held in the agency stockade, with the wild Indians shut out.
The treaty, already complete, was read to the chiefs. They must give
up all their hunting grounds of the Powder and the Tongue and the
Yellowstone, move to little agencies among the whites of the lower
Missouri or go south to the starving people of Indian Territory. The
chiefs protested, and were told they would be kept in the stockade

until the pen was touched, and there would be no rations for the women and children until it was done.

Stunned, the headmen sat silent in their blankets, Red Cloud surely recalling that only eight years ago the U. S. government had backed down and dismantled a whole string of forts at his command.

But one man was not silent here. That was Sitting Bull the Good. With the butt of a revolver sticking from his belt, the gift rifle in one hand, his great war club in the other, he harangued the commission and the chiefs. This was not treaty-making but trickery— with the chiefs locked up and the women helpless! It was foolish to talk of selling the Hills with so few people here, most of them away north, where there was still meat.

When Red Cloud taunted him with his friendship for the whites, Sitting Bull ordered the gates thrown open and not a word from the whites was spoken to stop him. Whipping the chiefs out, he roared, "Get out! Go north! Maybe there a man can still live in honor for a little while!"

With his war bag packed Sitting Bull the Good started north for the camps of Crazy Horse. He went openly and nobody challenged his departure. Safe from disturbance now, the conference reconvened in the agency stockade and the chiefs had to sign away the gold-bearing Hills and their hunting ground forever.

Up north Sitting Bull's heart fell down when he saw the poorness of the children of the hostiles, the scarcity of winter meat and of lodges and robes, with soldiers following them across the snow like wolves tracking the blood of a wounded buffalo. He went up to see the Hunkpapas too, and heard the messengers from the northern agencies try to coax those Indians in there. He heard the other Sitting Bull tell of his council with General Miles, saying that he wanted peace for his people but that he could not lay down his gun while the soldiers were in his country. So Miles had turned the council into a battle. One Indian was killed and the rest had to scatter because the women and children were along and ammunition was very scarce.

Hopelessly Sitting Bull the Good returned to Red Cloud. Everything was done. The military asked him to go right back with a message to Crazy Horse. He went. It was not that he believed the whites any more. While he was north Red Cloud and Red Leaf, long-time government chiefs, had been surrounded in the night, their guns and ponies taken so even the winter wood had to be carried on the backs of the women. Once more the Sioux were back to the

SITTING BULL COUNTRY

Key to map on facing page.

OGLALA SITTING BULL
Circles

1. Born 1841, below forks of Platte.
2. 1862—Studies Napoleon, Deer Creek Station.
3. 1864—Attacks that closed Overland Trail.
4. 1865—Attack on Julesburg, Colo.
5. 1865—Attack on Platte Bridge.
6. 1866—Attacks on Bozeman Trail, Fort Phil Kearny, and on Fetterman.
7. 1870—Goes to Washington.
8. 1872—Holds off warriors at Red Cloud Agency on Platte.
9. 1874—Holds off warriors at Red Cloud Agency on White River in Appleton killing and in flagpole affair. 1875 Goes to Washington, receives gift rifle from President Grant.
10. 1875—Helps save Black Hills Commission at Lone Tree Conference.
11. 1876—Breaks up Black Hills Conference at Red Cloud Agency.
12. 1876—Killed under flag of truce at Cantonment on Tongue River, Dec. 16.

HUNKPAPA SITTING BULL
Diamonds

1. Born 1831, on Grand River.
2. 1862—Fleeing Minnesota Sioux find him near mouth of Little Missouri.
3. 1864—In battle of Kildeer Mountain with General Sully.
4. 1865—Foray on Fort Rice.
5. 1865—Engagement with Cole on Powder.
6. 1866—Attack on Fort Buford.
7. 1872—Attack on Colonel Baker on Yellowstone.
8. 1874—Burns prairie before Custer as he returns from Black Hills.
9. 1876—In Battle of Little Big Horn.
10. 1876—Attacked by Miles in council for peace, troops firing into gathered Sioux.
11. 1890—Was suspected of planning treachery in Ghost Dance troubles, killed during arrest, Standing Rock Agency, Dec. 15.

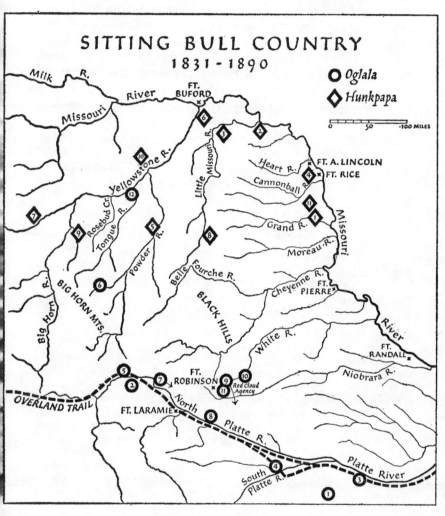

SITTING BULL COUNTRY
1831-1890

○ Oglala
◇ Hunkpapa

0   50   ·100 MILES

SITTING BULL COUNTRY
Key to this map is on the facing page.

dog travois they used before the coming of the horse, but now without the buffalo, or even the freedom to move to wooded shelter.

He went north carrying the word of General Crook: Come to Red Cloud, get food and blankets and peace. But that was two hundred miles over winter Wyoming, and into the power of the crooked tongue, as even he had to admit now. He was told that General Miles, settled on the mouth of the Tongue River, was offering them the same, right here in their own country. The Missouri Indians who went in there two moons ago were well fed and warm.

So Crazy Horse decided to go talk to him. Sitting Bull the Good, the friend of the whites, was sent ahead, carrying a lance with the white flag the general had sent for their coming. Beside him rode three others, all unarmed, and behind them four more, bringing some horses stolen from the post herds by the wild young men. A ways back several older men sat smoking, one holding the gift rifle of Sitting Bull until his return, while on a little knoll Crazy Horse and his headmen waited to see how it would be, and far back the women waited too, and hoped.

The story of that day is told in General Nelson A. Miles' report, dated December 17, 1876 (AGO Records, Military Division of the Missouri, Sioux War, 1877, National Archives), of which the following are briefed excerpts:

Unfortunate affair at this place yesterday. Five Minneconjou chiefs came in bearing two white flags, followed by 20 or 30 other Indians and were passing by the Crow camp. The five in advance were surrounded by Crows, 12, and instantly killed. The act was an unprovoked cowardly murder, the Crows approached them in a friendly manner, said "How!" shook hands with them and when they were within their power and partly behind a large woodpile, killed them in most brutal manner. At the first shot the officers and men rushed out and tried to save the Minneconjous, but could not reach them in time. The Crows were aware of the enormity of the crime as they saw the Minneconjous had a flag of truce and had been warned the day before against committing any act of violence against messengers or other parties coming in for friendly purposes. They tried to hide the flag and taking advantage of the momentary excitement, while efforts were being made to open communication and bring back others who had fled to the bluffs, the guilty Crows jumped their ponies and fled to their agency in Montana. . . . These five chiefs and the followers were within a few hundred yards of the parade ground, where they were deliberately placing themselves into hands of the government and within the camp of 400 government troops. These, with heads of others, would have given us leaders of the Minneconjous, Sans Arcs, and possibly the Oglala tribes, representing fully 600 lodges and at least 1000 fighting men of the hostiles and completed and secured beyond doubt the fruits of our efforts.

Sioux Chiefs to Washington, D.C., 1875.
Seated: Sitting Bull the Oglala; Swift Bear; Spotted Tail.
Standing: Julius Meyer and Red Cloud.
Photograph made at Omaha.
Courtesy Nebraska State Historical Society.

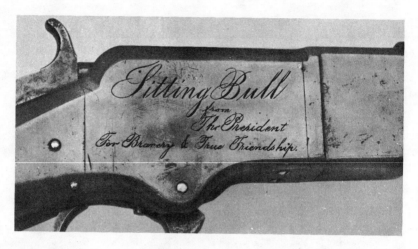

Inscription on Henry Rifle presented to Sitting Bull the Oglala,
at Washington, D.C., 1875.
Now in the Museum of the American Indian.
Courtesy the Museum of the American Indian.

Sitting Bull the Hunkpapa.
Barry photograph, 1885.
Courtesy the Smithsonian Institution.

The funeral procession of Crazy Horse passing through Camp Sheridan, Nebraska. *Frank Leslie's Illustrated Newspaper*, October 13, 1877.

"This illustrates the complete ignorance of eastern artists about the accoutrements of the Sioux, of their appearance. The horse wouldn't have a white man's bridle, the mourners would be in tatters of mourning, the travois is wrong, the saddle is wrong, etc." (77).

The Crows were immediately disarmed, 12 of their horses taken from them and with other considerations, together with letters explaining the whole affair, sent to the people and friends of those killed, as an assurance that no white man had any part in the affair and had no heart for such brutal and cowardly acts.

A note attached to a letter of February 1, 1877 from General Crook to General Sheridan reports that the Indian messengers returning to Cheyenne Agency said Sitting Bull the Good from Red Cloud was among those killed in the attack on the hostile flag of truce. Four fell where the Crows jumped them and the rest ran back, the Crows following and killing one about two miles from the post.

When their emissaries fell, the waiting chiefs had to get their women and children away. The old man who was caring for Sitting Bull's rifle ran and was overtaken by the Crows. In the fighting the unloaded weapon slipped from his hands. It was surrendered to Miles in the Crow disarming and was added to the Miles collection. Automatically, by its inscription, it became the former property of the Hunkpapa, although he had never been much nearer Washington than the east bank of the Missouri.

If there had been no Crow attack that December day, General Miles would have had all the hostile leaders except those with the Hunkpapa Sitting Bull. It would have ended most of the winter campaign that lasted to May. With a good word from Crazy Horse even the Hunkpapa Sitting Bull might have come in, instead of finally retreating to Canada.

Sitting Bull had been reported killed in the Custer battle and then turned up fighting, strong as ever. One more rumor of his death was just another shot into the empty air. So Sitting Bull the Good disappeared from the knowledge of most white men. But not his achievements, his name on the agency rolls, his trips to Washington or his gift from the President. They became divergent and contradictory elements in the character of the great leader of the Hunkpapas, and compelling evidence of great treachery, treachery that became the ready cant of every lover of Wild West shows. Presented as the honest and upright man that the Hunkpapa Sitting Bull was, he might very well never have died from a white man's gun in the hands of an Indian either. It was fear of treacherous intentions that sent the Indian police to root him out into the gray dawn of morning, naked from the sleeping robes, and to shoot him down. It was December too, the fifteenth instead of the sixteenth, and 1890—fourteen years after Sitting Bull the Good died up in the country of the Yellowstone.

X

The Burial of Crazy Horse

The home of my childhood was . . . at the edge of the region they called the Indian Country. It was close, or what seemed close in those open days, to the great Sioux reservations of South Dakota, to Fort Robinson and the Black Hills—the final place of refuge for many of the old buffalo-hunting Indians, the old traders, trappers, and general frontiersmen who looked with contempt upon the coming of the barbed wire and the walking plow. Such men, with their heroic times all in the past, are often great story-tellers. . . .

. . . most often they talked of battles in what the whites called the Sioux wars, from that climactic summer day on the Little Big Horn all the way back to the beginning, when, in 1854, the young Grattan with a few soldiers, a drunken interpreter, and two wagon guns foolishly pushed his way into a peaceful Sioux encampment and never came out again.

As I listened to these stories it seemed that through them, like a painted strip of rawhide in a braided rope, ran the name of one who was a boy among the Oglalas the day the chief of his people was shot down [by Grattan]. He must have been twelve then, quiet, serious, very light-skinned for an Indian, with hair so soft and pale that he was called Curly or the Light-Haired Boy. But by the end of those wars, twenty-three years later, he was known as the greatest of the fighting Oglalas, and his name, Crazy Horse, was one to frighten the children of the whites crowding into his country, and even the boldest warriors of his Indian enemies, the Snakes and the Crows.

—Foreword, *Crazy Horse* (27)

Crazy Horse has brought me the most satisfactory response, not in numbers but in quality of letters, of any of my books. Last month a mess of Indians, apparently Northern Sioux and Flatheads, mostly soldiers, came through and stopped off for a pow-wow. I'd never seen any of them, so far as I could find out, but one of them had a

108

copy of my book in his sack and while they all sat around my apartment he gave an old-time harangue, in the sense of the word French
traders speaking of Sioux orators used. . . . Then there was probably the same thing in sign language, with bits of the book read here
and there. All the while that circle of dark eyes never left my face,
although here and there a glint of amusement came to the surface.
And when it was done they solemnly gave me the double handshake,
first the right hand on top, then the left, and went away.

While it was funny at first, it got pretty awesome toward the last.
Somehow these young men, probably none over twenty-four, had all
the dignity and high seriousness of the old buffalo hunters left in
them. It was the finest thing that could ever happen in my house and
I felt terribly small and insignificant for a week (60).

SOMEWHERE, most probably in South Dakota, the passing seasons
chill and warm a little nest of bones that was once the most beloved
and the most feared man of the southern Teton Sioux—the man called
Crazy Horse, meaning Holy, Mystical, or Inspired Horse. Every few
years there is a new rash of letters offering the bones of Crazy Horse
for sale. To the query: Which Crazy Horse? there is usually no reply,
and even less response to the follow-up question: Does the upper
jawbone show the path and embedding of a bullet a few years before death? But evidently times are hard among bone-sellers, for
over in Iowa one man offered to fake such a bone wounding "to fit
the requirements."

Every few years, too, there is a spurt of interest in the burial ground
of Crazy Horse from serious historians, students of western Amer-
icana, and an occasional *tasunka witko kola*, friend of Crazy Horse.
The bones, if discovered, are to be deposited in a vault at the foot
of the Crazy Horse monument being carved from a granite mountain up in the Black Hills by Korczak Ziolkowski.

Jake Herman of Pine Ridge, apparently a Sioux descendant of
Jacob Herman, an educated German who worked at Fort Laramie
in the 1850's, wrote a long article (Sheridan County, Nebraska, *Star*,
April 15, 1954) about Crazy Horse and his burial between the forks
of Wounded Knee and White Horse creeks, at Crazy Horse Butte.
Blue Eagle says a man who helped with the burial showed him the
grave on a tributary of Wounded Knee Creek, near the battlefield.
The resting place, if it should prove so, was the last of several.

Crazy Horse died the night of September 5, 1877, from a bayonet thrust into the kidney by William Gentles, a bearded old soldier of the 14th Infantry who had evidently been with Johnston's campaign against the Mormons in 1857. Through the turbulence and keening of that night Gentles was sneaked out in an ambulance to Camp Sidney to save him from all the warriors whooping for his blood to make their hearts good again. Grouard, the breed interpreter whose misinterpretation had started the trouble, was hidden away too, and managed to escape the reservation in safety.

Early next morning the body of the dead Oglala was given to a delegation from his own b? ,d and hauled away on a pony travois. To the mourning and the } ,ening of the camps the body was started for the agency of Spotted Tail, the brother of Crazy Horse's mother, where, by matrilinear rights, the body would logically belong. The horse drawing the death travois was a clean young buckskin; the father had a blaze-faced, stockinged bay, the mother a brown mare with a bay colt following. With the loose and haggled hair and the tattered blankets of mourning, the older people walked most of the forty-odd miles.

The Indian widow, the ailing Black Shawl, her shins cut and bleeding for the death of the great leader, followed behind the travois until her strength failed. Indians mounted and afoot gathered in dark little knots on rises along the route and then slipped down behind the ridges to reappear again and again, so the pitiful little cortege was never unobserved. Below them the travois moved slowly along the worn wagon road but off to the side a little to make room for the small detachment of troops riding briskly on the trail in a great and energetic show of business today, their weapons shining in the hot September sun.

At Spotted Tail Agency the body of Crazy Horse was wrapped in his blanket and placed on a scaffold of four posts, the red and white calfskin cape he wore into battle laid over him. Some say that his golden pinto was shot there beside the scaffold, but others insist that this would have been against the man's unostentatious ways. Certainly there were none of the usual gaudy accoutrements to blow in the wind for awhile and then be laid aside for posterity. Beyond the little blue stone tied behind his ear and the occasional lone feather of his chieftainship in his hair, Crazy Horse had worn no adornment.

The parents squatted there beside their son for three unbroken days and nights, with no food and almost no water, until finally Major Lee, the Spotted Tail agent, sent out meat and bread and canteens of coffee and so finally coaxed the old people in. But it is said that the man's body was never alone, day or night. Always the parents, the silent Indian wife, or other relatives were there—or friends, men who had followed him all those last desperate starving, fleeing months along the Yellowstone.

Then in October word came that the Sioux must go to the Missouri River, do what Crazy Horse had so vigorously opposed, for he had been promised an agency in his own country up on the Powder River and he held that the other Indians should be allowed to keep their western homes also, not go where there was no farmland, no game, only the whisky of the Missouri River whites. But Congress had voted the Sioux appropriations, the Indians' by treaty right, only on condition that they leave their agencies in Nebraska. When no goods were given out, no flour or beef for the hungry women and children, the chiefs once more bowed their heads to the white man's wishes.

And once more the parents of Crazy Horse put his body upon the travois, this time to follow behind the exiled people. But as they moved along with the Spotted Tail Indians, parallel to the Red Cloud followers going to the Missouri too, disquieting gossip reached them. It seemed that Woman's Dress, of Red Cloud's band, had lied as surely as the absent Grouard. Both had misinterpreted Crazy Horse's agreeing words and actions into bloodthirsty plotting and defiance. At first the Sioux ignored the new talk, for surely no one would believe the words of Woman's Dress. Such people as he were only to be believed as diviners, as Pipe had been believed when he was sent out before the Fetterman fight to bring back his prophecy of one hundred white men to be killed. No Indian would ask such men as Pipe or Woman's Dress to report on something actually said or done. But gradually the Indians had to admit that perhaps the white officers had believed the lies of Woman's Dress too, and so arrested Crazy Horse for the guardhouse.

In addition, there was talk about the Larrabee girl, the handsome young breed woman who was given to Crazy Horse as a second wife when he came in last spring, to reconcile him to the white man and his ways. Now it was said she had been friendly with Lieut. W. P. (White Hat) Clark before that, and since the death of Crazy Horse was friendly with him again. Even now, on this sad moving, she was gay and flirtatious with the officers.

Ahhh-h, the Crazy Horse people told each other, so she must have been a spy in their man's lodge. The trickery to get Crazy Horse killed was not only from the jealous Red Cloud faction but from the white men also. Indeed, as they had discovered by now, there had been a team waiting to take the captured chief to a Florida prison the day he jumped back from the guardhouse door and was bayonetted.

Men who had been peaceful all summer were fired to anger by these stories, and harangued the warriors in hidden night meetings away from the little escort of troops along. Who could say what further treachery the whites had planned for those of them who were left, men like Little Hawk, uncle of Crazy Horse, the Big Road and He Dog and a dozen others? They could only expect death or imprisonment and perhaps as much for their families now that the only man who could stand up for them was dead.

Then one day over a thousand Indians, led by Big Road and Little Hawk, left the Spotted Tail column and, with the Crazy Horse bones along, swarmed over a ridge upon the Red Cloud Indians straggling along south of White River. "Let us all go north!" they shouted. "Let us go north before more people are killed!"

With taunts and the pitiful sight of the death travois, they whipped the younger men into a frenzy, and with only two little groups of cavalry along, the officers and the Red Cloud agent saw the futility of resistance. Instead they gave the Crazy Horse Indians a large quantity of rations and supplies and let them go, away toward the Powder and finally to Sitting Bull in Canada.

But the father of Crazy Horse was eighty, and with no winter supplies or shelter and sub-zero weather upon them, the parents did not go far north. They hid the bones of their son and went on toward the Missouri with the rest. Indians differ about this hiding place but at the best it was only used for a few months.

Most of the Sioux goods didn't get up the river before ice came in, and the Indians spent a starving winter. In the spring, without permission, they started back toward their old agencies, stopping north of the Nebraska line, where Pine Ridge and Rosebud agencies are now located. More of the Crazy Horse Indians had gone north on the way back but the parents still remained with Spotted Tail. Once more they moved the bones of their son, westward this time, and buried him again. Unfortunately there is a disagreement about this burial place also. According to the manuscript of Mrs. Susan Bettleyoun, daughter of Jim Bordeaux, trader at Fort Laramie and born there about 1853, Mrs. DeNoyer, niece of Crazy Horse, said his body had been hidden under a ledge in the cliffs of Eagle Nest Butte on the way east. In the spring of 1878 it was brought back to the new Rosebud Reservation.

The parents lived in Salt User's camp, two miles northeast of the agency. The mother died in 1879, the father about 1880. Even the Sioux around at the time differed about the final resting place of Crazy Horse. Black Elk told John Neihardt in *Black Elk Speaks* that some thought it was near Bear Creek in the Badlands. He knew that the old couple had brought the bones down Pepper Creek a little way south of his cabin, two miles west of Manderson. Later the travois was seen moving empty along White Horse Creek, which would perhaps put the burial near the sites favored by Blue Eagle and Jake Herman. But Black Elk says that the parents might have gone on into the Badlands with the body before they reappeared on White Horse Creek.

Both the father and the mother were dead when Sitting Bull surrendered, and Little Hawk, Big Road, and He Dog returned with over a thousand of the Crazy Horse followers belonging to Pine Ridge and Rosebud agencies. So perhaps none of these knew the burial spot firsthand. Crazy Horse's widow, Black Shawl, must have known, but she mourned all her life in apparent silence. The Larrabee woman settled down with a Sioux instead of one of the entertaining white officers. Her new husband, sometimes called Greasy Head, by good Sioux custom took the name of his illustrious predecessor and became Crazy Horse No. 2. He is apparently the dark little Indian with feather headdress and white-bordered leggins and breechclout in the photograph sold everywhere as the picture of the Oglala war chief Crazy Horse. As wife of Number 2, the breed woman and her children by him lived in the third house above Bat Pourier's on Wounded Knee Creek.

It might be interesting to find where this man's bones are buried, or those of the half-dozen other Sioux named Crazy Horse. There were three old enough and important enough to be signers of the Proposed Division of the Great Sioux Reservation, 1889 (*Senate Executive Document* 51, 51st Congress, 1st Session). The name has been going right on. The body of a Pfc. C. P. Crazy Horse was returned to Pine Ridge from the Pacific in December 1948.

But perhaps Black Elk spoke the important words on the burial place of Crazy Horse when he said, "It does not matter where his body lies, for it is grass; but where his spirit is, it will be good to be."

SHORT FICTION

My interest in human conflict
led me into writing . . . (62).

. . . perhaps you insist upon going into what is often considered the glamour end of the writing business—the short story. . . . Very well, think about a story idea until you can put the whole thing into a declarative sentence: the main character, his dominant trait or traits, the locale, the conflict, the crucial moment, and the outcome. Now you are ready to begin. Write the first draft, even if it is only the barest string of narrative, as fast as you can, to get movement. Then begin the actual writing, solidifying the background and the characterization, sharpening the dialogue, and improving the description —always by the selection of words and phrases that will stimulate the reader's imagination to fill in much more than you have given him. Learn to make a detail or two suggest a whole house, a whole person, or even town. . . .

. . . If you are interested in the story of man against his environment, either superficially or with some seriousness, your best field will probably be the longer story. Or if you are wondering about man as a part of a unit of society instead of the unit itself, the book length is the place for you.

Sometime before you reach the book stage, you will have made the crucial decision in your writing career—whether you are in it just to make money or to say something that seems worth saying. And then you may find that the decision has really been made for you long ago, that the answer was largely determined by your physical inheritance and by the traditions and the environment into which you were born. If you believe that all really is right with the world in the end, then read the popular magazines very seriously, polish the surface of your style, and may great riches indeed reward the honest craftsman. If you are, however, aware of certain injustices in the world, of certain antisocial urges and unescapable conflicts in man, then you are bound to collect rejection slips until you acquire some real distinction in style, some power in presentation. Even lacking the ability to attain these ends, your future probably will be in the novel, for where else will you be permitted to voice these things? Who, for instance, would let anyone but an acknowledged expert in the field discuss, outside of the novel, a will-to-power individual and her system for dominating her world as I did in *Slogum House*? Or make a microcosmic study of the civilized world selling itself into fascism as I did in *Capital City*?

Yes, you can learn to write; even given the greatest handicap a writer can have, a serious concern for man upon this earth, you can learn to write well enough to make a living at it (28).

XI

The Vine

Mari Sandoz has called Joseph Conrad her first literary discovery. "The force with which the analogy between the sea and the sandhills struck me left me a little bewildered at first. Conrad's description caught the same spirit of moodiness in the sea as one catches in the midst of vast reaches of sand" (55). On another occasion she remarked that Conrad and Thomas Hardy "fit the sandhills better than any other writers I know. There is in their work, always, an overshadowing sense of fatality, and their characters, like the people of the prairies, are helpless victims of circumstance. The inexorability of nature's laws is revealed in their novels as it is revealed in the tragic, desperate lives of the settlers whom my father brought to Nebraska" (56).

"The Vine," written in 1925, is the author's first published short story. It appeared under the pen name Marie Macumber in the January 1927 *Prairie Schooner*—the first piece in the first issue.

THE HILL NORTH of the little soddy rose tall and steep. Diagonal cowpaths, grassing over, marked it into a regular pattern from foot to sand-capped top. Soapweeds clustered about the highest dune, catching the first late winter sun. Perhaps the wind drove them over, like sheep, before the stinging sand, Baldwin had said. Meda couldn't see anything in that. She didn't see much in anything in Baldwin's world. She liked green things, like the glory vine.

Meda couldn't see the narrow valley, wrinkled plush of russet bunchgrass between the lower chophills with the wind ruffling the pile as it fitfully passed. She saw the greedy thirst of the long strip of gray that had been green corn in June. She didn't hear the soughing of the wind across the valley. She heard the crackle and snap of dry stems whipped by skeleton leaves.

Meda loved thick, green things like the glory vine that covered the window of the gray soddy and reached ambitiously toward the

117

sod-covered eaves. The great heart-shaped leaves bobbed on their slender stems in the wind.

Tall and spare, she held her faded blue-checked apron back with one hand while she poured a dipper of water, brimming full, around the slender stalks, like tiny green pencils. The hungry sand soaked up the little pool, and as it vanished, Meda pushed dry sand over the wet spot from the edges with her broken shoe. She smoothed it over until it looked just as before—just as dry, just as yellow. Straightening up, she shaded her eyes and looked into the west, the northwest.

"There'll never be any rain," she told the vine. "I'll just have to water you." The thick leaves seemed to nod to her.

At the corners of the soddy, small holes, blowouts-to-be, spurted tiny volleys of sand as the wind playfully attacked the vine. Here and there a grain hit the window with a ping.

Standing in the whipping wind, Meda's body, in a long, faded, blue calico dress, looked hungry. Her hair, faded, straggled in the wind like raveled ends of old, weathered rope. Her hazel eyes looked hungry too, only too hungry to be fed. The smoldering yellow flame that lurked in their depths was hunger itself. Baldwin had told her to be careful of too much sunlight.

The glare outdoors blinded Meda as she stepped through the low doorway but she didn't need to see. She knew every detail of that crude room. She found the rocker near the window and swayed gently back and forth; her toes, bare and brown as saddle leather through the gaping holes in her shoes, dug little holes in the sand. The yellow flame died from her eyes, lost in the green shade of leaves that filtered the flecks of sunlight on the sand floor about her.

Meda looked about the room, its bareness old, old and yet strikingly new. Not even Baldwin could deny the smallness of the place, nor its shabbiness. An old grocery box covered with a frilled newspaper held the washbasin. The water pail stood beside the box on the sand. Newspaper frills, yellowed, lined the clock shelf, empty now. A flour-sack curtain, bleached on the grass to a blue-white, shut in the bed. A tablecloth of newer, creamier squares covered the two-legged table fastened to the wall. The kitchen corner was Baldwin's pride. It was a pick-up, one pick-up stove, pick-up pipe and pick-up frying pan. Only a few things, like the coffee pot and the saucepan, had been bought.

Two chairs, legs sunken into the sand, completed the furniture. "Not much to dust," Baldwin had said. What mattered dust, thought

Meda, the yellow flaring up in her eyes. Even the walls would be dust if there were no roots to bind them into blocks. She sat still, her hands clenching and unclenching in her lap.

She compared it all to her Indiana home. She saw the cool porch, the shade trees. She wanted to see the rolling lawns of the chief citizen. She missed the small church bickerings and the news and gossip of the Ladies' Aid. Baldwin made light of the rivalry of neighbors over the parlor sets and crayon portraits. He despised the jealousies of the "folks back home." He even laughed at her charities "across the tracks," calling them inadequate, and he never could be dragged to a bazaar. Meda doted on these pastimes. She delighted in the slumming among what Baldwin termed "the unwashed." She felt she had lost her husband in this desert of soapweeds. He believed in the somnolent hills; he was a part of their simplicity, their strength. She thought resentfully of his frank enjoyment of their isolation.

Meda had felt nobly self-sacrificing when she came west with Baldwin. She had known they would soon go back home. But they hadn't, somehow, and now she hated it all. She hated the cold, she hated the heat. Blizzards, objects of wonder and delight to Baldwin, were days of disgust and loneliness to Meda. Not even the Indian summers nor the chinooks moved her. She cried for the cool green of the bluegrass meadows, never seeing the lovely, ever-changing browns and yellows of the hills.

A passionate fondness for green things grew on Meda. They made her think of Indiana. Crisp, green things, alien to the sun-yellowed hills. There had been a tall geranium that bore gorgeous red blossoms. A fall in the January mercury ended that. She had almost died; Baldwin had looked worried until spring brought the glory vine, with its deep red funnels against the slick, dark leaves. The red funnels died young; there was never any dew for them to catch, only heat, sun, and wind.

Meda had to admit she felt the hills, not like Baldwin, who felt a companionship in the purple hazes and the fiery evening sun. She feared the relentlessness of their long, lonesome days. But the nights were worse! Conversation was a skeleton of bones picked dry. She might look at the stars with Baldwin but they burned so far away. In the winter they were cold white lights mocking her from a blue steel sky. Meda hated them, as if they stood between her and the family circle where her brothers had always been frankly bored, but where her eyes hadn't burned, searing. . . .

Once, long ago, she had hated rain, too. It mussed the kitchen so, but now she would welcome it if any ever came. Then there was the cream and butter and fried chicken on Sundays or when the minister called. Meda remembered telling Baldwin that beans, always beans, palled so. He had replied, "They're a sure-fire crop."

Meda thought of dinner. She stepped out to squint at the sun. She saw windrows of dancing heat waves over the dunes south of the soddy. A tiny, puffball cloud of dust trailed its thin tail down the narrow strip of corn along the north slope. The crop looked even grayer than before. Nearer and nearer came the cloud until a team and then a man could be seen, the nucleus of the cloud. Baldwin walked, carefully jerking the handles of the corn plow to left and right. Meda knew the leaves of the small plants would rattle against the rusty wheels.

Back in the room, Meda lit the fire. Cowchips from the old candy pail (another pick-up) and a handful of hay roared up the rusty pipe. The woman lifted a black kettle of beans from the oven. She poured a dipper of water over them. There would be soup again. Meda set the kettle on to boil. She never did like soup; she didn't like beans, either, but hunger would be appeased, even if it could demand only beans.

Baldwin could be heard outside. The snapping of the tugs in place across the horses' backs and the clatter of rings as the neckyoke dropped made Meda hurry. Baldwin came stooping through the doorway. His overalls were covered with dust. His blue eyes looked strangely light, like milky water, against his dirt-caked face. The long hair under his greasy Stetson was bleached to a taffy color with a frost of gray dust on it. Meda did not look up. She was busy poking chips into the cookstove. Her face was red with heat and her eyes reflected the leaping yellow flames as she broke the fuel into small pieces. There was a curl of distaste on her lip even though her hands were hidden with mammoth cotton gloves.

Baldwin poured out a scant cup of water. It rattled in the tin basin. He dipped his hands and rubbed his grimy face. Streaks of water ran down his neck in little rivulets. Pawing blindly along the wall, he grabbed the towel from its nail and rubbed it into his eyes. When he was through he ruefully surveyed the wreck. There wasn't a clean thread left. Meda, slipping off the gloves, saw the towel. She bit her lip, the yellow flames under her lashes danced. Baldwin held it out from him awkwardly.

"Never mind, Old Girl, I'll take them all to Twin Mills and wash them, next time I go."

Meda did not answer. She set the two bowls of soup upon the table and poured the coffee. Baldwin stood for a minute, looking at her, a little furrow between his brows. Then he set his large frame to the ridiculous table.

"Think that breeze will blow up something, Meda. I saw a swamp swallow skim the valley just before I came in." Baldwin salted his soup and broke little pieces of bread into the bowl.

Meda sat still, looking at the man "I don't believe it can rain. It never does here. It's the going without water that is more than I can bear."

Baldwin looked up surprised. " 'Taint my fault it don't rain, or that the well went dry, is it? I'm no crazier than you about being just dampened 'stead of washed."

"It's not only the well." Meda's hands made a sweep of all the vast hills. "Three years of drouth, no corn, nothing but beans, beans. Is this what I left my home for? This—?"

She pushed her bowl back and, rising quickly, left the room. She stood outside, beside the window, her head touching the glory vine. The yellow flames in her eyes died sullenly down, like an ugly serpent before its charmer.

Baldwin ate steadily on. Meda heard the scraping of his spoon in the bottom of the dish and his cup being set down. After a few minutes she saw his pale blue eyes looking out between the leaves. They looked clouded, hurt. Well, she had been hurt too; just wait until he got numb. The flames flickered and flared up as Baldwin appeared at the door.

"Meda, you've said all that before but what can I do? Rain may come any day and fill the water hole, yes, and water that damned vine of yours."

Baldwin strode to the window and jerked away a leaf.

"Drouth don't seem to hurt it much. Probably gets my drinking water."

"No, no, I only give it dishwater, only dishwater." Meda shrank against the rooty sod beside the window. Her eyes gleamed orange.

"So? Only dishwater? And how much is that? Remember, I'm not skinning my horses, hauling water over seven miles of sand for you to drown dishes in."

Baldwin's lips had gone white. Meda watched as he viciously turned the corner of the shack. The yellow flames leaped and danced in her eyes. She flew to the corner in time to see Baldwin lift the heavy lids by their crosspieces from one barrel, then the other. He peered into the last and his jaw dropped. He slammed the lid down with a curse.

"Not even a gallon left and they ought to be half full."

Meda took a step backwards, then another. Not only had she lost her husband but he had turned enemy. Baldwin lifted the spade from its hook among the tools along the sod wall. Without looking at Meda he passed her and sank the blade deep into the soil at the roots of the vine. Meda's eyes grew round yellow flames, cold, hard. Her hands dropped limp as Baldwin stooped to snatch up a handful of the turned-up soil. He squeezed it and let it fall, a firm oval ball with deep finger creases.

"Soaked!" He looked at Meda. "Soaked, and I skimp myself and my horses while you . . ." Anger snapped in his pale opal eyes. He made one vengeful thrust at the base of the vine with the spade. Straightening up, he looked slowly at Meda. She was watching him, her hands covered, shielded in her apron. Baldwin walked stiffly to hang the spade in its place. Meda did not move or speak. Baldwin stood before her, expecting something, but she was puzzled. What could he expect? She had seen him angry before but usually he did something foolish before it melted.

Meda stood still as Baldwin led the horses to the wagon. With a rattle of rings and snap of teeth on bit the hitching up went on. Meda caught Baldwin looking at her over Old Bluche's back as he untied the lines. Circling the team around the soddy, Baldwin was out of sight. Two heavy thumps and he appeared from the north side with the two water barrels, blackened from sun and rain, in the wagon. Rusty hoops held down the flapping canvas squares that kept the lids on.

Baldwin kept looking back, over his shoulder, as he started down the valley. Standing up, feet wide apart, he flipped the lines and the team stepped up. His shout, "Be back before dark," came clearly above the bump-bump of the empty barrels as the wheels hit the bunchgrass. The wagon rattled across the valley and began its upward climb through the sandy pass toward Twin Mills. Meda stood at the door, looking slowly all around the valley, her narrow horizon.

There was nothing to see. Heat waves danced over the rolling chop-hills every day. Tiny whirlwinds often chased each other across the narrow field. She didn't see the corn blades, rising and dipping, merrily whirling upward and dipping again. They finally settled slowly into the tawny grass and the fickle winds left them and hurried on to find other playmates.

Meda turned from the heat and glare. Her eyes, resting on the solid green thatch of the vine, became hazel again. She held one of the leaves, cool even in the withering sun, between her hot palms. The larger leaves drooped a little; the sun was too hot for them, thought Meda, as she pushed the lump of soil Baldwin had lifted back into the hole with her foot. Stepping on it easily, she tamped it back level with the earth.

The sun drove her indoors and she cleared away the dinner dishes. There was no water to wash them, so she stacked them in the empty black kettle and threw a dish towel over them to keep out the flies. She wondered vaguely if there would be a letter next freight day. She always wondered that, but no one ever wrote any more. Why should they? Mail once a month discouraged correspondence easily with a piqued family who didn't believe in Baldwin or in homesteading.

Then, too, there was seldom any respectable stationery, and so the months slipped by and it was now a year since she had written to anyone. There was nothing to say. The struggle to ignore the winter's blizzard or the summer's heat left her with no news. She moved her hands, one over the other, as she swayed in the rocker. The fire, yellow and fierce, burned her eyeballs. She thought it was the sun, too. The sand crunched softly under the rockers, falling from the wood back into the trenches in fine streams.

The sun did not fleck the ground now. Crystal clear blue sky showed between the transparent leaves, like green veined glass. Meda resented the blue. There was too much blue, too much sky. If the whole sky could be green—that green of the leaves, seen from the inside of the room. Then she wouldn't have to look at the blue spots that made her eyes burn. She could look at the green. Somehow now she *had* to look at the sky; even closing her eyes didn't help much. She could see the blue over the rolling dunes that turned to blue and purple in the distance, turning all to blue where they met the sky. She tried to imagine her home, the apple orchard down the slope from the house, but the blues and purples and golden tans of the hills crept between, especially the blues.

Meda opened her eyes. There it was, blue, blue. Why, there was more blue than there had been, more than there was green, and the green looked brown, even gray!

Stumbling through the door, she ran to the vine and touched one of the leaves. It was limp. Another crumbled in her hands, almost powdery. She opened her palms and watched the wind blow the bits

from them until all of the leaf was gone. The yellow flames leaped
and danced in her unblinking eyes.

She flew into the house and carried the water pail to the plant.
Upsetting it at the roots, Meda waited. Time would not go. The
water seemed to stand, a little pool of blue sky. She crushed another
leaf. The pool was still there, still blue. The leaves turned yellow,
then gray. The pool was gone but the vine didn't grow fresh. The
leaves began to rattle in the hot wind.

Meda stood very, very still. She wished the sky weren't so blue,
it made her eyes burn. Suddenly she fell to her knees. She dug under
the dry, crackling leaves, her hands clumsy with fear. She found it!
The flame burned her; she buried her head in the leaves, the cut
stalks in her palms. Her head dropped to her knees. The tendrils of the
plant released the strings that held them and fell across her hair.
Meda did not move.

A fan-shaped cloud hung in the northwest, gray and thin. It grew
darker, slowly spreading its transparent fringe until the sun showed
through, a white, round ball, without light. The cloud thickened,
spread until the sun was gone. The rain began easily, a drop here and
there. Then it stopped. The sand lay yellow with darker splotches,
like freckles, but in a moment they were gone. Baldwin clucked up
his team. They raised their heads and swung into a long stride that
made the water barrels splash merrily. Baldwin looked at them and
pulled the horses back to their slow walk. He sat sideways on the
board used for a seat, turning his back to the rain that began again.
Dusk stole down the gullies. The hills moved away in the darkness.
The smell of wet horses came to his nostrils. He moved his foot and
it struck a rusty syrup pail under the seat. He hoped Meda wouldn't
mind too much when she saw what he had brought to replace the
vine. He smiled into the darkness as he recalled how the greasy-
looking woman at the cook house had gaped. Nesters weren't so
popular at Twin Mills and here was one who wanted geranium slips!
Well, he had them and a rooted wax plant "to boot."

Baldwin stripped the harness from the horses and turned them
loose. He was soaked but he didn't mind. Water! and there might
even be corn! He dug under the wagon seat for the syrup pail. As he
lifted it he noticed that there was no light and there should have
been a little, even through the vine and the rain. Perhaps Meda was
asleep, he decided. Pail under arm, he went to the house. He felt for
the knob, and didn't find anything, only a gap. Stepping nearer, he

tried again. His hand struck the jamb. The door was open. He walked in and called softly, "Meda." No answer came and he called again, louder. His hands shook as he felt for a match. The first one sputtered, wet. The second match flared up and the darkness fell back. The wind whipped the flame and, shielding it with his cupped hand, he looked around the room. He took two steps to the bed and pulled back the white curtain. Both pillows sat up against the pine head-board, smooth and prim.

Baldwin lit the swinging bracket lamp and looked all about the room. The wick smoked; a black smudge grew up from one corner and spread over the globe to its fluted top. He stumbled over the pail of geranium slips in the doorway. He called "Meda" loudly, hands to his lips. There was a dim echo from the rain, nothing more.

Then he saw her crouched at the window. The vine had fallen all about her. The light came through the window clearly now, making little glittery streaks of the rain as it fell on the head of the woman.

He ran to her and lifted her in his arms, begging her to say what was the matter. She didn't answer, only whispered, always whispered. Baldwin set her into the rocker, trying to catch a word, but he couldn't. He pulled frantically at her knotted shoestring.

"Meda, are you sick? Meda, answer me."

She didn't notice him, but looked down at her hands full of the withered, soggy vine. Her lips moved and still Baldwin could not hear. He raised her face in his palm and his eyes went black with horror. In the lamplight her eyes roamed over his unknowingly, glow-ing like deep orange caves, alive with fierce, intense flames. She shrank down into the rocker like a frightened rabbit, clutching the vine to her breast.

"Who are you? You can't take my vine, my pretty green vine, you with the blue face."

Baldwin drew back, his hands clenched and white-knuckled. He tripped over the syrup pail with the rooted wax plant. It rolled away, spilling geranium slips over the sand.

XII

The Smart Man

Most of my better stories were too *avant garde* for even the *Dial* in the middle twenties. Now the only two that I didn't burn back in 1933 (when I tried to put all the writing business behind me, once and for all) sound like echoes of the experimental writing of the 1928–1935 period (70). "The Smart Man" dates from the late 1920's and was out when I burned the rest. I don't think I would have burned it anyway, because it was not of the mood of the twenties so far as my writing went; not entirely. It was a sort of transition stage into the *Old Jules.* I once started to take a little of the twenties out of it for some editor who had asked for something at a lit'ry tea ... (73). The editor [was] one of several who thought the telling too bleak and would be happy to publish the story if—if—When I tried to make it less bleak I dropped the matter, as you can see. I am rather firm in my belief that the style of a piece should fit the characters and the locale (75).

THREE MONTHS OF WINTER lay deep and silent upon the Karr valley. In the sharp, gray air of morning the drifts showed post-high along the fence-line of the fields. Only the mail road broke the crusted snow, its two deep ruts winding cautiously along the higher ground, straight through the Karr yard and away to the far railroad.

From a snowbank a grouse rose cackling before the stealthy feet of a coyote. With a whirring of her wings she skirted the valley toward the brightening hills, making disturbed little clucks as the coyote watched her course, and then fell to digging in the snow holes again. The sun moved down the ridge to the huddle of buildings on the knoll. Slowly it crept over the old sod house to the frosted windows of the bedroom, where a baby was awaking, and of the kitchen where Emil Karr lay with his head buried in the pillow of his floor bunk.

As the first thin cry of the baby settled into a hunger squalling, the man pulled the covers over his ears. But outside somewhere a calf began to bawl, too, and from behind the kitchen range the runty pig came squealing to nuzzle the man's neck. Muttering, Emil Karr kicked the blankets aside and pushed the hair from his eyes. Up until daylight and now no sleeping, with all the racket going on. That Noreen woman in there better learn to take care of her yelling kid. She needn't think he'd keep on doing it. Not a smart man like him— the champion hog grower of the county, nursing another man's get.

But for all his complaining, Emil Karr did what he had been doing for a month. He fussed about the kitchen with his overall suspenders trailing behind him, warming milk and water with a dash of syrup in a saucepan. Carefully as for one of his young pigs he tested the temperature with a strong blunt finger, filled an old linament bottle, and laid it on Noreen's bed. Without looking at her at all he stalked back to the kitchen, knowing that she would be laughing in there like one of those goosey girls from over north, laughing at him out here in the kitchen feeding the runty pig with a bottle like it was a baby.

When the little pig was full and sleeping in the box behind the stove, Emil lifted his suspenders over his shoulders and scratched a hole in the white frost of the window. The bright sun of March that should make a young farming man feel warm and good came in and found only the cracked oilcloth of the kitchen table, the smoked lantern of a night's watch with a foaling mare, and an old stocking of Noreen's hanging across a chairback thin as veiling.

Heavily the man turned away to stuff the fire with corncobs and coal and then, instead of frying ham and flapjacks, let himself down upon a chair and waited, his face in his hard, broad hands. When the water in the reservoir boiled he filled two pails and started out to the morning chores. At the steamy bang of the door behind him a chorus of hog noises rose from the pens on the slope, followed by a romping of Poland Chinas to the feed troughs. But the man's face was as unresponsive to his prize-winners as it had been for the last month. He pulled his forgotten earflaps down and turned up the collar of his old sheepskin. Then, head down, he walked carefully along the icy boards laid end to end across the frozen mud of the yard, the steam from the pails trailing in powdery clouds behind him to the low barn. At last they too were gone.

At the sound of a car along the mail road Emil looked out of the feedway, a shovel in one hand, a pail of shorts in the other. For the moment he stared over the glaring snow and then ducked back. It

was that dudey Mike Watson, Web, as everybody called him behind his back, because of his duck feet. He was coming along early,
driving a new brown coupe instead of the slow old mail truck.

"Hello!" he called, stopping smoothly before the barn and opening
the car door a few inches. "How's the hogs this cold morning?"

Reluctantly Emil came out into the sunlight that made a reddish
stubble of his week-old beard. His eyes were murky as new snow-
water at the sight of Web, with his smooth face, his tight-kneed engineer pants and a necktie even on work days. And it wasn't because
Web looked toward the house and Noreen—that wouldn't get him
anything—but only because of the tie and the fine red-cuffed high
boot he was hanging out of the open car door. Showing off, the no-
good, putting every penny on his back and always making fun of
folks in sensible working gear.

But today Web didn't laugh at Emil's clumpy old overshoes, greenish with manure, or at the stubble—the buckbrush, as he called it—
on the windburned farmer face. He grinned a little friendly-like and
said, "Hear you sold some fine shoats the other day," as he held out
an initialed cigarette case. Getting no response he lit one for himself.
"Fetched a pretty steep price, I hear."

That thawed Emil. "Yeh, seven hundred dollars in one chunk." He
said the words slow-like, to let Uncle Sam's hired man taste them,
to make that Slick Pants see he wasn't taking a back seat for anybody.

Web whistled, which might mean that he was impressed or just
getting ready to laugh. Emil moved his feet uneasily. "That's twice
what others is getting—" he defended.

"Yeh—a lot of money," the mail carrier agreed, blowing smoke into
the sharp air and watching it float away. "A hell of a lot of money
for a sandhiller to make—"

Emil shifted the shovel in his hand but Web's smile looked all right,
like he knew the hogs were good. "Yah—well, I know how to feed.
So much of this and so much of that—" not giving any secrets away.
"Scientific, with hot slops on cold mornings. I got it all figured out.
I'm a smart man." He added the last by habit, as simply as he might
say that his corn was good, or his soil.

As always the carrier let his lip curl at the statement, his cigarette
sagging. "Yeh," he said. "You're a smart man, all right—a damn smart
man with hogs—and with kids, I hear."

A moment the farmer's beard stood out dark as a smudge of stove
soot on his gray face. Then the skin swelled ruddier than ever. "And
with women too!" he was driven to say.

Web pulled his hat brim to his eyes. "Yeh, a smart man with women," he drawled. "'Specially after nobody else wants 'em."

For a moment the taunt brought no words, no anger, nothing at all. Emil Karr just stood motionless as a horse might, a horse just off the range, or one struck over the head too often.

Web saw and began to laugh, opening his mouth until his broad white teeth gleamed, until his roaring filled all the empty yard and came back from the barn and the far hills.

"Thought you'd keep it quiet—nobody knowing! By God, you are a smart man!"

Now finally Emil began to move, slowly at first, as a stream stirs under winter ice. Then the anger in the man broke, and swinging the shovel over his head, he ran for the car, crying, "This time I fix you, you goddam' webfoot!" for all the valley to hear.

When the stench of the car was gone and the mail road empty as the winter slopes once more, Emil Karr flung his shovel ringing upon the frozen earth and started for the house. Now he'd have it out with that woman. He'd waited too long as it was, letting her make him a laughingstock—him with a handful of blue ribbons from the fairs in his trunk, seven hundred good dollars in the tobacco can behind the clock ready for banking.

A kick drove the house door inward, into the kitchen that seemed black as the depths of a badger hole to Emil's glare-blinded eyes. At his step the little pig in the box behind the stove awoke and came squealing for fresh milk. Shoving it gently aside with his foot, the man rubbed the blindness from his eyes and stalked to the bedroom.

But before the woman on the bed all his anger melted as snow before the south wind of April. The waved and blondined hair, so pretty, so bright and shining a few months ago, was faded brown-rooted stuff about her pale face now. Her cheeks were thin and the paper-white of an ailing little girl's. It was her lips, not yet red, but full and curving with contempt for the hog-grower that aroused Emil's fury once more. That and the hole scratched in the window frost where she had been looking out at the mail carrier with his necktie on, on work days. So, towering over the bed, Emil Karr demanded to know what his wife expected him to do.

"Do?" she asked, covering a pretended morning yawn with her small hand, in her pretending big-lady way.

"Do about that kid!" the man answered her, roaring out in his resentment, sending the little pig scuttling back into the kitchen and waking the baby on the bed into frightened squalling. Noreen stuffed the rubber nipple into the mouth of her son, filling it to quiet. Then she pulled the quilts and the faded voile gown from her slim young shoulder.

"You'll manage. You're a smart man, Emil," she said, giving him his name for the first time, making her blue eyes soft and round under her plucked brows for him. But when she saw that the man's face was unchanging as the frozen ground outside, she jerked the covers up under her chin. "Do about it—?" she threw up to him. "What you been doing for a month—!"

Emil straightened, flung his thick shoulders back. "You expect me to keep hiding another man's kid in my house?—me, with the best hogs in the county, winning blue ribbons every fair time?" he demanded. "I won't have everybody—people like that webfoot—making fun, laughing at me!"

"Oh, you won't?" Noreen sat up in bed. "What you expect people to think when a jane like me what's got everything marries a wet smack like you—you greenhorn pig-raiser!"

So, that's how it was. A greenhorn pig-raiser.

Once more today the man moved forward in anger. Before his coming the woman slid deep into the quilts, her hands over her face, squealing a little when the man's big farmer hands found her throat. The flesh was soft under his fingers, soft as a rabbit's belly.

A minute later Emil Karr was out in the blinding sunlight, clumping across the yard and past his hungry pigs as though they were not there. With a great triangle of blue denim torn on the yard fence flapping behind him he ran across the valley, the drifts cracking under his feet. He had no direction; like a wounded animal he sought the shielding chophills, farther and farther from the signs of man. As the March sun climbed and the snow softened he floundered hip-deep through cuts and gullies, plowed straight into soapweed clumps, their spears no more than dead grass against his legs. The shimmering glare on the snow burned his face raw, made bloodshot slits of his eyes. Sweat came down his cheeks, chilling as his feet began to slow, but still he pushed on.

Gradually a vague discomfort rose in the man's troubled mind, grew into an empty sickish feeling. He didn't remember that there had been no breakfast of pancakes and ham, no dinner of brown beans, salt pork and maybe wild plum jam and biscuits. He didn't even remember his hungry hogs because the feel of the woman's throat still clung to his fingers like the soft fur of a rabbit.

It had all begun with a dance at Sculley's late last June, and the

new cook's helper from Red Miller's hay camp. She was there with
Web, in a purple net dress with no more under it than a fringe of blue-
stem growing in a barbed wire fence. Nobody seemed to know anything about her and if Web did he wasn't saying. Emil hardly looked
at her before midnight supper, but everybody else was noticing her
hair, yellow as alfalfa butter, and her red fingernails that looked like
the claws of a hawk gorging on a pullet. And her not much older than
little Meda Sculley, just out of high school, the women told each
other. She ought to be home helping her ma, that girl ought, instead
of hanging around a hay camp and a-wearing that shameful dress
among decent boys.

She had a bold way; her eyes searched the crowd like a hunting
coyote's, but once when she passed him close, Emil saw that they
were really blue, and maybe a little scared. So towards morning he
asked one of the imported hay waddies for a knock-down to her. The
youth, a chap with checked pants and a knowing air, looked Emil
over, from his red farmer neck sticking out of the thick, dark suit
bought for his mother's funeral three years ago to the shoes blackened
with stove polish.

"Brother, she ain't the knock-down kind," he finally said.

After chewing on that for half an hour, Emil shouldered his way
through the crowd around the girl and asked her right out, blunt as
an old axe, for a dance. She pulled one net-veiled shoulder to her
cheek, looked at him through slanted eyes and laughed with her
pointed teeth showing.

"Can you tie that—Old Sour Puss wants to try a little rug cutting—"
she told the circle of grinning men about her, playing to them just
like a woman Emil saw with a carnival up to Union once, or like a
pretty red heifer in heat for the first time and making all the old
cows stand back. So he turned and, pushing his elbows out for room,
got away, but not without a big laughing to follow him. Like always,
that web-footed mail carrier's mouth was the loudest of all, and
Emil's neck reddened even more than usual. Besides, he hated that
chicken noise some women made when they laughed, not the happy
singing sound of a laying hen, but the silly cackling of the wandering
ones the hawks get.

With walk heavy from following the harrow and the plow Emil
went to stand in a corner, stiff as a cedar post. That dudey Web, with
not an acre or a hoof to his name, and probably not even the pants
he stood in paid for! When Old Man Shearer came by, just swapping
yarns, Emil told him he was planning to take his Poland Chinas to

the state fair "come September and things is going good." He had more important business to think about than women, he told the old busybody trying to whisper about "that new skirt-tail that's blowed in from Red's camp."

At the late July dance it had been a little different, only Emil was never struck much by anything different except an animal off its feed. Web brought the girl again but he didn't even dance the first one with her and the men noticed that, especially the hay waddies from town. She had on a pretty little blue dress, like a country high school girl, and none of that bloody-looking stuff on her nails. But Emil wasn't interested. Any woman who'd laughed at him— He could tell them all a thing or two, the silly ginnies.

Only the overgrown farm boys hung around the woman from the hay camp, a little sheepishly, with their mothers glaring and making up jobs for them, like opening stuck windows and bringing in the baby's bag. Everybody knew a lot about Web's girl by now. She was from up beyond Union somewhere in the Breaks. Big family scratching a living out of the gravelly knobs. She was frying chickens at a stand her pa set up for people come to see the oil drilling around there. But the rig was folded up and dragged away, and the mail carrier, who had seen her, brought her down to Red's cook tent, and turned her loose on the boys here. Anybody'd ought to be able to see she was fixing to find herself a man quick, one of the mothers told Emil. But she's going for the young ones, the kids, the woman complained, snapping her false teeth in her worried anger.

After midnight supper the girl from Red's, almost alone by now, smiled across the room to Emil. He blushed red clear up through the sun-shielded white of his forehead, but tried not to let on. He wasn't to be laughed at again. Besides, he was talking to a fellow from over in Brule County who was having trouble with a scrub stud horse of his neighbor's getting to his mares. He wanted Emil to come down to help take care of the animal.

Suddenly Noreen was beside the men, swirling the ruffled hem of her short, flaring, young-girl dress against Emil's knee. When she asked for a smoke he started doggedly away. But she put out a soft hand to hold him back and said she didn't really mean it about the cigarette. It was then he noticed the scared, lost look in her eyes again. Like the puppy he once found, long ago, left at a windmill by some movers. And when the girl told Emil how smart she heard he was with stock, curing anything, he asked her to sit beside him. When she talked about his fine hogs that everybody said he had, he took off his coat, threw it on the bench and swung her out upon the floor.

During Home Sweet Home, the tips of Noreen's small white fingers crept up under Emil's shirt collar, smoothening the band of his tie as she listened to him expand, lay plans for the greatest hog farm in the whole state.

And later, when he sat beside her in his rattley old car, the perfume of her hair made him forget his hogs, the meals his wife should cook, the chores she should help him do. Before long he was kissing the girl, his clumsy fingers in her hair, the golden threads catching his calluses. So he took her straight to town for the license and the prize-winning hogs missed a breakfast.

But within two weeks Emil Karr was sitting on the pigpen wall far into the midnight hours. People still talked to him like always, but different too, looking down their noses and laughing a little. Noreen laughed too, when he tried to get her to go to the dances. The first time he had been pleased that she would rather stay home with him, although the dances were something like the fairs, where a man showed off his woman instead of his pigs or his watermelons. But later, when he had to see how she felt about him, he thought that maybe he had hurried her too much, right at first—scared the little girl that was still in her. He'd seen a mare colt scared just that way once. But it would come out all right in time. He knew Noreen was smart as he knew a smart pup when he saw one, or a colt. She would get used to him and she would learn, maybe even help him get to be a Master Farmer some day. And if she didn't—well, she was a mighty pretty piece to have around and that toney Web hadn't got her, for all his dressing up.

Then one night she told him how it was with her. She said more, about wanting him to help her get out of it, like he did work mares who brought bad colts. But in his big excitement he heard nothing of that. And when she was asleep at last, a little girl in the nightgown thin as yellow smoke, the tears dried on her cheek, Emil Karr went out and breathed in the sky and all the darkness. He climbed to the top of his highest alfalfa stack, the smell of the new hay sweet about him, and sat there a long time. And that night the stars were very close and the earth cupped itself into a bowl around him.

He was very patient through all the trying months that he had to carry Noreen's breakfast to her, coaxing her into quietness when she cried to him to get out of her sight, or even threw the thick cups, coffee and all, at him. It was sometimes so at first even with animals when the male approached, he knew. Soon she would soften, find contentment. He longed to see peace in her stormy eyes, see her hands working quietly at fine sewing instead of fingering the confession magazines she got somehow, her nails red again as she fumbled the pages.

Later she quieted a little. Often from his corn-shucking wagon Emil Karr looked up toward the whole sod house on the knoll, the only one left in all the sandhills. But even so he strode with a finer step from one rattling cornstalk to the next, moving like a tall, a very tall man, who had to hold himself to this stooping work. But he fired the heavy yellow ears hard and fast against the bangboard. It would be a son, a smart man like his father.

That first day after Noreen told him he had gone out and scratched the little fellow's name on the finest of his Hubbard squashes with a nail—YOUNG EMIL—and watched the words grow and spread in silvery gray over the darkening green of the squash. Fair time he wrapped the big Hubbard in a bed quilt and hauled it to town in a box of hay in the pickup. For three days it lay there on display, the blue ribbon across the shiny dark-green shell. "We usually disqualify marred vegetables, but your Hubbard's by far the best—" one of the judges had said.

Emil had walked past the display a dozen times, seeing nothing of the nudges and the laughing at the name across the squash, grown into the hard, swollen letters. His mind was busy with other things. He had been looking at plans for a new house in the spring and selecting a glistening blue car to drive out to Noreen, who had not come to town, never came to town with him since their wedding day.

But although she said the car was fine, she let it stand in the shed all the golden brown days of fall. When the baby came, long before time, with no one except Emil there, two months of winter snow lay piled outside of the soddy. There was no time to ride to the telephone for a doctor. He was worried, of course, because Noreen was like a heifer that was too young, and not strong.

And when the new mother slept, like the white angel Emil saw once on a Christmas tree at a school program, there was the little fellow, his first-born son, to look after. Carefully the man tested the bath water in the wash basin with his elbow. Little animals born too early were very tender and puny, with thin skin, no hair, no real hoofs or nails, very delicate and likely to die. But this young one yelled loud enough, with his father's good hog-calling lungs. He waved a red fist around and scratched the man. Not deep, but still a scratch. He had fingernails, long sharp fingernails. . . .

Afterward, out in the barn among his familiar animals, Emil wondered why he hadn't drowned the brat right there. But he never could shoot as much as a bird-killing cat, and not even this night could change him.

Of course he hadn't touched the baby since, just left his feed and things on the edge of Noreen's bed and dumped the washing into the new power machine and set it going. Himself he moved into the kitchen, to an old strawtick on the floor, and when the baby cried so Noreen couldn't sleep she fed him from a bottle capped with one of the pig nipples. In the meantime the man went dully about his spring work, extra heavy this year, with the late winter dragging on into farrowing and calving time. For himself he cooked when he was hungry, for Noreen he prepared soft-boiled eggs and oatmeal and stewed prunes from the catalogue-house supply in the cellar. He had nothing to say, not even the first night that the young mother came out to supper, almost lost in one of the big aprons of the winter that Emil had washed and ironed so neatly.

Up to now it had been just between him and Noreen, and while he didn't know what to say or do, he kept on fixing the bottles for her baby, even put aside the seven hundred dollars toward the new house he would build with a porch and a big sun window on the south. But now everybody was knowing and laughing and even that webfoot throwing it up to him, right up to his face, and on his own land too. He'd been made a sucker by a woman in a fix—a greenhorn, pig-raising sucker for all the country to see.

So Emil Karr kept plodding the drifting hills with the feel of a woman's throat clinging to his hands. When he saw a horsebacker coming along a wind-swept ridge, he dodged into a blowout and kept his head down until the man was past. Even the first steel-blue sky of spring overhead and the snow that was soaking the soil to fertility right under his feet were nothing today. He didn't even know where he was, how far he had pushed from home.

By the time the sun had swung into mid-afternoon, the whiteness of the steep southern slopes was breaking up, the ridges between the cowpaths coming through like the dark wales of diagonal corduroy. The air was heavy with the moistness of planting time, and stirred a deep-seated longing in the man, drawing his feet back toward his own land, the earth his plow turned, sweet and dark, every spring.

Yet when he cleared the last ridge and looked down upon his buildings and fields they were as strange as the far hills had been, with no familiar thing. A truck or a car was leaving the far end of the valley, one that seemed familiar—the web-footed mail carrier heading back to Union with the empty mail sacks. And in that sod house down there was another man's baby in the bed of his wife and everybody knowing about it, maybe even more about it than he himself.

Clumsily, as a loaded wheel lurches into a frozen rut, Emil sank down to a wind-cleared bank of sand along the ridge. He dropped his head to his folded arms, shutting out everything of the house and the knoll, everything except the loud, open-mouthed laugh of Web, and the feel still on his fingers.

Gradually the air chilled into evening, crusting the grainy snow as the shadows crept up between the ridges. In the north a long cloud bank waited for sunset, and on the Karr knoll the hungry cattle once more raised their heads in a bawling that echoed far into the hills. The man heard and remembered that the cows hadn't been milked, that nothing had been fed since the night before, not even the new-foaled mare. A losing day for his Poland Chinas—for all his stock.

Stiffly Emil Karr rose, pulled the flap of his cap down over his ears, and plowed through the crunching snow toward his home. Inside, the kitchen was dark and empty, the room filled with the iron smell of a very hot fire gone cold. The runty pig squealed behind the cook-stove and through the open bedroom door came the choked wailing of a baby, the hoarse and tired end of long, long crying.

Automatically Emil started to the neglected child but a note on the table stopped him. He picked it up and looked at it curiously in the light of the frosting window. As he read he pushed at his cap until it went to the floor behind him with a soft plump. Noreen was gone. No goodby, only a note telling him that he was a smart man; he could take care of the baby.

In his confusion the hog-grower rubbed his snow-burned eyes. Why, she had no reason to go kiting off that way. Crazy as he was this morning he hardly touched her before the feel of her throat made him go sick. A greenhorn pig-raiser she had called him, and it was so. Yet he had been good enough to take care of her when she was in a fix. Now that she was light again she was off. Gone without a penny.

Suddenly he thought of something. Stumbling over his floor bunk, he reached for the old tobacco can on the clock shelf. It rattled as he tipped it. A nickel and three pennies fell into his palm. Only a nickel and three pennies left—the seven hundred dollars that were to go into a new house for that woman gone. It took a lot of feed and work to get seven hundred dollars, a lot of dirty grubby work, even for a greenhorn pig-raiser.

The second time that day Emil stood over the bed he had deserted long ago. The baby lay alone, purple with cold and long crying, but making only round-mouthed little gasps now, barely moving a feeble grayish fist. With the woman's note still in his hand Emil looked down upon the cause of all the laughs and jokes he would have to take if he stayed in the sandhills. He crushed the paper to a wad, flung it to the floor, stomped it, ground it into a wet pulp with his snow-soaked overshoes.

But Emil Karr was the man who coddled every poor runty little creature. And so he wrapped the faded bed blanket around the baby and carried it into the kitchen. When the fire roared hot under the lids and the infant seemed to doze a little after a few spoonfuls of sweetened water, he ran out to get fresh milk. Already the sky was clouded to the barn peak, dusk dying fast. More snow before morning.

When the baby and all the place was fed and quiet at last Emil pulled off his frozen overshoes and hunched himself upon a stool before the hot stove, his face weary in the dim light of the smoky barn lantern. Once he got up to put away the torn stocking hanging over a chair back, one like those Noreen had on the morning they were married. He folded it gently, freeing his broken nails from the cobwebby threads, and then put it away in the till of his trunk, with the picture of his mother, his eighth-grade diploma, and the handful of gold-lettered blue ribbons from the fair.

When he came back he stooped to look upon the baby sleeping in his bunk on the floor. Finally he settled to the stool before the fire with the baby in an awkward bundle across his knees. Gradually he shifted the child to a more comfortable position in the crook of his arm. Unfolding the blanket, he held the tiny bare feet to the glow of the hearth. In the close warmth he fondled the velvety skin and grew drowsy and full of thought.

Such sound joints the little fellow had, and straight, long bones, like a fine colt. He would grow up into a strong, wide-standing man, with feet solid on the ground behind the plow and harrow. Strong feet already, with the pretty little toes no bigger than young gooseberries but soft as willow pussies in the spring. Young Emil he should be, like on the Hubbard squash at the fair. With Noreen gone not even Web could prove it wasn't so. Young Emil Karr.

But suddenly the man sat up, struck a match over the little feet, spreading the tiny buds of toes apart. It was true—between them were folds of skin, thin, but plain as the web on the feet of a new-hatched duckling.

A long time he held the match, letting the flame burn down until the red end of the wood curled and broke, falling upon the little foot. The baby kicked and screamed and the ember went in a streak to the floor and lay there, darkening.

So that's how it was. Here was the proof, and everywhere the brat went people would be seeing, knowing, be talking about Emil Karr's wife whelping a webfoot. By God, he would stop that!

Kicking the stool away, he reached for his straight-edge razor, heated it in the steam of the teakettle. Then he held the toes apart, and one after another slashed away all the paper-thin membranes.

When he had walked the hurt and frightened baby into quiet at last, Emil Karr went back to the stool before the stove, the salve jar at his elbow. Once he pulled the lantern nearer, to look at the toes, scarcely seeping a reddish dew, at the white down on the little head, the heavy, tear-swollen eyes. Then he settled back, the sleeping baby lost in the shadow of his strong arm.

XIII

Pieces to a Quilt

The whole allegorical aspect of my fiction . . . has been almost entirely neglected, partly because each book draws new reviewers. Many of my readers find in my first three novels the allegories I intended them to be. Now and then one of these readers runs into "Mist and the Tall White Tower" [page 154] or "Pieces to a Quilt" and sees the allegorical intent there also. But for this the approach apparently must be through the novels (74).

THE LANG EIGHTY contained not even a shirt-tail patch of level ground. Most of it was a deep gullied cup of gravel and crumbling sandstone, sloping abruptly into a dark pool. Now and then a glimpse of a summer cloud lay on the still surface but its whiteness only accentuated the dark reflections from the ten-foot bank of volcanic ash just above the water line. Even the cress-grown spring didn't bubble but welled up with slow complaint of green water under ice.

Back from the pool, under a solid nose of stone, squatted Lang's old shack, weathered to the gray of ashes. A silent little creek slipped past the sagging doorstep and out between sheer sandstone bluffs toward the hay flats north, as though eager to escape the deep pool, the stark canyon walls, and the shack, empty since the man who built it hanged himself there with a silk muffler.

At least it was assumed he hanged himself. Sarah Reimer, schooled in patience with her slow-witted son, asked no questions when he brought home a square of figured silk with a corner cut off. He washed it and ironed it and made blocks for his crazy quilt. It was all right. Somebody was always giving him old silk pieces.

A week later, when the mail carrier mentioned that Lang's newspapers were piling up at the box, Rusty flung his clumsy hands about in a frenzy at the slowness of his tongue.

"I-I-I forgot to tell. Lang died."

The father and two neighbors went over and found that it was so.

Lang had died, of hanging, probably with the muffler, as Rusty tried to explain. He had seen the man and, fancying the pretty silk, cut him down. It was August. The sheriff came out that night.

They took Lang outside, burned a little plug tobacco on a stove lid, and looked around, but there wasn't anything, no papers, no letters, not even a trunk, only the name of a New York tailor in his coat, which didn't mean anything. Lang's hands had been small and soft, never touched work. Just another hide-out.

Although Lang had lived in the canyon five years, not even the neighborly Jacob Reimer knew anything about him except that he was graying, never got farther from his place than the mailbox, and always seemed to have money for the groceries the mail-carrier brought out. None of his neighbors had seen him more than once or twice, unless it was Rusty.

"That half-wit ought to be looked after," a suspicious newcomer suggested.

"Aw, Rusty wouldn't hurt a fly," the sheriff defended. "His father's a damned good neighbor; too good to get ahead."

And there it was.

A week after the write-up of the Sad End, as the local paper called it, a woman, a young one, came to the county seat with the clipping. She made a fuss because Lang was already buried. No, she had no idea who he was.

A few days later Sarah Reimer spoke to her husband over Rusty's empty chair.

"He took his quilt blocks away this morning and then came back for that old revolver. I haven't seen anything of him since."

Jacob brushed his thinning hair back decently and looked with friendly blue eyes upon his wife's uneasiness.

"I will see to it," he said.

After supper he went out to smoke his pipe and wait for his son. On the way through Sarah's flowers he picked a golden calendula for the bib of his wash-bleached overalls, as Rusty often did. Then he leaned both tired elbows over the garden gate and looked off into the sunset, into the evening haze over the meandering creek and its soft green clumps of willow. Perhaps he should straighten the bed as he had helped his neighbors do long ago; cut out the willows. But a stream laid out by compass, hurrying away between weed-grown ridges of dirt and sod torn from their place in the earth—no, he preferred the first yellow-green of spring creeping shyly into the willow clumps, long grass dipping into the little stream in midsummer, thin sharp knives of anchor ice around the backwater in the fall.

Sometimes he could not forget the drouth and hail, or that his wife had once been ambitious to have a big house too, and a broad red barn, but she never complained. She had been as ready as he to spend the butter money for those five little Meyers last week. She even sewed all night so they could have dresses to wear to the funeral of their father who started home with too much Short Grass moon aboard and drove off into a canyon. Jacob was glad about the dresses. There should always be something nice to remember about funerals.

By the time his pipe was cold a black speck broke from the bluffs toward the Lang eighty, followed by a grotesque shadow down the long, sun-gilded slope. It was Joseph, Rusty, as the neighbors called him, on flea-bitten, stiff-kneed old Sarry. On her back lurched the top the sun-sensitive Rusty made of two forged rake-teeth fastened to the broken cantle of his old saddle, with canvas across them. Bobbing up and down like a jockey in his short stirrups, canvas flopping and rods rattling, Rusty rode towards his home.

When he saw his father waiting between the hollyhocks, his flat face softened into a broad, short-toothed grin and his eyes flecked with yellow glints. After the old mare was fed and curried he picked up the sack of water cress he brought his mother and walked beside Jacob to the house, the silence of good feeling between them.

Once or twice the father looked past the lamp to his son's thick mat of coarse sorrel curls, his heavy shoulders stooped over the clumsy fingers. It seemed foolish to ask Joseph what he had been doing. Never in his twenty years had his father ever known him to harm a living thing. Even after a day of fasting he was eating very slowly because this unreasonable procedure seemed to please his mother. Because Jacob saw this he was a little ashamed and hid behind talk of his work. Tomorrow he would help the Johnsons, and the next day Ivan Vach.

Rusty went to bed unquestioned.

Not until a year later did the community discover the cave that Lang had dug in the bluffs overlooking his shack and the canyon. The opening was concealed behind a big sandstone boulder with just enough space to slip in at one side. He even had a little fireplace opening into a gully.

Rusty had evidently found it long before. At least that seemed to be where he took his quilt blocks and later the phonograph his father bought at a sale for a quarter, with a stack of French and German records nobody wanted thrown in. Rusty liked them. He pulled out the carved wood front of the machine so he could get his head closer to the sound and kept it going. When his mother's impatience became too evident, he shambled out into the yard with the phonograph in a gunny sack. That was how the cave was discovered. A visiting geologist examining the bank of volcanic ash heard a scratchy but unmistakable rendition of the Jewel Song from Gounod's *Faust* drift thinly down to him. He followed the sound. As his shadow struck the mouth of the cave Rusty sprang up, swinging an old revolver like a club.

"I-I-I thought you was *him*," was all the explanation he would give. The geologist catalogued Rusty at a glance and dismissed the incident. But he was pleased when the youth took him into a deeply washed draw where a ledge of rock with bones in it lay exposed. In return he sent Rusty two records by the mail man, a Tyrolean yodel and a laughing Chaliapin. Rusty liked the yodel best.

News of the cave spread. Lang *had* been hiding out. But when nobody could produce any details, the sightseers soon tired of his cave. Rusty went back to it now, but openly, begging cookies from his mother or potatoes and eggs to roast in the fireplace so he wouldn't have to come home at noon. Several times tough fellows from town came out with bottles. They tried to get him to do things fit only for pigs. When he wouldn't, they wanted him to drink Short Grass moon with them, but it burned his mouth and choked him and that seemed reason enough to refuse it. So he sat away from them, watching under his bushy brows as from behind sandstone boulders. Their kind laughed at him away from the cave. They could go.

When they kept coming back he got a skunk carcass from old Amos, who trapped a little. After they went away the last time he scooped the contaminated sand down the slope, carried in clean dirt, and built a smudge of twisted mint from the creek bank in the fireplace. When the cave was sweet again he listened to the yodel and tried to forget the black mist of things that had been said and done.

After that nobody came to the cave to bother him and from the earliest spring winds until the narrow tongues of grass along the creek were the autumn brown of young beaver, Rusty's old mare, Sarry, spent many days picketed above the bluffs. When the July noon heat made Rusty's head ache, he spent hours on the crazy quilt, arranging and rearranging the blocks a hundred times before he sewed them, taking joy in the feel and the color, although all dark, shiny things were red to him. He never went near the Lang shack, even before people said it was haunted.

Once several squirts from the community brought a Hallowe'en fruit jar of white dynamite. They went home pretty well scratched up and muddy, as though their departure had been a hasty one. After that Rusty had the canyon to himself, he and the cat, Bidge.

That was his own name for her, as the cat was his own. His mother, tired of the constant mewing of hungry kittens underfoot, told Rusty to take the old gray and white tabby out and drown her.

"B-b-but she don't like water. She swim out," he argued, trying very hard to manage his tongue well for his mother.

"Of course," Sarah Reimer agreed. "Get the old clothesline hanging on the post and tie a rock to her neck."

Rusty scratched his head, exposing his short teeth in a doubtful smile.

"Please do as I tell you."

Rusty got his equipment on old Sarry, and with Bidge mewing across the saddle before him, the clothesline snaking along behind him like an Indian's picket rope, he disappeared toward Lang canyon. The mother watched him out of sight and then returned to her churning.

The next morning the cat was crying outside the screen door.

"I just knew it would be like that. Now take her out and tie a rock to her tight so she won't come back. Maybe I had better do it myself."

Rusty pulled at the lobe of his ear and grunted. The cat didn't return. After that he tied her up in a web of clothesline in the cave every time he left.

In corn-plowing time Rusty usually helped. Wearing a water-soaked red handkerchief under his rush hat, the corners flopping about his face, he wielded a hoe against the weeds in the rows. He didn't like it and when the heat dances shimmered before his eyes and the sweat trickled down his broad shoulder blades, he loitered along, wondering if he was certain enough which were sunflowers and which corn. But only until his father came by with the walking cultivator, his round shoulders furry with dust, his horny hands reaching out to pull the weeds the shovels missed. Then Rusty's head felt better. He could tell the difference between weeds and corn quite clearly, and after supper he could have music.

One evening as he plodded down towards his cave, the window in the Lang shack suddenly glowed as from a lamp. Rusty looked toward the moon, standing big and full on the horizon, but it was not that, for the canyon was a deep cup of shadow.

He wanted music but he couldn't have drunks in his cave, so he sprawled out on a sandy cliff, the cat across his chest, and looked into the face of the moon. It had dark spots like black canyons. Perhaps throwing pebbles at the shack might scare them away down there. But it was too much bother, after hoeing.

Sometime after the moon rose high enough to light the sandstone bluffs to a blue-white, Rusty realized there was a splashing in the little pond. He dumped the cat away and, sneaking down the gully, squatted on a knee of rock overlooking the water. A girl swam the moon-gilded pond as smoothly as an otter, then turned and, flailing her white arms upon the water, made a crystal and silver showering all about her. At the far side she climbed out upon a bit of rock, her wet body gleaming like pale silk. Folding her palms together she cut the air and water, disappearing as completely into the still pond as though she had never been. Rusty hugged his knees and watched her come up, shake moonlit drops and weeds flying from her streaming hair, and stretch out upon a bit of sand, breathing in soft little gasps almost lost under the mournful complaint of the spring.

Suddenly far up the slope the deserted cat mewed and came bounding to Rusty, arching her back against him. The girl heard but she did not retreat from the watching figure hunched dark on the rock.

"Who are you—spying on me?"

When there was no answer, she picked up something, a dark garment that shimmered like the moon on black water, slipped it about her and approached the youth with the green eyes of the cat beside him.

"Who are you and what do you want here?"

Still Rusty gave her no answer, staring instead at the lounging robe tied with a long, loose bow.

"P-p-pretty ribbon, red ribbon," he said, as though to himself, reaching out a finger for an end.

"Oh." The girl was relieved. Then she smiled coyly, running the end through her fingers. "Do you like it?"

"P-p-pretty," he said again, rubbing his thick hands together.

"Have you a knife? I'll give you one."

But he had no knife, as his shaking head indicated, and so she deftly twisted one tie about her to hold the robe and ripped the other off. Rusty took the ribbon from her hand, making a little sucking noise between his teeth.

"I-I-I show you my quilt —"

"Quilt, did you say *quilt?*"

His head waggled up and down as he stroked his rough thumb over the silk.

The girl snapped a casual finger at the cat and asked if they lived near. Rusty pointed off towards the north. The woman nodded a little and strolled away to the shack. A long time after she was gone the two plodded up the steep incline. "Pretty ribbon, red ribbon," he told the cat, speaking easily enough now that there was no one but Bidge.

After he had been in bed an hour, his mind a vague pattern of moonlight on the dark robe of a girl, he remembered that he still had his shoes and pants on. Growling like a dog disturbed at his rest, he pulled them off. At last he slept.

After that he watched the woman almost as much as he listened to the phonograph. A few times he perched on the bank outside her doorstep, delighted with the sheen of her dress, the play of her spiked heels. At first she moved in a cloud of annoyance, perhaps even of fear, but later she got so she waved to him, tried to dawdle away a little time talking. One evening she approached very close to him with a letter.

"Will you take this to the post office and tell no one where you got it?" she asked.

Rusty shook his head, remembering a blur of faces there that laughed at him.

"The mailbox then?"

Yes, he could do that, bobbing his head vigorously in delight. When she tried to give him a quarter he growled and made a grab at her dress.

"S-s-scraps!"

Scraps? What did he want with them? Didn't he get enough to eat?

Scraps! He insisted upon scraps, fingering the material of her skirt. When she still did not understand he brought a canvas-rolled bundle from his cave and spread his crazy quilt over her lap, clinging to a corner all the while.

"P-p-pretty," he said.

"Gorgeous!"

Rusty regarded the strange word dubiously, turning it over in his mind as he might a stick of chewing gum from a stranger, afraid it was a joke.

"But I didn't make the dress. There are no scraps," the girls said, and dragged him back to the matter of the mailbox. He rushed off and was back in half an hour, motionless, watching her swim from the knee of rock, now and then rubbing fat blue sparks from the cat. But the idyllic isolation of Lang's canyon couldn't last. A woman, particularly a strange young woman living in the shack where the man had hanged himself, was a welcome diversion, even in the busy haying season. When the first investigator reported that she was slim as a movie actress and had hair like a brass washboard, there was an epidemic of grouse hunting over that way. Women with straying men suddenly developed a taste for water cress. But the shack door remained closed to all of them. At the post office and at sales there were conjectures. Perhaps a constable might go over to find out who she was. Still, as no heirs ever appeared for the place, there wasn't much to do. The mail carrier admitted that he brought her out, left groceries for her every week at Lang's old box. She got no mail and gave him no name.

Then somebody saw Rusty sitting on a hump of rock, watching the house, the gray and white cat at his side.

"I'll talk to him," Jacob Reimer told his wife and she had to be content.

After supper Rusty seemed eager to escape but his father motioned him to stay. "Want to help me catch sparrows tonight?"

Rusty's short upper lip drew back in a grin. He liked catching sparrows if his father held the lantern and let him run along the stringers and reach into the nests and nooks until his pockets were full. But it was only a game, for he could never bear to see the little birds killed, and after counting them, stroking the quivering backs, feeling the pounding of their little hearts against his palm, he let them go, one after another, until all were lost in the darkness. Then he liked to lie back in the hay, his arms under his head, while his father talked of his own boyhood, and his three brothers.

"B-b-brothers," Rusty would say, almost as though his impediment of speech were all that made him different. "Brothers fine."

Then his father always looked away into the darkness. There could never be any others, but Jacob was thankful. Almost he had lost everything—the son and the mother.

"Bedtime, son," he would say, very gently. But tonight there was more. "You aren't bothering the woman on the Lang place?" he asked.

Rusty moved his head in the hay. "S-s-she give me ribbon, red ribbon," he said after a time.

So? Then it was good. And now to bed.

The next evening a dark cloud leaned out of the west and sent low rumbles of thunder before it as Rusty started old Sarry towards the Lang eighty. The mother looked after him.

"It is good," the father said. "She gave him a ribbon—red, he calls it."

The mother was not entirely satisfied. "What does she want here—such a woman?"

Her husband looked up from his paper. "It cannot mean anything to us and to Joseph."

At the cave Bidge, neglected for two days, her pan of water almost dry, rubbed against Rusty with loud purrs. He pulled her ears and stretched out on the sand to watch the woman. She came from the spring with a pail, stopped, looked all about as she always did lately, and then disappeared into the house to make the window full of light.

In the west the thunder cloud was sending a long arm around behind them and the lightning brightened. A car roared along the mail road. Rusty looked for the shafts of light against the clouds as it climbed Peeler's hill, but there were none.

Just when he first saw the man creeping through the dusk towards the shack Rusty could not tell. It was as though he clotted from the gloom across the creek, taking form as he circled the house. He sneaked to the window, then to the door, as a cat stalks a bird. Silently Rusty slipped down a draw and flattened himself against the shack.

Inside there was a little cry, not loud, but like that of a young badger he caught once. There were words, quick, fending ones from the woman, slow, hard ones like stones dropping into deep water from the man. A stirring in his mind troubled Rusty, a memory almost tangible. Then he had it. It was the *man*. And after he left, Lang had been dead.

Rusty's lips curled back from his teeth. He threw a handful of sand over his head and loped up the steep incline to the cave. Gripping the old revolver by the barrel like a club of stone he charged down the slope. From the window he saw the woman was not yet hanging. She had the table between them, but the man clutched her wrist and ran a taunting hand up her arm while she flinched like a wild horse that would paw a man down when the moment came.

In the doorway Rusty blinked once from the glare of light, took aim and brought the gun down upon the bald spot at the man's crown. He swayed, half-turning, and slumped into the shadow of the table.

"Well," the woman said with a little laugh as she rubbed her wrist. "You killed him. Now we better get him out, bury him."

Rusty looked from her to the floor, his eyes blurring. He wiped at them with thick fingers. They cleared a little and, dropping the revolver with a clatter, he vanished into the darkness. At his heels ran a faint patter of rain.

For a moment the woman hesitated, but when the man stirred, groaned, she grasped the revolver and with flat lips she brought the butt down into his temple. It gave like ice-crusted mud.

Before she could straighten up, Rusty was back with the clothesline. Not looking at her at all he dragged the man away to the pond, tied him close to a big rock, and rolled both into the water. There was a deep *plunk* but the lap of the far ripples was lost in the increasing patter of rain.

Rusty wiped the sweat from his face and, trying to remember something, went back into the shack. Before his approaching bulk the woman once more took refuge behind the table. Rusty stopped in the doorway, eyes blinking and searching the floor.

"G-g-g-give me the shooter," he demanded, his voice suddenly harsh.

For a moment she faced him, then slowly she laid the gun on the table. Rusty took it, wiped the skin and blood from the butt on his overalls, and went through the door.

"Where—where are you going?" she asked, in new fear.

But the doorway was empty.

In the cave Rusty sat on a rock for a long time, his hand making rhythmic poppings of sparks from the back of Bidge. Now and then sheet lightning set the hunched figure into bright relief against the deep blackness behind him. The rain quickened.

Somewhere west a car started up; the lights cut the clouds in a half circle. As the roar died away Rusty had a queer prickling of fear along his arms. Once more he plunged down the slope to the shack. The lamp burned in an empty room. The woman was gone; everything was gone except the dark robe, folded on the table, as though for someone. Rusty lifted it. The folds swept downward, gleaming like moonlight on dark water.

XIV

The Birdman

I can't recall [writing] any Indian fiction beyond a short story in the Omaha *World-Herald,* February 10, 1935, about a prehistoric, earth-house Indian boy called Birdman. A student finishing up a master's on my writing ran this down and thinks it was the spiritual forerunner of the boy in *The Horsecatcher* (72).

LONG BEFORE THE SUN struck the face of Lookout Mountain, curls of smoke rose from the earth houses at its feet. Women hurried to the springs for water. Boys ran through the village. Dogs barked. The men brought out the weapons and gear of the hunt for admiration and repair. Today would begin the preparations for the ceremonial that would bring the buffalo from the land of the warm wind.

It was time. The long snows of winter had eaten deep into the caches of dried meat and corn and pumpkin rings. But soon there would be new meat for the pots and the drying racks, new robes and skins for sewing with the bone awls and needles of the women. And with these things would come great glory for the buffalo hunters.

Seeing this, young Birdman drew his robe around him and stalked out of the village, carrying neither bow nor arrow—only his flint-headed spear which everyone derided as much too heavy and much too strong for birds and rabbits.

Climbing the steep slope out of Reams Creek to the high plain spreading away southwestward, he circled back to where it broke in the high limestone-capped bluff called Lookout Mountain. There he squatted in his robe and scowled down upon the gray earth homes of his people, scattered in little groups far up and down the benches of the creek valley.

Below him the women moved about their labors. Several were working with bone diggers and willow baskets at the warming clay pits, for there was pottery to make, and the winter-bared patches of willow thatching on the house roofs must be covered before the late spring rains came. At the creek an old woman tied a long string of buffalo bladders to a stake to soak, complainingly, Birdman knew, and with no faith that there would soon be fresh ones for the moulding of the pottery.

About the earth houses the men were preparing for the buffalo ceremonial and the coming of the herds from the south, the older with pipe and story and the sacred things for tomorrow's rites, the younger with mighty testing of bow and arrow and great plans for the surround. Others sharpened the knives and spears that might, with one blow under the shoulder, bring the buffalo to his knees.

But the testing of buffalo bows and the sharpening of spearheads was not for him on the top of Lookout Mountain. He was a birdman and sat long hours in the chill waters with an eye-holed pumpkin over his head. When the ducks came he moved slowly, very slowly, as though drifting in the evening winds, until he was among the gossiping birds. Then he pulled them under by the feet, each so swiftly that there was no time for outcry, their mates noticing only to watch this curious diving until Birdman had all his two hands could hold. And twice a year came the flying wedges of geese out of the evening horizon. Once he caught two white-throated geese at one time.

But Birdman was not so named for these things alone. Upon a far bluff was an old pit, and when the hunting eagle soared the sky like a flake of soot from burning cornstalks, the hunter threw the drifted sand from the pit with the shoulder blade of a buffalo and repaired the light covering of willows. When it was old to the eye he caught a young antelope or a rabbit, and with its side opened red, tied it firmly to a center pole. Then he waited in the pit and when the circling eagle dropped like a stone upon his prey, Birdman reached up from below and swiftly clutched the powerful legs. He must get them both, and in one hand, to leave the other free for defense against the sharp tearing beak, the threshing wings.

In the first fierce rush of his anger, the eagle would beat down the light network of willow and strike again and again upon Birdman's unprotected head and shoulders, his sharp beak cutting and tearing the flesh, while the wings were as war clubs. But never once did the bird hunter release his hold and at last his thumb always closed on the sinewed, pulsing throat.

Sometimes it was hours before he could rise and bear his kill to the village, the wings spread longer than any man and the torn flesh of the hunter speaking of a battle that would bear recounting for many a moon.

He knew that it was no small thing to be called Birdman, but it was not enough. He would be a buffalo hunter also and as he looked down upon the earth houses of his people on the second bench above the river, Birdman was angry. Even now the house builders were perhaps seeking him to help place the center posts about the fire pit in a new house or to mould the clay about the firehole in the roof. Or perhaps his aunt wanted him to help plant the pumpkin in the creek bends where the sod would yield to the shovel of bone from buffalo killed by those who were now sharpening their spears for the hunt.

As the sun climbed in the sky, a drowsiness settled over the gray earth houses above the tree-tufted creek. They were greening fast today, and on the horizon shimmered a pale heat dance. No wind stirred the spare sand grass upon the slope. Two grouse flew across the valley, cackling low, uneasily. Birdman marked their flight, but not as carefully as was his habit. The sun was as the ash fire in winter, soothing. Gradually he was drowsy too and slept for a long time.

He awoke to hunger and to a breathless stillness and a green-gray sky. Below him the women were flying to finish their work, to gather in the soaking bladders, the garments and the robes spread to air. Over them the clouds darkened and began to roll and tumble like the floodwaters of the creek rolled when they rose over the cornfields or perhaps even the lower houses, crumbling their earth shells.

Birdman watched the valley below darken into an unnatural opaqueness. The air sang with a high, thin sound that grew into a roar. A dust cloud swept out of the horizon toward Lookout Mountain. Then the wind struck, from every side at one time. The grass ran like milling buffalo. Trees leaned, turned half around, and went down like sticks.

Hard on the wind came sheets of rain and earth-shaking thunder. Birdman dropped over the limestone cap of the mountain, squeezed himself under an overhanging cliff, and pulled his robe about him. Let the storm howl like the wolves in midwinter, the thunder fall like great boulders from high places!

A long time afterward the silence came back. Birdman stretched his cramped knees and looked out from his robe. Reams Creek was a swirling, gray river, scattering mud, branches, even whole trees over the lower cornfields. The new yellow clay was washed as paint over the ground. The trees tucked in the draws were broken; many that stood alone bared their uprooted feet to the air.

The creek lapped sullenly at the houses along the lower bench. The women ran for the higher ground with their bundles, shooing their children before them, while the men threw up earth embankments. Birdman saw that he must return to the village. As he wrapped his robe about him he heard a faint roar as of far but mighty thunder—a low, steady thunder that shook the earth. He looked around. Across the horizon lay a dark line. At first he could not believe it. But even as he watched, it grew—the buffalo were coming, stampeded by the storm.

One moment he hesitated before giving the customary signal. Then, without warning his village, he grasped his spear and clinging to his flying robe, he ran over the plain toward the herd, leaping gullies and washouts like an antelope. As the dark mass neared he saw that it was breaking. Little herds, unpressed from behind, were gradually swinging to the sides.

One of these dark fingers pointed along the breaks of Reams Creek. Birdman, recalling the many accounts of the great hunters of his people, thought swiftly. To the left was the broad plain down which the larger herd was sweeping. Coming straight toward him were about a hundred of the muddy animals, heads down, running blindly, certain death to everything in their path. For one instant he was only a birdman and wishing to rid himself of spear and robe, wanted to run as the antelope and the coyote ran, with no pretense of courage. But instead he threw himself into a washout to wait, the earth trembling under his body. Even now he wondered if he should not signal to the village for those who make the surrounds, those who do it well and bring meat to the drying racks. But already it was too late. Besides, his anger with himself stiffened his determination. As the dark herd was upon him he rose and with a loud cry he waved the dark robe before him.

For a second the leaders hesitated. Then the thrust of those behind drove them on. Birdman leaped sideways, flung his robe into the mud-caked faces, and with a mighty thrust buried his spear under the shoulder of the nearest. Inexpertly he overbalanced and went down but the herd, already swerved, swept past him toward the bluff. At the brink the leaders could not stop and those behind followed.

Birdman found himself unhurt. As he looked down upon the muddy, bleeding side of the dead buffalo, his spear deep, an exultation rose in him and he threw back his head and began to run. At the edge of the bluff overlooking Reams Creek he stopped and looked down. Below was a writhing mass of buffalo; some, less crippled, were dragging their heavy bodies onward.

And already up the benchland from the village came the first of the runners with their spears. Birdman stood straight and tall against the sky and signaled to his people. Here were robes enough to keep the women tanning for a long moon, fresh bladders about which to mould their pottery. Here was much meat for the pots and the drying racks and tongue and hump enough to feast all the people—to whom he would be Birdman no longer.

XV

Mist and the Tall White Tower

The setting of this story, written in 1936, brings to mind the author's 1939 novel, *Capital City*. Of the latter she remarked in an interview: ". . . *Capital City* took up much of my idle thinking for years, ever since I sat through a frontier course in the University here [Lincoln]. Elsewhere in the world cities justified their existence industrially and commercially, and were capitals incidentally. Here, with the exception of Des Moines and Denver, they [midwestern and Great Plains capitals] produce almost nothing and are becoming increasingly parasitic. This parisitism wouldn't matter so much if they didn't dictate, in large measure at least, the thought and culture of the entire state" (59).

THE CAPITOL TOWER stood straight and tall over the shimmering, dusty heat of the flat prairie town. Alone it pierced the sky—timeless, enduring, a fluted shaft of stone and gleaming windows rising high from its broad base on terraced lawns to the banding of blue thunderbirds. Upon the gilded dome the sower plodded his dark and solitary way, scattering his futile seed over the July plain, aloof from the sweating, heat-exhausted humanity barred from the grass by day guards.

But at the first yellowing of twilight between the hot buildings of the town, the walks darkened with people plodding listlessly toward the soft moistness of the capitol grounds. Among them came Irvy Snell, a thin-shouldered boy of thirteen, timid as a strange colt, following close upon the heaving buttocks of two old women so his aloneness would not be seen.

At the first clump of shrubbery he dropped down, away from any chance lift of the dead air but well hidden. A long time the boy hunched there, tense, motionless in this his first trespassing on public property. At last he unhooked his broken cowhide shoes and jerked them off in one jerk. Tenderly he nursed his road-blistered feet in his

154

palms and tried to forget that his empty stomach was wet canvas rubbing together and that the road was dark before him.

With the evening, groups of boys trailed in by twos and more, the dust of long travel upon their shoulders, to drop wearily to this cool grass that seemed free for the taking. Several stretched themselves not far from the bush that hid Irvy, so close they were somehow not strange; seemed almost of him, a little like his own people, talking around and over him as his father and grandmother used to talk at home. But he didn't let on. He kept clear of the bigger fellows on the road since he got away from Butch up at Broken Bow, with lips so nasty to see, thick and brown as pigs' liver at butchering time.

Between velvet silences the boys talked of the things of the road: of women, food-getting, the dust, the heat, of women again. But mostly of food. And always with the alert watchfulness of animals, hunted animals, upon them.

Yet nobody came to move them on. Not even when the tall brass lamps around the four blocks of capitol grounds flashed to life and showed the grass dotted thick as with tired cattle in a pasture lot.

And still the people kept coming along the lighted walks. A mother, with three fretting little ones and a circle-stained pillow. Old people, who groaned as they lowered themselves to the grass and perhaps busied their hands in crumpled paper sacks, scooping out the last crumbs, or fanned themselves with old newspapers. Young couples, hungry hands upon each other. Lone men, many lone old men, dispirited, their faded shirts vaguely dark about the armholes.

At last the boy in the shadow of the shrubbery relaxed and lost his immediate need of effacement or flight. He wiped his damp face and his sun-weary eyes on his sleeve. Then slowly he stretched out, his joints a dull aching from long undernourishment. Gradually he let himself settle upon the earth with the cloud of misery that was always with him. But he did not lose his vigilance entirely. He kept one hand on his shoes and the other in his pocket, on a sliver of yellow soap moist against a smooth nickel.

As the night thickened, the light from the neons of the business section spread in a fan against the sky. The spire of the capitol reddened in the glow and grew until it was lost in the blackness overhead. To the boy it seemed tall as the Milky Way, tall as his grandmother's tower of Babel had been planned. "The most beautiful building in the world," Lela Gray, his teacher, had told him. And as he thought of it, and of her, the ache in his stomach became only a vague uneasiness long with him. The grass was soft as his mother's goose-feather bed, and gradually the drowsiness of the day's tramp crept into his arms and over him.

He was startled from his dozing by a sudden flood of light that poured over the wide tier of stone steps leading to the main entrance. It came from the panel over the wide doorway, a panel of pioneers pushing Westward, just as the teacher had said, a stone carving of them against the background of gilt: the ox team, the neat bowed wagon, sturdy frontiersmen walking, followed by a pioneer couple, the man with his gun across his arm, the woman with her sunbonnet turned like the wagon, hopefully, bravely, toward the West.

Irvy pillowed his chin on his palm and thought of his grandfather who stood off three of Dull Knife's raiding Cheyennes in 1878. Alone, with his wife to reload his guns, he saved their home and horses and then died a year later from a rusty nail. The grandmother, who had looked after Irvy since his mother died, often told him this much, but he knew more. He knew how she had looked out upon her land over the heads of her four children and refused to go back East to her folks. Her plowing was still held up as a mark to shoot at in Koya County—plowing smooth as the blade of her pancake turner. When the cattlemen came she stood them off her watering place and corn patch with a rifle until it took her two days to bury the dead steers. They never came again. And Saturday nights, at the square dances, she always led the sets and knew every call.

But that was long ago, more than fifty years ago, and the good times were long gone. For years cattle and hogs weren't worth taking to town. And then, on top of that came the drouth and the land grabbers. Now, this last winter the government woman was at her all the time, picking on her, like a dog worrying an old cow. She was getting along in years, would be much better off in town. Make it easier about the grocery orders and all. While the woman talked the grandmother stood by the window, looking out, her hands folded under her apron.

"We couldn't just find us a little shirt-tail patch somewheres?" she asked. "Irvy'll soon be big. He's good as his grandpa was with horses right now—"

But they kept at her and at last she had to give up. The boy didn't remember much except the smell of the moth balls from her old beaver neckpiece the day they came for her. She hadn't said anything, only looked back once to her row of bridal wreath along the fence. They didn't tell her until she was in the government woman's car that he wasn't coming along. Even then she didn't make a fuss. Just sat there saying something that sounded like "Poor little Irvy" over and over to herself.

Itching uneasily at the recollection, the boy scratched his ribs and turned upon his back to look up at the capitol tower. "A covenant eternal as the rainbow in the sky," the teacher had said, "an abiding promise of equality before the law."

It was a fine thing to think of her talking, with her eyes misty and blue as the sky over the Running Water. And she lived somewhere out there in the darkness of the city and tomorrow he would find her. He didn't think beyond that, hadn't since the morning he ran away from old Jillery. The government woman wouldn't like that. She thought it a very fine thing for the boy to stay on the place where he was born, and his father before him.

So he had stayed, and every night, after the choring lantern was finally darkened and hung in the shed, he slipped away from the house for a few minutes to the hill overlooking the river far below. He would sit there in the spring chilliness and the starlight, with maybe a belated wild goose honking by and the good smell of the water coming up to him. Sometimes he thought of his grandmother breaking the sod of the west eighty, and of his father tearing up the south strip when he was just tall enough for the lines around his neck. And now it was all gone, only he, Irvy, left, and heavy as his grandmother with old thoughts. . . .

He had tried to tell his teacher about these things the day school was out, but she said it was wrong to harbor such notions. That he must keep of clean mind and cheerful heart.

Finally Jillery, the renter, caught him sneaking away to the hill at night. Mooning around, was he? And almost no getting him up in time to do the milking in the mornings!

"Damn you—I'll learn you to work—I'll show you how to make money where your folks starved into the poorhouse!"

After that Irvy tried to do as the teacher said. But when Jillery worked their old Spot mare until she fell in the harness and then kept clubbing her with the neckyoke even after her hide quit shaking, he couldn't stand it any more. Slipping under the fence like a rabbit, he had run toward the river and ducked into the thick brush to hide. But not from Jillery. Let him come with the horse whip or even the neckyoke. Kill him and get it over with. Better off like old Spot anyhow, better off dead.

Then suddenly the boy had remembered his father, and with

his arm over his face he was up and running, through the rose brush and plum thicket, his clothes tearing to rags as he ran.

At last he had had to stop. Walking, he had made no plans, except that somewhere, four hundred miles away, was Lela Gray and the beautiful building. He went by way of the little shack where they kept his grandmother and the other old women like her. A long time he stood in the dark outside the pale yellow light of the window. Then he turned to the road.

Because he had only a quarter he tried to hurry. He rode the backs of trucks at night with the cattle, maybe, or the cream cans or in the grain, slipping out in the dark when they stopped. He slept in haystacks and under trees, eating from vegetable gardens along the road. Once he caught two fish in a little creek and cooked them on a stick without salt. Mostly it was only an empty road before him, a hot, dusty road with gravel coming in at the holes in his shoes, or maybe sitting humped over on a bank to rest, like his father used to, after the sale, hunched on his stool in the empty kitchen—the stump of an old dead tree moldering. And moving past him would be the grandmother, not saying much, her soft old feet slow on the bare boards, and feeling bad for the man that was her son.

Looking up at the tower, rising high into the night, Irvy wished she were with him. He remembered the one time he got to go to see her in town. The old woman stood a little away from him, her face covered, clear drops of water running down between her bony fingers. He hadn't known until afterward that she was crying. She hadn't cried when they found his father in the barn that day, his head sticking forward from the rope like a jumping-jack on a string, his work-knotty hands hanging open. Together they had cut him down. He was floppy as a dead cat, but they managed because he wasn't so very heavy any more.

At the recollection a sob rose from the emptiness of the boy, but because he knew that Lela Gray would think it wasn't manly, he clenched his fists and stared up at the tower. Gradually he calmed. He'd get a little paper somewhere, maybe from the teacher, and write his grandmother how fine it was, this capitol, and the pioneer panel with the gilt and the light and the men and women like her and grandpa marching West to conquer a wilderness. Once he had tried to explain it to her from a picture in a book the teacher had. "I guess it wasn't just like that," the grandmother said. "I guess we weren't planning to conquer no wilderness, mostly just looking for a place to set down our stuff, rest some and plow a patch for corn and truck."

The teacher had nodded her wisdom at this. Poor old woman. She had forgotten the splendor of her coming. Old people were like that sometimes, she said pityingly. It made Irvy just a little mad, but the teacher put her arm around his shoulder and told him not to mind. He would grow up fine and strong and full of humility and idealism.

And tomorrow he would find her. As he thought about that, and about her curly brown hair and her pretty dresses, a lightness as of the winds of the river at home came over him. The talk about him had died down, the air moved a little even behind his bush, and the dark evergreens tucked along the building were fragrant.

Gradually the small light in the dome of the tower receded into a long and troubled dream, broken by an occasional low dispute or a worried voice that too died away into silence at last. . . .

After a long, restless stream of shadowy, meaningless pursuit, Irvy was back at home, pushing through the plum thicket, gathering a syrup pail of very ripe wild plums, knowing how sweet they would be upon the tongue, popping the pits of the softer ones at the wasps that buzzed over the rotting fruit on the ground. Then suddenly all the thicket was gone, and the air was gray and chill and the pail in his hand was heavy with dark frog jelly and toad strings. It made him sick and swinging the pail he threw it far. He never heard it drop. Already he was on a sandbar in the river, digging up the deep end of the furrow left by a little clam. But it wasn't anything except plum pits and his grandma calling him from somewhere in a far haze and him trying to answer but no words coming, and so hungry that his stomach was rubbing together all the time.

Gradually the dark hills of the boy's mind stirred, walked as a giant walks, head bent under a lowering sky, a thunder of hammering against his ears. Then he was up, and awake, fear like sand in his throat, his body shaking. The noise came again, a patter of rain running over the bushes and the grass like little animals in dry leaves. Overhead a small cloud moved away. The rest of the sky was clear, with a low slice of moon in the west, almost behind the dark tower.

Complete awakening brought a wave of nausea to the boy. He hunched over his stomach and ran his hands down his aching thighs for the comfort it gave him in his aloneness. Vaguely he wished for the old Spot mare. It would be fine to go to her stall and rub her down with a handful of straw, the feel of her rough skin under his hand, the gentle nip of her satisfaction on his sleeve. Instead, about him lay the silvery gray lawns dotted with the sleeping, the desolation of watery moonlight over them all.

In the morning the boy opened his pale, red-rimmed eyes to the heights of the brightening tower above him, its flutes of windows dyed by the red sky of morning. He lay still, afraid to move, afraid of the pain that slept in his legs, the gnawing under his ribs. And as he contemplated the beauty about him, and the sun-torn clouds overhead, the easy ecstasy of hunger lifted him. He was light as a fluff of seed from the old cottonwood at home. Today everything would come right; today he would find Lela Gray.

By the time the sun spread its gold over the tower there was a general stirring on the grounds. Most of the boys were up, trailing across the grass and away. Several stopped before one of the great carven buffaloes guarding the main entrance.

"'Arise with the dawn,'" a slim, girlish youth read from the carving, his voice a little solemn.

> Arise with the dawn
> Bathe in the morning sun—

"Bathe where?" another cut in. "Arise, it ought to read, Arise and go away before the day guards come, And take your filthy carcass with you."

Irvy crouched behind his bush, watching. He saw one of the boys spit upon the buffalo and make an obscene gesture. He was angry and offended, and made suddenly aware of himself and his own need. At last one of the older men got up and went around to the door under the steps. The boy hurried after him, across the paper-strewn lawn and into the building. He followed in awe down the long arched stone corridor to a gray marbled room with many swinging gray doors.

The boy washed his hands and his face, using his own bit of soap because he didn't know the purpose of the dispensers. Wiping himself, he stopped at the sight of a gaunt, burned face in the mirror before him, only gradually seeing it as his own, so thin and hungry it was. He felt for his nickel in his ragged overalls and slipped away, seeking a place to eat. A block from the capitol he turned to look back. High above the sun the sower plodded dark against the clouding sky, a flock of white pigeons circling about him.

With the nickel gone for a hot dog, the boy followed the flow of workers to the business section. Dodging the hurrying cars, he walked up and down the streets, looking in at the windows now and then, but mostly searching the faces of the women. At first he ran after every curly brown head, and each time he looked into a strange face. At last his feet began to lag and he saw that there must be thousands of people in this city, thousands and thousands.

Finally, when the clouds were a low gray blanket and a faint drizzle was darkening the streets, Irvy dared to inquire of an old man where the post office was. Timidly he asked for the teacher's address at the window. The white-haired woman thumbed carefully through a book.

"Not in the directory—" she said regretfully, watching the boy turn away, dragging his hand along the wainscoting as he moved vaguely toward the door.

Not knowing where to go, he followed the white finger of the tower back to the capitol grounds. But now he was driven away from the clean, smooth grass, so soft and moist under his tired feet. He stood out at the walk in the thin mist a long time, his ragged overalls turning dark on his lankiness, thinking that now it was raining, but not on his father's fields, or his grandmother's.

A stream of visitors moved past him, up the steps and under the pioneer panel. Two large busses stopped. Forty or fifty children, about his age, trooped out and were urged toward the entrance by two fussy women. Almost without intention Irvy trailed along and walked, unchallenged, under the pioneer panel.

He edged in at the door, bewildered by the high vestibule with its bright mosaic arch, the soft buzz of subdued voices coming from the queue of people reaching down the long corridor, and a strange, moist, sweet smell of flowers. The boy could not see ahead but high above him were the colored mosaics of workers in the fields, and the motes in the quartz light made golden dances.

One of the stiff young men standing along the stone walls motioned the boy into line and timidly Irvy slipped in behind a large and protective woman. Slowly the line moved him forward, down the corridor, into a wide shaft of yellow half-light. He looked up the height of the rotunda, almost as tall as the tower, to the mosaic dome in bright blues, purple and gold—a circle of slim, friendly women with clasped hands. Head tipped back, he forgot everything that was behind him, and before, even the Lela Gray that he could not find. He moved automatically at the pressure from the impatient, out toward the center of the rotunda, until one of the guides pushed him back into line. At his touch the boy shivered a little, and the sweet sickish smell was strong in his nose.

Under the yellow light of the rotunda stood banks of flowers. Large, flat pieces like pictures made of roses and lilies and carnations were propped against the marble pillars or stood side by side, man high. In the midst, on a lower bank of pink roses, was a long gray box, open. When the boy saw it he tried to get away but he was caught in the slow, silent marching file, the men with heavy, serious tread, now and then a woman sobbing.

Then the boy was alone with the dead face—still and white and remote as the stone carvings outside. It was not the face of the governor or any great person he had ever seen in the papers. It seemed to be just anybody and with truckloads of flowers and a funeral in the beautiful capitol, the most beautiful capitol in the world. A bitterness came to the boy's tongue. All this for one man and only a painted box for his father, with not one flower, not one.

Suddenly the boy threw his arm over his face and ducked out of line into an alcove, down a dusky stone stairway and was lost in a milling of picnic children, excited and dusty, in the care of a tall, tired girl. A door slid open and they all pushed forward, sweeping Irvy with them into the elevator. The jammed cage shot upward and the boy clutched his stomach. Then they stopped, the door opened and the children crowded out, into a high, roundish room of black marble, awesome, and completely empty.

"Sh—" the girl warned the noisy group. "This is Memorial Hall, the Hall of Heroes."

The children were quiet. They looked about uneasily and finally slipped toward the door, one after another, until only Irvy was there, leaning against the shiny black marble wall, waiting for his dizziness to pass. Vaguely he heard complaining voices, and when the elevator came back, loud protests: "Can't see a thing for the fog!"

"Too bad. Are these all of your party?" The door slid to and they were gone.

Alone in the shadowy coolness and the silence, Irvy felt a little better. He looked around. Memorial Hall, the black marble hall of heroes, smelling of lonesomeness and death. He moved a foot and an echo came softly out of the silent emptiness that was all about him. Quietly he tiptoed to a door. It opened outward, upon the stone parapet and the fog. Cautiously the boy approached the stone wall that struck him at the bib of his overalls. Beyond it and above, there was nothing except a moist mistiness, below only a white tower rising from the downy, gray fog.

Gradually the boy's sickness left him and a peace came, a great and good aloneness. The whole world was gone, fallen away, even as his father had dropped his hard life like a slack string. He was alone with the silent fog, soft as the down of his mother's featherbed. He leaned into it and the heaviness began to slip from him, the weariness and the sorrow. He pulled himself upon the outward sloping stone of the parapet and edged a foot over. He pulled the other foot up and slid himself forward, inch by inch, toward the white softness as of down that was a rest and a forgetting.

Then a trailing length of the mist broke and the boy saw, far below him, the ridge of a black roof. Frantically he dug his nails into the stone to check his slide. Slowly, very slowly he stopped, pulled himself back, up the sloping parapet, inside at last, to the stone floor. A moment he lay there and then he dragged himself back through the heavy door into the murky light of a tall room. Face down, he crept to the security of the wall and lay there shaking, his wet cheek against the black marble of the Hall of Heroes.

XVI

River Polak

This is a strange situation, it seems to me: that with the common complaint against the complexity of modern life, not more serious writers have made Nebraska their locale. Here we have the period from the dispossession of the so-called savage to transcontinental air service, some industrialism and much tenancy, all in the span of a living man's lifetime. It makes no difference where you may come from in Nebraska there is always someone who has seen the Indians moved out and the settlers rush in. Here, within one lifetime, we have assembled the conflicts of nationalities and races from all over the world, from the first settlers who came in by way of Bering Straits to the last Mexican smuggled, perhaps only last night, into the sugar beet region of the North Platte Valley.

Here then, before us, is a comparatively simple society from the stone age to the present, one whose processes are not lost in antiquity, one with all the conflicts, the hopes, the dreams and aspirations of man visible and free for the taking. . . .

We have our county seat fights, our ghost towns, Antioch for instance, that spot of hilarious mining boom for a day, not even a village now. The hoped-for coming of oil, the actual coming of the railroads. Man's battle with nature, as in the Republican Valley flood. . . . And then there is Lincoln. A dozen themes have been suggested to me but if I were to write of Lincoln and could choose my talent, I should want to be a modern Aristophanes and do a biting satire of our city called "Light on the Tower." And why hasn't anyone written a good novel on the Winnebagoes and their degradation under the hand of the conqueror? . . .

But for me the most important themes of Nebraska will always be those of the farmer and his dispossession. Hamlin Garland's "Under the Lion's Paw" grew out of the nineties, yet our much more serious depression has produced not one authentic vital story of the farmer of this region during the last seven years. Doesn't anyone . . . see that the story of the man who broke out the first sod on his government

164

claim thirty, forty years ago, clung to it until 1929, and lost it is a theme worthy of a Nebraska Hamsum or a Reymont? Why doesn't anyone who really understands the farmer's weaknesses, his strengths, his triumphs, and his problems—and appreciates the fierce affection that grows up in him for his not always friendly plot of soil—write of him (19)?

I

FOR ONE WEEK in the spring the Niobrara River jammed its bed with broken ice. Its gray floodwaters rose over the bottom lands, piling trash at the feet of the ash and box elder along the bluffs, with here and there a bridge plank or a drowned hog in the willows. From then until fall the tepid little stream flowed tranquilly past the old cottonwood leaning from the cutbank of sandstone, making a soft, friendly little sound as it ran past the Polanders'.

On quiet June evenings a blue plume of corncob smoke rose over the Smolka house in the little ash grove and hung in thin threads along the shadowing bluffs. Now and then a bell tinkled somewhere, not loud or often, for the cows had learned not to disturb the clapper overmuch.

But this evening there was no hand cupped to the ear for cowbells. Instead, Yonak Smolka was squandering his time on Indian Bluff, at the feet of the bare-legged little American girl, Eckie Mason, making a wreath of wild flowers for her. And as he selected one sprig of bloom after another from the girl's apron, he forgot that his tongue had a way of escaping his lips when he worked, that his shoes were manure-yellowed and too large to pass in a plow furrow.

At last the boy shook his hair that was bleached and unruly as weathered binder twine from his eyes. Then he arose, unbelievably long and awkward, holding the thick wreath of purple and yellow wild peas like a thing of fragile china on the palms of his broad hands before the waiting girl.

"I—c-crown you," he stammered, breathing hard, "I c-c-crown—" But his voice broke and he jammed the wreath down hard on the girl's dark hair, glad to be rid of it. There it hung, over one ear and the delicate nose as on a post.

Seeing that Eckie still waited, he fell awkwardly to one knee, touched his lips to her extended hand, and sat back on his haunches in relief.

"The glass," Eckie prompted in a whisper.

Yonak wiped a bit of broken mirror on his overalls and held it up. The girl straightened the wreath, and, seeing only a blur of purple and gold and no sunburned face, she sighed. "I wish I could be like this all the time, with no sick baby to mind and no cows to get."

At the mention of chores Yonak let the glass clink down his overalls to the gravel as he straightened up and peered under his palm toward the shadowed grove across the river. "Gee, I bet Pa be home and I have not the cows. . . . Maybe he knock me down."

But the sun stood large on the bluffs, powdering the quiet evening air and spreading a bright path over the moving water. And suddenly for him there was no angry Polish father with eyes red from the jug under the bed of Ignaz Kodis.

"Look it!" he cried, wanting Eckie to see that the water was like mice running under a golden sheet and that the purple stealing down the draws was the flying veil on his sister Olga's new hat. But before his thick tongue could move to it a woman's voice called up the bluff. "Eckie!—Eckie!—Come away from that dumb Polak and mind this baby!"

Holding the wreath to her head and without a look or a word for the boy, Eckie ran down the shadowing slope to throw clods at the two milk cows switching indolent tails in a patch of sandburrs where she could not follow barefooted.

With the bright sun still upon him, Yonak watched the girl vanish along the path through the brush. Then he kicked a pebble bounding after her and plodded down the slope toward the river. Dumb Polak— dumb, left-alone Polak. Sometimes even Olga wanted to be American, with an American name, Ollie Smith, not a greenhorn Smolka. But only when she was angry with her father. Other times she laughed and strutted a little, like her black Leghorn rooster, saying, "Pretty good for dumb Polander, no?"

II

From the time Yonak's thick baby legs could keep his sister in sight they had played together. Often it was games like going to the market in the Old Country, under the cottonwood leaning over the Niobrara River. They played selling syrup buckets full of wild flowers, the cat and her kittens, their pet rooster, or the runty pig that wouldn't stand still and so fell off into the water and had to be dragged out. And once, when the house was dark and empty, they sneaked out their mother's black Sunday shawl. And then Olga was the queen of the market and made music with the accordion like a fine big dance with many rich city people.

When she was fifteen the father heard that his countrymen down the river took in much money from their sons and daughters who worked for the Americans. He got Olga a job at Union, waiting tables, and once a week he stopped at the back door for her pay.

It was during his first summer alone that Yonak found the American girl across the river. She was watching a bull snake try to get the bulge in his middle that had been a gopher into a mouse hole. It was very funny and they laughed together. After that they were what the Americans called friends, and so she took the Polish boy up to her house and showed him how to make good races with the Leghorn roosters. Her mother said it was bad, but she didn't think so. The roosters liked it. Yonak found it truly so.

After that he often hit the wire fence between the two places with a stick and made it sing to let Eckie know he was going down by the river. Sometimes she could get away and came running, dodging barefooted through sandburrs and rosebushes. Then Yonak cut whistles if the willows were sapping, made bows and arrows for them both, or scalded crawdads to a blood red in an old tomato can to eat with salt.

And now, today, he had made the wreath.

When the house was filled with warm, dark silence, Yonak lay in the little half-dugout bedroom under the picture of the thorn-crowned Christ, and thought about it. Gradually he forgot the throb of his head from Big Steve Smolka's willow whipstock and the hurt of the American woman's words, calling him a dumb Polak. The memory of the girl's hand against his lips was like sweet, gritty bumblebee honey from the nest in the meadow. And below the grove the river made its soft, busy little sound as it ran past the Polanders'.

The next day Olga came home for her birthday. She was seventeen now, dark hair short, eyes swift and blue as the kingfisher's, and with only red-lipped contempt for the old bachelor Ignaz Kodis who hoped to trade a daily drink from the jug under the bed for the high-headed Smolka girl. She would give Ignaz a bellyful of fight, Big Steve promised loudly after the third tipping of the jug. She was a bad one, that Olga, standing up to her father like the August thunderhead, making the ground to shake with a great wind and fire and noise, until the little mother hid her face in the headcloth.

And Ignaz licked his brown lips and passed the jug once more.

A week later Steve Smolka brought home a full bottle of whisky and walked so straight that there must surely have been more. He filled a cup half full of cold coffee and brimmed it over with the paler liquid.

"Tomorrow I get Olga from the town and the next day it will be a wedding," he said through his floating moustache.

With shaking hands the mother wiped up the ham fat she spilled on the hot lids and moved quickly to put the supper on the table. Once or twice she coughed into a white rag that she hid in her slit pocket. Steven talked big. No more cutting corn by hand, Yonak! From now on it would be the binder of Ignaz Kodis, and perhaps a ride to the town in his car on Saturdays.

After supper Yonak slipped through the dark trees to the soft-looking gray clumps of buffalo-berry brush. They were really not soft at all, but stood thick and thorny about him, shutting out everything except the fragile lace of the fireflies and the square of yellow that was the window of the Americans across the river.

Before the sun stood man-high the next morning Big Steve was gone. A sad murmur as of fall insects rose gradually from the darkened bedroom where the mother knelt before a dim candle. Yonak put the milk away quickly and went into the yard where he need not hear. His pet rooster gave a high cackle and fled. When there was no pursuit, he came back curiously, looking sidewise at the boy, scolding. Slowly Yonak roused himself and the rooster was gone again, under thistles, over fences, dodging, scolding, squawking. At last the boy caught him, stroked his gleaming black neck, and watched the American girl, the baby across her hip, come to the bridge to fish in the deep hole at the pilings. He threw the rooster a handful of wheat and made business at the sweet-corn patch across the river. With the doubletrees balancing across his shoulders he stopped on the bridge.

"What you using?" he asked casually.

"Grubworms."

"Grasshoppers is better."

"Maybe," the American girl admitted, flipping a silvery chub from the water, "but I bet you couldn't catch many grasshoppers neither with a sick kid like Dickie hanging onto you."

"Oh, I dunno." Yonak spit into the water and went on, his big feet clap-clapping on the planks like a horse, pretending he never made a wreath for an American girl, never a purple and gold wreath, and that there was no soft, sad noise in his mother's bedroom.

That night there were violent words over the oilcloth-covered table in the Smolka kitchen. Once the mother dared remonstrate, but Steve sent her back into the shadows with the flat of his hand and Yonak had to lead her away to cry in the outside darkness. Olga better give up; only get a smashed mouth for her wedding.

And at last she tossed her short black hair out of her eyes and, grabbing her red accordion, played like drunk or crazy. Her teeth, white as corn in milk, flashed; sweat beaded her forehead. Finally she went to bed. Yonak lay tense and still as she crept into the cot across the dugout from him. Until the rooster crowed she cried softly.

In the morning she was gone. It was Yonak who found her, hanging from the cottonwood over the river. When Ignaz came in his old car to the wedding, Yonak had to tell him. Red moustache bristling, the man swore that Big Steve had cheated him. Without going in to look at the girl laid out in her new white dress, he went home to his corn. A dead woman is no good to a man and the sunflowers do not wait.

All the June day Steve Smolka sat with his fingers over his face while his Polish neighbors hammered together a long box and covered it with black cloth. That evening they buried Olga near the little white church on the Flats, where the roads going in and out cross, as was fitting.

Yonak stayed behind in the dusk at the leveled grave. Suddenly the American girl was there with him. Softly she laid a wreath of bluebells on the new earth and ran away. Yonak put his hand out to the flowers. They were cool as the waters of the Niobrara.

After Olga was gone the mother leaned lower under the sacks of weeds she carried home for the pigs; she huddled closer into her dark headcloth. Big Steve drank less and went to church, but the river Polanders avoided him. It was not right, this that Steve Smolka had done. Olga was sweet as the chokecherry blooms in the spring. Here it was not like the Old Country. One must use less of the club and more of the sugar on the colts.

The mother coughed steadily from the days of the black frost to the white. By spring she lay still in her dark bedroom. Because she would not have a doctor, Yonak steeped camomile and brewed wild-sage tea in an iron pot, but it was as nothing. *Na,* what must be must be, she tried to tell this boy with the man bones pushing through his round cheeks. Only fifteen and already high as Big Steve, and no catalogue shoes big enough.

Then one night when Steve was in town with the fat pigs she called the boy to her. He cleared away the blood-soaked pillow and washed her white face. She smiled up to him, like a tired little child. He must not be afraid.

When the father came Yonak left him alone with the still, white woman on the bed. He walked fast to the old cottonwood. The tree still leaned a long arm over the river. Somewhere far in the high blue of the sky a bobolink sloped and sang. Only to him and to his father was everything different.

A sound of running feet came up the cowpath and Eckie stood before the Polish boy. He turned his light eyes upon her. "Why you come to bother me?" he cried, and could have bitten his tongue out.

Mutely the girl pushed something hard into Yonak's hand and ran, her faded blue dress flying across the bridge and into her own yard, and on the boy's calloused palm lay a round, shiny disk—a pyrite, a sheepherder had said—Eckie's lovely gold dollar.

The next day Mrs. Mason brought the geranium blooms of all the Americans for miles around in a washtub to put over the town-bought coffin. Yonak scarcely knew that, or heard the good words she made for him now. He stared straight ahead, gripping the gold dollar until it cut his palm.

III

That summer Yonak looked often toward the house across the river. Sometimes he sneaked through the brush to watch the American girl pick black currants or gather wood. She was growing straight and fine like the young cottonwood, and her hands were gentle as the night winds in the leaves. But he never spoke to her after her sick little brother died. There was nothing he could say to the American girl. And soon she was going to Union to high school, to work for her board, be a teacher.

Once she saw him there and stopped him outside of the trading store to ask how it was with them on the Niobrara. Two of her classmates, scrawny in their dirty corduroys, saw them. "Migod! Look at the big Polander!"

The girl tried to laugh up at Yonak, to make it good. "They're just sorry they're such little runts."

But the boy turned away and went down the middle of the dusty street to where the team was eating from the wagon. He hunched down on the tongue and kicked a hole in the ground. Town was no good. And the American girl had no business talking to him, not with a dress the color of wild-grape wine, her short black hair like wild geese flying before the wind.

IV

In the summer Yonak and Steve worked the fields and watched the wind-streaked sky. If rain came, like long blue brooms sweeping across the dusty flats, it was money in the bank. If not—chickens one year, feathers the next. Anyhow, the Polanders still had the river.

But to Yonak the Niobrara was not just water for grass and cabbages and sweet corn. It was something to see suddenly from under a fork of hay, to hear in the aloneness of the night. It brought a fine hurting to his arms when he looked down upon it in October, the cottonwoods lemon yellow, the ash trees slim golden flames against the gray of the bluffs: or when he came down the spring slope, walking behind the deep-breasted mares, the chain tugs rattling.

When Big Steve's wife was dead three years he got a gallon jug for under his bed, sent for a new suit and a tie, shaved his moustache, greased his shoes, and started to Mass again. Several times he drove to the Polish settlement on Snake River, to come back smelling of bad alcohol and cursing the American Poles as pigs.

Yonak, eighteen now, looked on in silence. At night, lying where the mother had died, he had to hear the heavy breathing of Big Steve beside him. Dark thoughts came to the boy, partly because his father breathed so, like the boar pig in the pen, but mostly because he was writing to a countryman in Chicago for a mail-order wife.

It was said that the matchmaker was a good one. For forty dollars he got a wife for Ignaz Kodis, not too old and only a little lame. She worked well and gave him strong children, one a year.

In a few weeks Steve was talking big of the wife he too would get, with the good name of Jadwiga Hajek, only thirty; and if a little older, what matter? Sixty dollars down for the match and one hundred for the wedding garments.

She met Steve at the depot in a pink silk dress like a costly American woman. Her kiss brought another red than that of the wind and the jug to the Polander's face. But she would not marry yet. "Be better to wait and see if we fit together," she told him in awkward Polish.

"Na, it gives bad talk so!" he protested, which was enough.

But it was not enough for the woman from Chicago. She laughed with open mouth, her gold teeth and the black stuff on her round parrot eyes shining, free for all the loafers to see.

She did not laugh when she saw Steve's place. Did rich farmers here live in dumps like that, she asked, pointing a red-nailed finger at the two-room soddy with its dugout lean-to. Seeing the man's flush of anger, she kissed him on the mouth, her round eyes already seeking the son.

Not until dark did Yonak come to the house, and slowly then, seeing a woman with hair that was burnt cornsilk, and a mouth like blood, on his father's knee. He stopped in the doorway, the light from the high lamp spilling over his hair, over the smooth tan of his face and the faded blue of his overalls. The woman sucked in her breath. She went to him, close to him, and looking up under greasy lids, she asked, "You are Yonak?"

Standing on tiptoe, she mussed his blond hair and ran her fingers down his cheek line to his lips. They smelled like flowers in the late spring, flowers wilting.

"Big, strong man," she said. Turning the lamp down, she pulled him to the bench beside her. "Now you are not Yonak, Polak, but Jack, American," she told him.

Afterward Yonak tried to forget the violence of that week between his father and Dolly Hall, as Jadwiga Hajek would be called. She was no greenhorn Polander, she told Big Steve, standing up to his anger. But always her eyes, her hands, were for the young Yonak, so tall and fine, even with the dirt of the milking pen on his shoes.

It was the son she would marry.

Steve threw his head back and opened his mouth wide: A good joke, good Polish joke.

But already the son was gone, out into the night. The woman was after him, holding to the doorknob, looking into the darkness. The father stopped his laughing and his anger broke like the gray flood-waters of the Niobrara, but the woman stood against him like the pilings of the good-built bridge. Yes, it was the son she would have. The son. The son.

And then it came over Steve that he could not let her go. So he became sly. Yes, yes, the son. Ah, he was a young fool, this Yonak, but if she would have him, *phutt*, so it should stand. Let them talk of it tomorrow.

No. Tonight. Now.

But Yonak did not come when Steve called from the doorway, not the next morning or all the next day. Steve cursed; the cows bawled. At last, when the woman went to call from the hill that it was only a joke, American joke, Yonak crawled out of the buffalo-berry brush, his face gaunt. his eyes light and hard. He came in for the milk pails and went out again. In the morning he looked down upon Steve, still in a sour, drunken stupor, and then he went away to the field.

And when the son returned in the evening the woman met him at the door in a fresh house dress, with a nice red drink for him. It was cool to the dusty throat and he had another, many more, until the woman's words were gentle upon his ear, her hair sweet to his lips.

The next morning Yonak roused himself as from the muck of a river flood. When his eyes cleared a little he ran out across the bottom land that smelled of dew, the boggier portions blue-tinged with violets. A coyote slunk away from a handful of feathers, all that was left of a Leghorn rooster out too early because Yonak had forgotten to close the henhouse. He kicked the wet feathers sadly and went to stand at the old cottonwood over the river, his head against the rough bark, his face shiny as wet, gray clay. This time Eckie would not come. Last week she had finished the high school. In the fall she would be a teacher.

After a while Yonak fell to cutting into the old tree with his knife, far back under the bark. He let the sun play on the bright disk that was Eckie's gold dollar before he pushed it out of sight under the bark and painted the spot with mud.

Then he tried to look over into tomorrow, but it was dark as the smoke of a prairie fire. And so he washed his head at the river and was surprised that the water could still be cool to him.

V

It took Dolly Hall just one day to spread the news, laughing at the Polish women who stood away from her when they spoke of their part in the wedding feast. The next day she got Steve to take her to town. They came home singing through the dusk, in a new car that the woman drove. Yonak plodded up from the milking pen between two brimming pails to the house. Ah, but there was news, Dolly cried to him. They were sold out—land, cattle, horses, everything. They were all going to Detroit in the morning, to Dolly's brother working in the automobile factory. He would make the wedding feast. Yonak set the milk pails among the cats and walked away, up the hill and through the corn, his boots bruising a fragrance from the young, green leaves. It still smelled the same, like his field, his home. He belonged here, with the river and the plowed land under his feet, deep-rooted in good soil.

Tonight he did not go to the cottonwood, although he knew the little winds were in its leaves. Instead he went to the bridge, so white in the moonlight, and sat on the willow-grown approach where he could see the light in the Americans' kitchen.

After a long time someone came along the railing toward him. Suddenly it was Eckie, there before him, in a light dress like river mist. She turned away when she saw him.

"You don't have to be afraid of me," Yonak said bitterly through his fingers.

"Oh, no," she answered quickly, but without returning.

"We go away."

The light oval of the girl's face moved, indicating knowledge. She wished them luck. It would be fine in the great city.

"It will be bad—bad like a sickness and a dying!" the young Polander cried, and stumbled away into the brush.

And when he did not return to the Smolka grove that night or the next morning there was much talk. So!—like his sister. But they could not find him hanging from a tree anywhere.

Dolly Hall was angry. Greenhorn Polak! But she did not wish to lose everything, and so she married Steve at Union—Steve and his three thousand dollars cash.

VI

Yonak, working in a packing plant in Chicago, knew nothing of the wedding, not until the three thousand cash had vanished and Old Steve, hearing of his son through a countryman, came to him. *Na*, it was bad. The American Polish woman was worse than two or ten of the English-speakers.

He brought word, too, of the Americans across the river, the Eckie and her people. The mother was dead and the girl she must come home to care for the sick father, sick from a horse kick in the back— not walk for a long time.

Yonak listened and then went out through the town, to the bridge over the river that did not smell like the Niobrara in the spring. A long time he looked into the oily water.

The next day they rented a little house and Steve cleared away the cans from the back. He would grow the cabbages and the onions for his Polish neighbors.

After a few months Dolly came too, for Steve still held a five-year mortgage for half his place. Greenhorns, she called the men when they would not move to an apartment. But she stayed, entertaining her drunken friends in sleazy satin pajamas. It was not good, Old Steve grumbled, but there was none to listen.

If Yonak hoped that the stench of the fertilizer dumps that was close as his skin would rid them of his father's wife, he was mistaken. She complained about it and her friends made fun, but that was all.

Then, one night in late April, Yonak lay on his hot bed with the moonlight across him and thought how fine it would be to walk along a fence once more, making the barbed wire hum under a tapping stick while his shadow grew long on the evening grass. How fine to see the faded blue dress of the little American girl come running through the brush. And soon it would be time for the purple and yellow flowers he had once made into a wreath.

The next morning the heat was like a dirty featherbed to the face. At noon a wind grew up from the far land, cool, gentle, wet as the mists of the spring Niobrara. To Yonak it brought the smell of new ground, warm horseflesh, and slopes snowy with wild plum and chokecherry bloom. A joy ran through his dead arms like the first cracking of winter ice in the river. He sent his unopened lunch pail against the shed so the wood splintered and broke, the tin flattened, and the gray coffee splattered out. But Yonak did not stop to see. He ran like a wild animal, wild with spring.

Two days later the young Polander was headed across the Flats to the Niobrara and knew, from the curious look the mail carrier gave him, that in spite of soap and hot water and new clothes he was still a packing-house stinker. He looked away over the shaggy prairie moving past as slowly as the flow of earth into the valley. Everything was so small, so drab, the Flats like a palm dusty with the thin green of early spring. Many homes were gone, broad fields unworked, gray with weeds. Three years' drouth, hand-running, the carrier said. That, with seven years' hard times, just about cleaned up the farmer. Old Phipps closed out most everybody across the river.

Yonak nodded. He knew Phipps and bad times. Chicken one year and feathers the next. He was watching a curlew drop whistling to a knoll, pinkish-brown wings folded over the back like praying palms. There was still time to clean the rusty plowshare with sand and coal oil, put in corn. The rains would come.

"The whole damn country's for rent," the mail carrier told him. "There's your old place, empty. The renters couldn't raise the money and was put off. On relief up to Union now. Old-timer down that way too, crippled bad."

He rambled on, but Yonak did not hear. He got off at the graying, deserted little church, the mail carrier shouting back that he'd be along again in a couple hours, glad to pick him up. When the truck was gone, Yonak went to his mother's grave, level now, the little wooden cross down in the weeds. And over the spot where the roads going in and out of the cemetery crossed, where Eckie had brought the wreath of bluebells to his sister, dead sunflowers rattled in the wind.

Heavily Yonak started through his old field, mangy with patches of spreading rye grass. Poor farming. It was not good to do the land so.

At the brow of the bluff he looked down upon the Niobrara and his sadness grew. This was not the river that had come to him on that rare, soft wind over the soiled city. This was little more than a creek, with a deep canyon of greening trees tucked against bare sandstone. And across from him was a bald knob, the Indian bluff where he had once made a wreath for an American girl.

Then he saw that Eckie's house was gone, the gray stones of the foundation scattered like dirty chickens over the bare yard. Suddenly afraid, he ran down the hill toward his own home, the shadow of a hawk circling over the ground before him. Only a dozen cattle-rubbed ash and box-elder trees were left of the grove. The sod house stood vacant-eyed as an old woman, the windows gone, the floor covered with newspapers, not yet yellowed, and fresh chicken droppings.

VII

At last Yonak moved to plod past the sagging door of the henhouse and to the old cottonwood. It, too, was gone. Undermined by spring floods, it had crashed into the waters, the branches catching trash until the river turned its back and shifted the channel to the other side, leaving only a rain-dappled sand bar around the bleaching old trunk, with the lacy tracks of a turtle across it.

Slowly Yonak started away, along the river to the road that led over the bluffs and off toward the railroad. The water rippled past him over yellow sand wavy as a woman's hair, but he did not see it. The tangled swamp grass caught at his shoes and he did not feel it.

Suddenly there was a high cackle at his feet, and a bunch of black and russet feathers rose from the water's edge and fled squawking past him. It was a rooster, a brown Leghorn, the tail gone, probably lost to some coyote. But the fowl did not go far. Under a buffalo-berry clump he stopped to look back, scolding.

With a whoop Yonak was after him, his heart pounding with excitement as the rooster ran and flew toward the grove. He turned the corner of the henhouse in time to see the Leghorn flutter off the ground and scramble into a rusty oil barrel through the six-inch bung, just wide enough for the scrawny body. Yonak leaned against the rooty old sod wall, puffing, laughing. The little devil! He was tailless, bedraggled of feathers and with frozen comb, but he stayed on.

Inside the barrel the cackling had died. Yonak tried to look into the blackness and was met with a vigorous clatter of claws on metal and an alarmed squawk. He started to shake the barrel a little, and stopped. Under his hand, across the dirty metal of the top, was a name—E. C. Mason. It was the Americans. Eckie.

So that was how the rooster could race.

Then Yonak remembered what the mail carrier had said. Old-timer, crippled. And Phipps closing everybody out for his cattle. So it happened that the Smolka field was grass. She who was slim and fine as a young cottonwood trying to hold the plow.

Once more he began to laugh, harder this time, like a March wind that clears away the dead things of a long, long winter. To the cackling rooster he promised Eckie, the American, and her father back. "I make them come," he said, "and once more it be good farming and fine racing, no?" Then he started toward the road again, walking very fast, to catch the mail truck for Union. And behind him the Niobrara flowed tranquilly on, making a soft, friendly little sound as it ran past the old grove of the Polanders.

XVII

The Devil's Lane

Since 1927, when "The Vine" first appeared, the author has published only five short stories in the so-called slicks—the large-circulation national magazines. "The Devil's Lane," which was written in the winter of 1937–1938, was the second of two stories to come out in the *Ladies' Home Journal*.

THE DEVIL'S LANE cut like a knife scar through the pasture, the field, the garden, and even the house of the two men who had once found refuge from the blizzard's cold in the same bed. For over thirty years it lay between the two old friends, a double spite fence of barbed wire, deep-stapled and tight enough to keep out everything except the wind. But the beginnings of the lane went far behind the bachelor bunk Mac and Duncan once occupied, back to Ohio, when the two were boys, each carrying home, instead of a bloody nose, half a kite or a fish trap they had quarreled over and cut in two.

They couldn't divide the girl in high school that way, and so someone else got her. But their first vote split on the free-silver issue, one following Bryan, the other McKinley and gold. All that winter and spring they ran alone, but when the conviviality of an old-time Fourth of July celebration wore off they found themselves side by side in a covered wagon headed for an Indian-land opening in the Dakotas.

On the reputedly very dry plains west of the Missouri an unexpected general rain came up. There was no wood in sight, cow chips were scarce and soaked, and the team too worn to fight the hub-deep mud. Three days in a covered wagon with cold gray rain all around became three long, polite days, and finally Duncan was driven to apologize for the half-cooked coffee he poured from the blackened sirup bucket.

"Looks like the Java's fell in the creek."

"Looks all right to me," Mac protested.

178

"Well, it ain't all right. Guess I know when coffee's weak."

Today that was too much. Mac jumped to his feet, banging his head on the low wagon bows, his boyish face purple-red under the sandy stubbles.

"Implyin' I don't know good coffee?"

"Implyin' nothing that ain't plain to the naked eye."

By the time the gray blanket cleared from the sky and the sun shone fresh and young, they had sawed the wagon into two pieces down the middle, bows, tongue, and all, and rigged the halves into crazy two-wheeled carts, higher on the hind-wheel side. The poles for the splicings and shafts they got at the timbered creek that had been running through the rain-hidden hollow below them all the time.

With the clumsy one-horse carts piled high they drove abreast along the narrow Indian trail, neither willing to let the other be more polite and take the rear.

Their coming to the tent saloons of the Indian Strip diverted the waiting homeseekers and loafers, who took them to different bars and bought them frontier whisky with chewing tobacco and rattlesnake heads in the bottom of barrels. When Mac and Duncan awoke two days later, they were in the same gully, behind the same saloon, and everything except the crazy carts was gone—the money for the land drawings, their two horses, even the blackened coffee boiler.

Choring around on the dry tableland for the next few years was so unremunerative there was little to divide. Finally the two decided to homestead together down on Willow Creek at the edge of the sandhills. They built a long one-room shack across the line of the adjoining claims, with a double bed in the middle so each could sleep on his own land. They painted the shack, planted a cottonwood at each end, plowed a garden plot before the door, and rigged up a pump jack so one windmill pulled two wells. They lived together, yet each had established a complete residence on his own land.

Then they met Mary Sears at a dance and argued all the way home about her hair, Mac having it brown and Duncan chestnut. It happened when rain was long overdue and the sod corn was already curling at seven in the morning. Without stopping to sleep they cut the house in two, each starting at one eave and working toward the ridge, the dry, hot wind blowing pieces of shingle and sawdust around. When they came together they slid off the roof and, with neighbors to help, pulled the halves a hundred feet in, each way. Then they boarded up the open ends and strung spite fences on each side of their homestead line—through the creek, the meadow, the garden, between the halves of the house and over the hills, with a devil's lane between. The staples were countersunk and the fence posts set deep.

The raw ends were never painted and for years the houses looked like a chunk of painted stove wood sawed in two. Better times came; the cows increased; the crops did well. Both Mac and Duncan built on two-story ells, on the far ends, leaving the scars to weather.

Mary Sears, only a visitor in the Willow Creek community, was gone before Mac and Duncan were done sawing.

The two might have made it up as they did in the past, but before the Fourth of July and its celebrating, Miranda, Mac's younger sister, came out. The post-office loafers noticed her firm mouth, her fine, thin temples, her dark cloudy hair. "She'll manage those two young fools," they told one another, relieved. There was no telling where spite fences might lead. Lawsuits, maybe even killings. Square, soft-spoken Duncan Burns would make a fine husband.

But that year Mac plowed corn on the Fourth and the next week he put another wire on his side of the devil's lane, doubled the posts and strung chicken fencing up to the first rise. Of course Duncan did the same thing, only his netting had a finer mesh and was six inches higher. He'd keep his Plymouth Rocks from pestering anybody's White Leghorns.

Soon the neighbors were saying that while Mac was steady and unbending as a cedar post, Miranda was neat as a new coin and as hard—like a nickel, without the warmth of a penny. They shook their heads as they repeated that these devil's lanes were bad business in a community. No telling what would come of them.

After twelve years without a bad word or any word at all across the devil's lane, Duncan brought home a bride, a quiet, gentle little woman from a one-room soddy with ruffled curtains at the window. There was a wedding dance in the loft of his new barn, free for all, and a written invitation for Mac and Miranda. But Duncan watched the trap door of the barn all evening for nothing. His friend never came.

A year later Duncan was alone again, with a tiny baby boy to be called Joel. For three days and nights Miranda had run back and forth through a wide gap cut in the spite fences. But after the funeral, firm-lipped, she nailed Mac's side up, double-stapled.

Two years later lightning struck Mac's barn while they were away. Duncan turned the cows out into the night, threw his coat over one horse after another until he had all six out, and even backed the truck from the tottering walls. Mac put a thank-you note in the county paper. When Miranda pulled the four-year-old Joel out of the stock tank, Duncan used the same columns.

It was a community joke when Miranda's yellow Persian had a mixed litter of kittens, one yellow, the rest spotted or black, like the big tom blinking on a flat-topped post on Duncan's side.

None of the kittens grew up. Miranda set out a piepan of milk and made Mac pick them off one after another with a twenty-two rifle. It was the spring Joel was getting over the scarlet fever, and the *ping* of the gun and the kicking around the piepan made him sick to his stomach, and when Mac picked the kittens up by the tails and buried them in the middle of the devil's lane, the boy ran out into the hills. It was night when Duncan found him, face down in a blowout, asleep. The father wiped the sand from the boy's tear-streaked face and carried him home.

"No telling what a pie a fool'll bake for others to eat up."

The summer Joel was seventeen a girl came to Mac's—a girl slim as a young tree, with misty hair the color of brown cottonwood bloom. When the boy first saw her she wore a dress like the violets on the bunch bogs along the creek, and Miranda's white chickens were flocking around her. It made him late with the cows, but he whistled while he clipped their tails to their legs and drummed two strong streams of milk into the pail. He squirted foam into the faces of the old cat and the two kittens sitting hopefully about, and all the time he was thinking about the girl in the dress like pale violets.

After that day he often heard her singing through the shimmering sunset of a dusty day—perhaps as she leaned over the railing of the bridge across the Willow, or, when Mac was extra busy, as she stepped along behind the milk cows, with a weed baton in her hand. They were simple songs, with no words that Joel could hear from the barn, soothing—like the lullabies he had never heard.

Once he tried to ask his father about the girl, but Duncan was stooped over his paper, his shadow large and unapproachable on the calcimine of the kitchen wall. So Joel sneaked a look into Mac's mail box until he found a letter with a neat, auntyish address: Miss Mahlia Seaton. Mahlia—like the brown tassels of her hair—so soft.

That evening he talked until Duncan looked up from the biscuit he was buttering. "What's set your tongue to running so, son?"

Joel blushed through the smooth brown of his skin, but his father's eyes were friendly blue slits and he took courage. "Did you know anybody back in Ohio called Seaton?"

"One married Mac's sister, but he's dead, and his wife too."

That was bad, Joel thought. Not even a father. Duncan saw and his weathered jaw line sharpened.

"We keep out where we ain't wanted."

Joel nodded and pushed the plate of biscuits back.

The first time the boy saw Mahlia away from the place was at the fish fry, with a least a hundred people around. And crickets had been at his bathing suit in the car.

"Hi—look! Young Joel's been shot at an' hit! Musta been making up to that girl at Mac's," one of the Rinker boys shouted, pointed out the holey black suit.

Joel's flush turned his white body red as a turkey's wattles through the holes.

"Here, I got a couple bachelor pins," Mike Andrews, from up the creek, offered.

But two safety pins didn't help Joel much. He should have remembered to look at the suit that morning, but they came down early—Duncan to set the fires, he to join the seiners. So he tried to let on he thought the holes were smart.

By this time the grassy bank of the lake was triple-tiered with cars, and a smell of water, seaweed, and swampy ground hung over the valley. Twisting streamers of pale heat smoke curled from the red fire piles. Beside them tubs of cleaned fish waited for the long-handled frying pans.

The tired seiners got the first of the platters of golden-brown crappies, with potato salad, bread, butter, lemonade, and a stack of cold pie. Joel sat on his haunches behind the rest, a slab of cherry pie on the flat of his palm, looking toward Mac's old car, far off by itself. He tried to ignore the two Rinker girls circling the seiners, their arms around each other, giggling.

"Are you gonna invite us to your coming-out party, Joel?" Narcissa called over her shoulder.

The boy flushed again and hunched deeper into himself before the laugh that spread from group to group.

When the picnickers began to move toward the dusty baseball diamond, Miranda took up a basket and led the way to Mac's car. And when they were gone the fish fry was done for the boy. With his short-tom gun on his arm he started home, not seeing anything on the way, not even the chicken hawk that sat on a fence post within twenty feet.

That night the father watched his son under the hanging lamp.

After a while he took his hat and walked along the devil's lane to the top of the hill and sat there at the edge of a blowout, where the wind had scooped a deep hole from the yielding sand. At last he started his pipe and came back to the house. But the boy's room was dark.

Joel watched the wild sweet peas, the bluebells, and the roses in the canyons bloom and fade, but when the yucca on the hills pointed waxy spikes into the sky he pinned an armful into butter paper; and as soon as Miranda's skirts vanished into the chicken coop, he took them across the devil's lane, threw gravel against the far tank, and then went whistling to the barn. From there he saw Mahlia pull back the paper and press the creamy blossoms to her cheek. It was so fine that he had to take his Goldy horse out for a gallop, bareback, over the hills, his sun-bleached hair waving like the brush of a wolf. When he came back there was one steady star standing in the west and the comforting wool of dusk blurred the scarred houses, the old cottonwoods, and the lane into one friendly mass.

After that Joel took to wearing a tie every day—old ones, mostly.

"Letting hair grow on a mule's tail never made a horse out of him yet," Duncan pointed out.

"Maybe not, but you oughtn't to blame him for wanting to lay his ears down a little," the son smiled to his father's graying reflection in the glass.

The next week the bull-tongue cactus in the horse pasture opened its yellow-satin blossoms, broad as Joel's strong hand. He potted two of the flowers in a small green crock of sand and threw gravel at Mac's tank. But the girl only shook her head and the newspaper bundle yellowed against the post in the devil's lane.

After that Joel put his ties away and watched the days move past dry as puffballs, dusty to the tongue, and bitter as ragweed—good haying weather. Duncan hired Jed Rinker to help, and the three of them worked long hours on the second cutting of alfalfa along the creek west of the house. In the evenings they ground sickles, repaired haying tools, or walked to their knees in purple bloom and estimated the probable tonnage, while on the other side of the lane Mac and his hired men were doing the same things.

But from his place on the stacks, Joel could watch Mahlia under his hat brim between sweep loads of dry alfalfa, even though she never looked toward the devil's lane any more. He watched for her every day; and once, while she was digging something, he saw her beat the earth with her hoe and then walk triumphantly homeward, bearing the thick, writhing loops of a dying rattlesnake the hoe handle's length before her. It was a fine sight and, forgetting the hay, Joel leaned on his fork.

Below him Jed Rinker licked his tobacco-stained lips. "Your boy's stuck on that girl over to Mac's," he called to Duncan, coming in with another sweep load. "He'll be lurin' her out into the hills one o' these days—"

"You shut your dirty mouth!" Joel shouted from the overhanging hay, his pitchfork poised as a spear upon Jed, making him jump and swallow his cud.

"Now, now, son," Duncan advised calmly. "If you're goin' to get overhet up there I'll be comin' up on the next load. Guess maybe I'd better do the topping out anyway."

Shamed, Joel moved back over the loose hay and rammed his fork deep into the heavy alfalfa.

But the mouthy Rinker talk had given the boy an idea. He began to drop weighted notes across the devil's lane. At first he only got frightened little headshakings, then a timid acceptance, and finally a shy thanking for the yuccas. This he put in his Sunday vest with the yellow handkerchief he found blowing against the fence early one windy morning.

Then he wrote the most daring note of all and flicked it to Mahlia in the garden while Miranda was in the cellar. After that the day dragged away toward evening, dark-banked with clouds. When the thunder rumbled nearer, Duncan brought his team in, the lines trailing through the dust.

"You'd better get the cows early tonight. I'll finish supper," he called to his son.

At the door where he could see the other yard Joel hurried into his overall jacket, dropped a shell into the short-tom gun, and slipped around up the blowout in the devil's lane. At Mac's fence he waited; and when he saw Mahlia coming, it was good that he had a small bunch of purple lupines and must busy himself arranging them. Not until she was before him did he look up, and then only to hold out the flowers. She put them to her nose.

"No, not to smell," he said, blushing that they must disappoint her in so vital a lack. "For your dress—there," he told her, indicating the point of the black lacing at the waist of her yellow peasant dress. From the brim of his old hat he produced a strong pin. Purple was fine against the yellow.

"Ah, you are nice," she said to the strange boy, and embarrassed them both. Once more the lupines helped. "You have a good eye for color," she told him.

"Yes—maybe I have," Joel admitted, pulling a long sliver from the cedar post against which his gun leaned. "I did best of all in art in high school."

That was good. For a long time they looked at each other as strange colts might.

Then: "Well, you came."

"Yes." She admitted it shyly. "And thank you—for the pink arrowhead in the note this morning."

"Oh, that! That's nothing, only rose quartz, but just a little scarce here. Was it hard to get away?"

"Not so very. Uncle Mac's repairing the stacker, so he was glad to let me get the cows for once, but Aunt Miranda said I'd better hurry."

"I thought about you all day, and about the old settlers' picnic next Saturday, and that maybe you'd dance with me, once," all in one breathless rush, as though she might escape, not hear him out.

"Oh, I couldn't do that. They—I mean I never have, with anybody, only girls."

Joel's jaw line sharpened like his father's. "I know. They wouldn't let you."

The girl didn't deny it, only stood looking at him, her gray eyes the disturbing color of the gathering storm, her hands tight about the stems of the lupines.

"I better go now."

"No, not yet!" Joel made himself laugh. "Look at that arrow hawk out getting his supper of mosquitoes—isn't he funny? And the swamp swallows, those gray things like gulls. Aren't they silly—and fine, too, cutting the storm like swords? When they come into the dry valleys it means rain." He had to stop, finally, afraid she would go now.

Mahlia did look doubtfully back toward the rolling clouds, but Joel picked up the gun. "Can you shoot?" he asked, swinging the stock into place against his shoulder, pulling the hammer back, letting it down with his thumb. "It was Dad's, when he and Uncle Mac used to go hunting together. They got snow in it once and busted the barrel. Now it's only a scatter-gun, but it could blow your head off."

While Joel talked, the clouds in the west crumpled into piles of green-gray wool, rolled into a long sausage, and raced over the valley toward the blowout in the devil's lane. A gray wall of falling water swept toward them. Before it a bolt of lightning fell, violet-red, through its own thunder.

"We better get away from the fence," Joel shouted over the turmoil. He slid down into the cup of the blowout. With a powerful heave of his shoulders he jerked the shallow fence deadman free. The wires flew up, pulling the one post in the hollow from the ground. Mahlia ran under it and together they dropped to the warm, yellow sand of the blowout under an overhanging bank of loose sod as the rain broke. They pulled their feet back, laughing a little.

"It'll be over in a minute," Joel comforted and Mahlia nodded her trust as another flash of lightning ripped the clouds and jumped in yellow sparks along the fence. A flood of water leaped over the banks into the blowout; the swinging post of Mac's spite fence swayed a little in the gusts, like a dead body, shiny wet and reddened by lightning. And at every bolt Mahlia closed her eyes quickly.

"Don't you have lightning—at home?"

"Yes, some, but not like this, and Aunt Adelaide draws all the blinds, puts her trust in God, and has me play the piano, fortissimo— you know, very loud. Rachmaninov and things like that."

"That must be grand, with the thunder," he said, sad that he could not hear her. "Dad says these are nothing to the storms they had up on the Indian Strip, where they went first."

"Were—they together then?"

Sure. Didn't she know? They were good friends.

Joel was disturbed by the girl's unhappy eyes. They must have been running somebody down, over there. They had no business. But he soon lost his anger in the contemplation of her slim hand on the sand, the tiny little finger the color of an icicle in winter evening sun. It didn't seem possible that she could kill a rattlesnake.

As Joel talked and let the sand run through one fist into the other, like an hourglass, Mahlia felt free to look at him—at his neck, brown as those round, peeled posts, his broad, strong shoulders tapering to the narrow waistband of his riveted overalls.

A warm pleasantness grew up between them.

But in the meantime the wind increased, the lightning was almost continuous, and the water leaped in yellowish streams into the blowout. Suddenly a new thunder shook the ground. Joel, understanding, threw the girl back against the wall, shielding her with his shoulder. The next instant Duncan's horses, wet, terrified, crashed against the fence. It ripped, went down, and the animals leaped into the blowout and out of it, down the devil's lane, throwing wet sand from their hoofs. Behind the bunch lagged a young mare, her colt running with his head in her heaving flank.

When they were gone Joel brushed a bit of soil from the girl's hair and blushed hotly because a tendril clung to his rough fingers.

For a long time after he let her go Joel held to a bit of her skirt under his hand. Finally he moved farther away and wiped the sand from his face. Then gradually they talked as friends again, but looking at each other with braver eyes now.

"I was afraid the horses'd come through on us. They go crazy from the lightning."

"But they might hurt themselves, get killed, running so."

"Old Bluche, the one that was pushed through first, probably has her breast ripped open. They usually do."

The girl looked at him with horror-darkened eyes. "Oh, the poor things! And that sweet little one, running with his mother! There was something heroic, as our literature teacher used to say, about them all."

"Yes," Joel acknowledged slowly. "Something wild and strong, like the mustangs of the prairies."

"Or white boats flying for harbor before a storm—I saw them once."

Yes, it must be fine too—the ships with the sails stretching. But it was even finer, talking so, and every time Mahlia remembered that she must go home Joel pointed out that the rain was like a waterfall and that the lightning popped and snapped most dangerously along the fence. They would think she had run in at Andrewses'. This minute she might be listening to his talk of million-dollar inventions while Mrs. Andrews washed dishes in a pan with rags in the holes. Together they laughed at this as at a very good joke, and knew what a fine thing is laughter when so shared. And after a while they learned that silence is a precious thing too.

The girl broke it first. "Do you like Narcissa Rinker?" she asked slowly.

"That girl—with her painted lips like a mouth full of blood?"

Comforted, Mahlia looked off into the gray rain darkening into dusk between the flashes of lightning.

Joel picked a harmonica from his pocket. Wrapping his fingers about it, he played softly the jolly, teasing old tunes Duncan had taught him. But when the wind shifted, blowing water in upon their knees, he stopped.

"Here, get back close to the wall." He helped her move from the cramped position. Her bare arm was cold as the rain. "Why, you poor kid! Here I sit and tootle and you freezing." He slipped out of his denim jacket.

"No," she said firmly. "You'll be colder than I, taking it off now."

"Tut—you talk foolishment," he teased; and spreading the jacket next to the wall, he made her lie upon it, buttoning the third button and the fourth about her. For a while she was strange and far away, then she relaxed and listened to him, playing softly.

As she got warmer the thunder seemed to recede, the rain to fall like early snow on a stubble field. After a while Joel put the mouth harp away and looked down upon the peaceful face lighted by the red webs flickering through the clouds. When she did not answer to her name spoken softly, he bent lower and touched her cheek with his lips so lightly she could never, never feel it through her sleep. Then he bowed to the rain again. For a long, long time he sat so, with something holy, something sacred and a little sad, too, within him.

A steady glare of light in Joel's eyes cut through the haze of sleep. He started up, awakening the girl. They were all there: Duncan in the fringe of light where the horses tore through the fence; Mac where his post and deadman swung in the air; Miranda at the edge of the blowout, gaunt and forbidding over the smoky lantern.

Stiffly Joel helped the girl climb out of the blowout and, holding tightly to her cold fingers, went before her to Miranda. But the woman struck his hand away, jerked the denim jacket from about Mahlia, and threw it to his feet.

"You! Luring an innocent child into the hills!"

Before her meaning the girl hesitated, then she flung her arm over her eyes and stumbled back, shaking. It made Joel sick, sicker than the time Mac shot the kittens about the pan of milk. He couldn't stand it; and grabbing up the old short-tom scatter-gun, he was gone, through the torn fences, toward the chophills, and not even Duncan called to him to stop.

Gently Miranda nudged the girl homeward. Slowly Mahlia bared her eyes to the emptiness of the circle of light. "Oh," she cried, and stiffened against them, "you and your devil's lane—you drove him away!" Then softly she added, "And all he did was—was kiss me, once." A flash of far lightning outlined the boy on a high point; and before the night closed down again, the girl had the lantern and was gone through the spite fences after him, crying, "Joel! Joel!" the swinging lantern lighting up one chophill after another as she ran.

And in the darkness behind her the three waited, motionless as the deep-set posts, the width of the devil's lane still between them, but the wires broken, the spite fences down at last.

XVIII

Bone Joe and the Smokin' Woman

"If you find that the short story form seems almost as rigid as that of the sonnet, or that the market for anything at all experimental has almost disappeared," the author wrote in a 1944 article, "you will tend to move into the longer field, the novelette, the serial, the novel" (28).

"Bone Joe and the Smokin' Woman," the author's first published novelette, was written in 1938–1939 and appeared in *Scribner's Magazine* in March 1939.

THE MORNING SUN of June lay warm and friendly over the sprawling knoll of buildings that was the home ranch of Rutherford Bills. Out on the wide sweep of meadow the shadows of a few clouds seemed to loiter before they ran toward the hills like playful colts in the wind. On the road a high-racked bone-picker's wagon was headed away from the ranch through hub-deep timothy, the little man hunched on the load prodding his four Indian ponies along as fast as he could make them go.

Although Bone Joe had been stopping at the Bills place for ten years, today was the first time he ever came with a tie around his dusty collar, and even Hippy had left his dough pans to see the sight. "Stickin' feathers on that buzzard's neck ain't gonna make no eagle outa him," the cook predicted.

"No, maybe not, Hippy," Cap Bills admitted, stuffing a long envelope away in his inside pocket. "Maybe not. But if a buzzard'd have the sense to fly high enough, few could tell the difference."

Hippy swung around on his good leg to look up at his boss, and then went limping back to his dough-punching. He had come up from Texas in the eighties with Rutherford Bills as a kid, worked with him and for him all the thirty years since. He wasn't listening to such talk. No buzzard was a-flying so high a bullet from a Bills rifle wouldn't fetch him down.

189

But outside, the old cowman still looked after the top-heavy bone wagon, watching it lurch slowly across the meadow toward the sand pass, the hind wheels rickety, one lower than the other, and running fast to keep up.

Until he was out of sight of the ranch, Bone Joe did his best to hustle his thin-necked ponies along with the sharp end of his willow prod. But as soon as the trail cut in between the steep hills of the pass he settled back on his load of bleached bones, letting the old rope lines sag, the sore-shouldered ponies nip at the weeds alongside as they plodded the heavy sand.

As the bone wagon passed the Gaylor fork, an open roadster swept in on the trail from the town. It was Hortense Bills, old Cap's daughter, her red auto veil flying, the wheels throwing sand at every curve. When she saw the bone rack, she turned in close behind it, hit her klaxon hard, and swung out around. Barely missing the tailboard, she was gone toward the ranch without looking back, scattering dust behind her, and a scrap of bone man's song.

"Stinkin' old bone-picker, ye ha ha," she sang, for all the hills to hear.

The man knew the words well, but this time they brought no red to his wind-burned face. At the crash of the klaxon and the rush of the passing car his sleepy little ponies had shied sideways, cramping the wheels hard. The top-heavy wagon teetered a moment and went down over the small wheel, breaking the old tongue out and spilling the man in a white avalanche of bones. Caught in the stiff lines, he managed to hang on, and was dragged away on his stomach over the bunch grass and through fragrant prairie roses into a nest of bull-tongue cactus, golden-yellow with bloom.

The winded old ponies finally stopped. Slowly Bone Joe lifted his head to wipe the dust and blood from his face, moving himself cautiously, afraid the wild-eyed animals might shy again, afraid he was smashed like the old wagon rack. But he was tough as the barbed wire of a feed corral, and unbroken, though his clothes were ripped to strings from wrist to knee, his skin torn and bleeding, his tie and one shoe gone.

Carefully he went over himself, jerking the thorns away, digging with his knife blade at those broken off close, until the tears stung his raw cheeks. And long before he was done he was pulling himself up to look back toward the pass where only a thin haze of dust along the hills remained to show which way the daughter of Rutherford Bills had gone.

The dry shell of moon hung low when Bone Joe finally pulled into his own little valley. He was hungry and tired from the long job of repairing and reloading his wagon, stiff and sore from the dragging, his arms and face swollen, the cactus spines broken deep in his flesh burning like new boils. But the pale moon made a pewter saucer of the little alkali lake, and the bleaching bones scattered about the dugout looked like white chickens undisturbed by the crippled old coyote always gnawing at a dry joint or a hoof. At the first creak of the wagon, the little scavenger lifted his sharp ears and bounded off into a gully, silent as a shadow. He couldn't know that Bone Joe had no interest in him until winter primed his hide.

With the fire going in the dugout and his skinned arms and chest wrapped in flour sacking soaked in badger grease, Bone Joe stirred up a batch of flapjacks in his old syrup bucket. But long before the last one was fried he was thinking of Hortense Bills again, of her black hair, shiny as a magpie's wing, her eyes gray and straight-browed as a man's, her walk ornery as a wild colt's.

When the last of the flapjack batter was fried up, Bone Joe balanced himself precariously on the top of a nail keg to reach down the elk head over the ridgepole, a fine one he had found years ago in a grassy old blowout, the antlers wide-pronged and weathered to a dead white. With a little red velvet over the skull, stuffed out good with sawdust, it would make a mighty pretty thing, even for a high-toned young ranch lady.

II

It was a week before Bone Joe got out again. By that time he had slept the anger from his tortured muscles, soaked the last of the festering thorns from his flesh, and got into an old pair of pants some duck hunters left behind last fall. He looked better than any time since he drifted into the freeland region ten years before. Although only twenty-four then, he wasn't much on duding up or for Saturday-night girling.

"That little bone-picker looks like some poor old broomtail that's been clubbed over the head and kicked away from the feed so often he can't seem to eat with any confidence," Rutherford Bills had told Hippy pityingly the first time Joe stopped at the cookhouse.

But even the cook wasted no sympathy on the bone-picker. "Them teeth a hisn bucks out so from reachin' for grub," he said in disgust after he saw Joe Leems clean up a kettle of Irish stew and all the stuff usually left on the oilcloth table, including the horse-radish and the ketchup.

Most of the other ranchers wouldn't hand out so much as a cold biscuit to the bone man, claiming he picked up stray tools, pulled their cedar posts, and left every gate or take-down open. But mostly people looked on him as a harmless runt, furnishing diversion around the post-office heater or at sales where there was always a free lunch. Not even the lone women homesteaders were afraid of him, probably because he never stopped at their doors, nor stood off looking after them as he did Hortense Bills since the first time he saw her climb up the stirrups to the back of Cap's old buckskin.

Although Bone Joe came in early enough for alfalfa land, he sneaked away into that dead little pocket, with its briny lake that smelled like a nest of old mallard eggs in August, the grass around it so gray and woody no cow would eat it—land that frosted white with alkali in the spring, especially where he broke out sod enough for his dugout.

But Joe Leems, who brought his bone wagon with him, wasn't sensitive to smells and had no farming intentions. He found that the hills hadn't been worked since the buffalo-bone men skimmed them thirty years before. By the first winter he had a long rick bleaching on the right of way at Gaylor, ready for shipment, and had heard the rollicking bone-picker's song many times as cowboys dog-loped past him out on the trails. Even the ranch children sang the one verse their mothers would countenance, shouting out the last lines good and loud and slapping their saddle leather to the chorus:

> Wagons pull in from the prairie dry
> To ricks of bleaching bones piled high.
> Four dollars a ton, but not for Sed,
> A rattler was a-watchin' that buffalo head;
> One settler less to bust up the sod
> And pray for rain from a deaf old God.
>
> Stinkin' old bone picker, ye ha ha,
> Robbin' the coyotes, eye ye ha ha.

From the first, Bone Joe got no mail and he could never be tied down to a definite statement about anything, particularly his origins. To the latecomers he was as much a part of the drab, ragged, smelly little alkali flat as though he had grown from its soil. His hair was to his neck and gray with dust, his dark and bony knees always sticking through several ragged pairs of overalls that he had picked up around some bunkhouse or livery stable where the former occupant shed them like the faded skin of a snake.

He cashed some pretty fair checks at the bank the last few years, but the money was never there long before some hard-pressed rancher slipped around to the dugout in the dark to do a little business. Once when a fresh wave of settlers came in, the new women, with ladies-aid ideas, made him a Christmas quilt. The ranch hands slapped their leather chaps hard at that one. "With you a-feedin' him, Hippy, most a the cowmen payin' him blood interest and them nester women takin' him beddin', he ought to make it to grass—"

But he really was a hustler, and so far as anybody knew Hortense Bills and her squawking klaxon were the first to interrupt his work, and then only until he could move around enough to catch up his ponies.

With his thin whiskers scraped off around the brown scabs of his healing face and the elk head in the wagon, he stopped in the Bills yard, not going in to Hippy as usual, or up to the big house as he did sometimes lately. Just waited, making no answer to the choreman's yell, "Hi, there, Joe—looks like you got you a snoot full a itch somewheres—" and pretending not to hear him whistle the bone-picker's song.

Finally Hortense came riding in from the pasture, wide-hatted, her silk shirt bright as a clump of golden sweet peas against a hill, the fringe of her gauntlets scarcely stirring, so easy was her seat on her loping pinto. At the gate she swung her arm around the stick and opened it without dismounting, closing it as handily as any cowboy, or Cap Bills himself.

While she watered her horse at the tank, Bone Joe shuffled forward, very small in his baggy clothes, holding the whitened elk head out awkwardly before him. With the pinto shying, jerking at the bit, Hortense tried to understand the man's stammerings. Suddenly she began to laugh, head thrown back, right out for all the yard and the bunkhouse to hear.

But as the man's mousy little face darkened, his knob of a chin set, she stopped. "You mean it—for me?" she asked.

"Maybe—" the man began slowly, not able to commit himself, the high apple of his neck bobbing. "Yeh—I guess maybe I could let you have the horns."

Now Hortense was laughing again, but quietly, with dimples and friendly white teeth for the man. Slyly she touched her heel to the off side of the agitated pinto and set him to an impatient crowhopping. "Oh, I couldn't let you rob yourself," she called back to the man as the horse carried her away into the yard. "But thank you for letting me see the fine horns," she added, over her shoulder.

So Bone Joe had to take the elk head back to his wagon, with the choreman and Hippy and anyone at the bunkhouse knowing, seeing it all. And when he was gone the father came out into the heat and sun of the yard, his hair blowing, shaggy as an iron-gray mustang in winter.

"You might have taken the head," he told his daughter quietly.

"From that smelly old bone-picker?"

"He picks the best bones in the country," Rutherford Bills said.

III

From his first coming, Rutherford Bills stood out tall among the cattlemen of the sandhills, his gray cowman's hat well above the rest, like a spruce rearing out of a forest of slim pines. He went at everything as he straddled a bronch, swift and confident, not sparing of bit or spur. There were some who claimed they remembered when he came in from the south like any other cowhand, with a slicker tied behind his saddle, his soogans and other traps on a pack horse. But even then his horses were good ones.

After looking around a little he settled on Fall Creek, and while the hands threw up some log buildings and pole corrals, he covered the region on Gold Dust, his buckskin. He bought up a small herd of the better Texas cattle from the later trailers, grazed them into meat on the free range, and made money selling beef to the Indians, while he built up his herd. By the time the railroad came he was ready to ship good grass-fat stock. His word was better than paper to the bank and his thick, black hair, graying early at the temples, better than gold with the ladies.

When the country tamed down some he brought in a big flat piano and a pretty little Eastern bride, with a waistline two hand-spans around, a blue chip hat with green wings pinned to her mass of light curls. He showed her off by candlelight in the ranch living room, playing sentimental little snatches at her harp or on the piano.

But soon it came out that the little bride was really as fragile as she looked and didn't like the country. The wind dried her soft, shining curls, coarsened the delicate violet-rose of her cheeks, darkened the pale shadows of her eyes and made her head ache. The people were so uncouth, the country so wide, so dreadfully empty

and plain. Only one spot seemed to please her—the headwaters of
the south branch of Fall Creek. The little pocket was ringed in by
hills, the low marshy meadow about the palmful of lake blue with
the violets of May. A few slim young cottonwoods stood shyly together at the pool springs of the upper end. Diane Bills filed on this
bit of land, and her tall husband put up a little doll's house for her
beside the peaceful, grass-hung thread of stream, with the hills standing firm against the winds. In the fall the ailing little Diane went
East and by spring there was only her portrait over the closed piano
in the ranch living room and a new baby, Hortense, to remind Rutherford Bills of the few months that were like a moment of sun on a
knoll ringed in by a low, gray sky.

Cap Bills was a good cowman and always made money so long as
the grass was free as the wind ruffling the long timothy of his
meadows. But the time came when browning fence posts marched
away to all the hazes of the horizon, when the yellow streaks of new
settler trails crossed the prairie in every direction, the dark blocks
of their soddies cramping the sweep of the eye, their hopeful windmills joining earth and air. Neighboring ranchers hired men with
six-shooters to keep the range clear, covered the land with fraudulent
filings, and ate up the homesteaders' crops in the night. Cap Bills
watched the covered wagons trail in, treated the newcomers like
neighbors, and leased their grass, even went to the school elections
to vote the maximum levy of taxes for the teacher's salary. The settlers called him damned white, but the other cattlemen stood away
from him at the Stockmen's Hotel.

He didn't seem to be making much from his cattle any more, either,
now that the sodbusters had so much of his hay land, and so he went
in for good horses—but the swamp fever got them. Next he tried
Mexican cattle, at five dollars a head. They were gaunt range stock,
wild as mustangs, and tore through barbed-wire fences like so much
string every time they caught sight of a woman's skirt blowing. At
the first snowfall they stood in little knots out in the wind, shivering,
humped up high as the back of a snaky bronch. That winter was the
worst since the eighties, and when the snow broke up in April, only
a handful of the new stock were still on their feet. That meant good
picking for Bone Joe after two, three years of sun and rain.

All this time Hortense was in school in the East, with an aunt. But
since she was eight she spent the summers loafing around the old
ranch house or riding the hills with Cap. She had his dark skin that
turned to a smooth, ruddy tan in the wind and sun, and two thick,

dark braids with red ribbons flying out behind her as she kicked old Gold Dust into a broken-kneed little run to catch up with her father or maybe some dog-loping cowhand who had to tuck in his flapping shirttail when he saw her coming. But they liked her, teased her in a heavy way that she soon caught on to, and showed her where there might be blue Indian beads in anthills.

They taught the girl to hold a calf down with a knee on its neck, and let her roll their cigarettes that they called fish worms when she finished them. From that a story got around among the older women of the region that the Bills girl was a young cigarette fiend, a smokin' gal, as they called it.

Rutherford Bills tried to remember that his little girl was growing up, would soon be a young woman. But she seemed so natural, so free and gay with her cronies of the corrals and the cookhouse, that he couldn't bring himself to spoil her summers.

And then gradually Bone Joe noticed the Bills girl. His little eyes, like glistening brown chokecherries in the sun wrinkles of his face, began to seek her out, follow her as she rode the range alone for flowers, perhaps for little blue lizards or for sand cherries.

At a ball game the summer Hortense was twelve and growing fast, Bone Joe held out a stick of chewing gum to her, and because the ranch hands were nudging each other, she took it and was teased all the way home by the sly humming of the bone-picker's song. When Cap heard about it he told her she'd have to go back to her aunt if she couldn't learn to be a lady, saying this red-faced and angry. Hippy, with his own opinion of old maids fetching up children, got Hortense into the cookhouse. While he ironed her shirts, he told her some of the things he thought a girl ought to know with buzzards like Bone Joe, or any of the rest of the boys, for that matter, around loose.

"Life's a mighty good hoss and'll carry you a long day's travel if you learns her tricks early," he advised. "Don't never let her get her head bogged down, or clamp jaws on the bit—"

That was talk the girl could understand and with her overall pocket full of cookies she threw the reins over Gold Dust's shaggy mane and rode out into the hills to contemplate this new and appalling world that Hippy had showed her.

During the next four years Bone Joe seemed to be spreading himself pretty thin. The cattlemen had tried buying up the range, getting it safely this time. But that took money, and with a drop in beef prices and a hard winter they were borrowing running money where they could, and paying high for it. One after another, Bone Joe got to them, even risked a little on a fellow boiling potash from one of the alkali lakes down on the south road. Half-interest in the business, no matter how far it spread.

Then suddenly Germany was at war, her potash shut off to the world, and Eastern magnates came talking big production, big money to the little lake owners. But Bone Joe still scouted the range seventy, eighty miles each way for bones, except the weeks Hortense Bills was at the ranch. Then he picked the home region, his wagon crawling like a slow, awkward bug along the slopes, his little eyes always out for the darker patches of grass and for a glimpse of a girl and a horse, perhaps only for a moment against some far sky.

IV

The August after Bone Joe brought the elk head to the Bills ranch, Vangie came from school with Hortense for a visit. Before the round-cheeked, jolly blonde girl had been at the ranch a day she knew everybody's nickname and had heard about Bone Joe, especially how he trailed Hortense around at the Fourth of July picnic down at Piller's Grove. She thought it was wonderful, so romantic. Even more romantic than Nickie, the poet, who wrote sonnets to Hortense. The hands winked to each other, openly, largely, suggesting that poor Bone Joe wouldn't have a chance to slip up his gully this time. But the girl didn't mind, went right on teasing to be taken to his dugout. So the girls got into their riding knickers and shagged over the hills toward the Leems place.

Quietly the girls circled their horses down the gully used by the old coyote to sneak up on the place. The wagon was home, standing, tongue down, among the piles of old iron and bleaching bones. And under it, his hat over his face, one foot in the air, was Bone Joe, asleep with the smell of old and stale death all around him.

At their sly giggling, the commotion of the snorting horses, the man sat up, bumping his head on the wagon bed above him. Red under his bristles, he crawled out between the wheels, rubbing his scalp and staring at Hortense in her bright silk shirt. The girl told him who Vangie was, and without waiting to be asked the two slid off their horses and tied them away from the wagon and the bone piles. Then, as though the path were made for their feet, they started toward the door of the dugout against the hill, with Bone Joe stumbling along backward before them, trying to wave them aside as a woman might, to stop a determined milk cow from a cabbage patch. Calmly Hortense walked toward the old door on leather hinges, Vangie close at her boot heels.

Inside, the dugout was a dark cave to sun-blinded eyes, the only light coming through the open, glass-paned door. Against the far wall an old cot spring hung between posts driven into the ground. Near the door a legless, two-hole stove sat in a box of ashes, with an armful of cow chips stacked on the dirt floor, and from poles of the roof dangled a low forest of dusty sacks and bundles. Even from the doorway the place smelled like the nest of an animal.

Vangie stopped, but Hortense pulled her in, to sit beside her on the cot. The girl let herself down reluctantly, touching only the barest edge of the swinging springs, and jerked at the yellow sleeve of her friend, anxious to go.

But Hortense Bills was already acting the young lady calling on a gentleman, even though it was only Bone Joe in tattered shirt and overalls standing in the doorway of a dugout, stammering. Before he could get his words made there was a scratching under the cot and a soft, furry animal looked out, sniffed the air, and started to climb up the boot nearest him.

"Shoo—git, git!" The man flapped his arms, his short upper lip jerking like a rabbit's. "Git, you—touchin' a lady—"

At that, little Vangie let one high giggle escape her and started Hortense too, laughing free, as though she were out on the open range. "A coon!" she finally cried, pretending it was the animal that was so funny.

Slowly Bone Joe began to grin, the thin skin of his mouth twitching over his buck teeth. In the meantime the young raccoon had settled himself in Hortense's lap and was pawing at the white thistle bloom in a buttonhole of her shirt, his bright little eyes on her face, his feet, like clawed hands, cautious, on the prickly flower.

Together the three watched the little fellow. He was the cutest thing, the girls said politely. Where did Mister—Mister Joe get him? And wouldn't it be nice for him here, out of the cold this winter!

No woman had ever spoken like this to Bone Joe, just as though he were anybody, and surely never Hortense Bills. So he let himself down to his nail-keg stool, dropped his hands between his knees, and began to talk a little, tasting the words cautiously. Yeh, sometimes the little bugger did seem kinda cute-like, he admitted, not committing himself completely. Guessed he just picked him up somewheres—out— Yeh, it might be nice here, round the fire, come winter. Maybe the little bugger wouldn't be here mucha the time—

Hortense understood the last. He wouldn't be here at all, not after the cold primed his hide, made it worth a dollar or so. But the young coon was sound asleep.

As their eyes accustomed themselves to the duskiness of the room, the girls looked around at the earth walls, almost covered with almanac pictures of pretty women with blue-black hair and considerable white skin showing. Half a dozen were of the same red-cheeked girl combing her loose hair beside a pool. And all the pictures had transparent clothes sketched in with pencil crosshatching.

Bone Joe noticed Vangie nudge Hortense toward the pictures and his pinched little head filled into the puffy redness of a hairy turkey gobbler. His confidence gone now, he tried once more to get the girls out. Maybe—maybe it was a-gettin' pretty late, and five, six miles to ride, with badger holes and bums loose in the country—

"It is getting late, isn't it? I guess we had better stay to supper," Hortense said, as to a heartily appreciated invitation.

"Oh," Vangie gushed, dimpling as at a beau, "it's just lovely of you to ask us, isn't it, Hortense?"

So they prodded the flustered man on between them until he lighted the smoky lantern, scooped out some of the powdery gray ashes from under the stove with an old sardine can, and stirred up such a dust that even the little coon hid his head under Hortense's arm. With the cow-chip fire roaring, Bone Joe broke off a piece of brown chicory stick for the coffee pot and got out a greasy black skillet.

"I—I guess maybe I better fix up a few flapjacks," he said apologetically as he pried at an old syrup bucket. Outside the tin was streaked and rusty and when the lid finally popped up, the inside was really lined half an inch deep with old batter, as the cowboys said, the sour smell filling the whole dugout thick.

Now it was enough for Hortense. Dumping the coon to the ground she ran for the door, and with Vangie at her heels, swung to her horse. At the first jump of her pinto she began to laugh, and all through the valley the horses ran uncurbed, the girls rocking in their saddles, laughing aloud until they had to hang to the horns, gasping.

When the girls were gone, Bone Joe let himself down on the sagging old cot. But the gloom didn't keep him from knowing what a boar's nest the dugout must have seemed to the fine young ladies. And he had hoped to walk right up to the Bills' ranch house someday, without stopping at the cookhouse for grub, without bringing money for Cap's urgent needs. Just walk up to the house like a visitor, like any man.

Several times during the winter Bone Joe stopped at the cook-house to eat up whatever Hippy set out for him and to get a little news. Once or twice he tried to lead up to Cap's sister, living in the East someplace, and to Cap's girl, going to school there. Maybe—maybe the cook knew the town?

Yeh, Hippy admitted, Miss Hortense was a-goin' to school. But he didn't say where.

So Bone Joe finally had to watch the ranch mail sack on the route for the address. And late in February a huge valentine drifted in at the college for Hortense. It came addressed in pencil, in a box like a fiddle case, a full-sized, gilt-paper violin standing away from a lacy background, with a swirl of pink roses around it. Hidden, but readily discoverable, were the letters J. L. Only the Gaylor postmark and the soiled fingerprints made Hortense think of Bone Joe at all, or remember that his name was Joe Leems. With the valentine and the wrappings in the apron of her uplifted skirt she ran to Vangie's room. Together they laughed until they were breathless. That bum in the dugout and his flapjack bucket! "To my Beloved," it said on the white ribbon among the roses. They howled it to each other as they popped candy into their mouths, candy the poet who made son-nets for his cowgirl from the West had sent them.

Next summer—just wait until next summer. They'd think of some-thing rare for old Bone.

V

The day Cap Bills met the two girls at the depot, the bone-picker was there in a khaki drill suit, waiting. But Hortense didn't see him. She was crying that her father looked so thin and aged; burying her face against his coat, she wiped her eyes and pretended it was joy at seeing him again.

So Bone Joe, standing off to the side, alone, stiff among the cream cans of the farmers, didn't get the greeting he hoped for—nothing at all but a hasty nod of recognition from Cap Bills.

At the ranch, while her soft little friend napped from the three-day trip, Hortense went to the cookhouse for an hour's serious talk. For the first time in his life, Hippy left the salt out of the pie crust he was mixing, and with company home, too. But it was pretty hard to admit to Hortense that every acre and hoof her father owned was mortgaged tight as a tick in a sheep's ear, and long overdue. The girl nodded slowly, her eyes still level and straight-browed, and once more she came away from the cookhouse with the world a strange, appalling place about her.

"You can't go a-lettin' on to Cap," Hippy had said.

She promised she wouldn't, and so, although the father was away on business much of the time, probably trying to raise capital or a partner, Hortense plunged into a strenuous, boisterous summer with Vangie, always on the go, mostly by saddle because the horses came free. They went to every picnic, dance, rodeo, and celebration for miles around, always with plenty of Cap Bills' old friends to ask them to dinner or to stop for the night, if it was far. Always, too, with plenty of boys, the Pillers, or other ranchers' sons, for dancing partners and to buy them pop and sandwiches at the stands, or to shoot for kewpie dolls.

"That bob-haired smokin' gal!" envious mothers told each other when they saw the arms full of silk-frilled, painted dolls the girls always had to carry around through the crowds, although none of them had ever seen Hortense take even one puff from the cigarettes she rolled so swiftly and well.

Once the girls rode clear down to Sully, the potash town where Bone Joe was said to have his investments. It was ten times noisier and dustier than the summer before, the tar-paper hulks of the refining plants spreading wider, rearing higher, pointing great chimneys into the windy sky. The thousands of workmen slept in the hot, single-board sheds, thrown together in boom-town style, or in the rows of tar-paper shacks a quarter the size of Hippy's smokehouse, each with one window and a door, set up on high blocks, only separated far enough so a horsebacker or a hurrying woman could slip between.

As the girls ate hamburgers with pop at a stand, they spied Bone Joe's old wagon in the surging alley beside the bank. Soon he himself came out of the building, and the crowd parted for him, hats and caps sliding off, men making excuses to call his name, "How'do, Mister Leems," "Nice day, Mister Leems," while farther back there were nudgings, laughings, and hurried searches for a place to spit.

As Joe Leems swung his wagon past one of the shack rows, a woman in a yellow kimono waved to him, trying to coax him in. At her first sign he prodded his ponies into a scattered, broken run, escaping with a great banging of the empty bone rack, leaving a whirl of fine, boom-town dust to settle slowly behind him.

"Must be pretty hard up for customers," a couple of old cow-punchers riding along the road shouted to each other over the racket, as they watched the bone-picker go.

When Hortense and Vangie got out on the clean, golden prairie of evening, they slowed their horses, hooked their knees around the saddle horns, and ate bananas as they considered Bone Joe's consternation at the woman's approach. It gave them an idea for the joke they planned last February, when the fancy lace valentine came for Hortense. The next morning they hunted up one of the matrimonial papers the hay waddies and ranch hands had around the bunkhouse. Between them they made up the five dollars required for the publication of a man's letter, with photograph. After reading the papers through, they described Joe Leems as the owner of "a fine cattle ranch, a large, comfortable home, well-furnished, overlooking a beautiful lake," and gave his name in care of Rutherford Bills. With a picture of Nickie's lean and beautiful face, his thick, pale hair mussed a little, to draw them, the letters began to pile in, as the mail carrier complained to the girls. "Why's your dad let that bone-picker fill his box up?"

There were packages, too, odd shapes and sizes. Debating for an hour or two the ethics of the situation in the stilted manner of their most unpopular teacher, they decided upon opening everything not strictly sealed, since, in a way, the mail was more theirs than Bone Joe's. Perhaps the purple fronds of feather sticking from a broken envelope, the crumbs of fudge leaking from a bundle really decided them. The feather was fastened to a lady's garter, a rich purple, and big enough, at least the girls decided, to go around Bone Joe's syrup bucket. There were hand-knitted socks, sleeve-holders, several ties, and in one the wedding picture of a widow, with "sod" written under the mustached man beside her.

Among the practically unsealed letters were some pretty good ones. "My beautiful curly-headed baby boy," one began, in good penmanship. Some were painstakingly done, in unaccustomed ink, with "Dear Sir" and "Yrs resp." Some of the women were kittenish and coy, pretending to have money and many admirers but romantic enough to prefer a great, strong man from the West. One came by special delivery. "Please wire Two Hundred Dollars for Fair and expenses immediately." Enclosed was the picture of a high-bosomed woman with earbobs and a commanding eye. Hortense, who had taken a minor in history, suggested that she would have made a fine general for the Prussian Army.

When the girls got tired of the mail, they rode over to the dugout in Leems' valley and emptied the grain sack full at Bone Joe's feet, the packages rolling, the cream and lavender envelopes scattering like corn leaves in the wind. The man looked at the lot and up at Hortense in confusion. There he stopped, boldly, for he saw that now the girl's dark eyes were the troubled green-black of hail clouds and not gay any more, as her mouth would make them out to be.

It was as well that the girls had their fun before, because Bone Joe didn't do anything, no stammering, no turning red, no sweating, no asking what it was about. Today he just stood there bold as a ferret, his little eyes unblinking as glass on Hortense until she hurried Vangie away to their horses. Nor was there any laughter as they rode out of the valley. Not even the daily letter from Nickie could make Hortense forget the waiting look of Bone Joe's eyes.

The next time Joe Leems shipped a car of bones and scrap iron he thumbed late through the catalogues by the light of the old lantern and finally sent for a red-satin box with sea shells all around the edges. "A gift fit for a queen," the description said, and filled with two pounds of assorted bonbons, finest quality, nineteen cents a pound, extra.

The day Joe brought the box over, Vangie and Hortense were on the top plank of the corral wall, watching the choreman provide a new mother for an orphaned white-faced calf. Hortense saw the bone wagon turn in at the yard gate, but because it was too late to get away, she waited as the man crawled down and came toward the corral, stiff in his wrinkled drill suit that was still too large, even after two hard sandhill showers on it. With his cap under his arm, he handed Hortense a package in crumpled brown paper and waited for her to open it, his short upper lip twitching in anticipation.

Once the girl started to make the bone-picker take the package back, but she remembered what Hippy had told her. "He's got both Cap and the bank where the hair's short." So she unwrapped the box, and Vangie's little squeal of delight seemed to compensate for her own silence. As she opened the lid, the choreboy came up to look over the outfit, as he called it. With much skepticism, he bit into a bonbon, nodded, and spit the candy out. "Old as them bones you pick," he grumbled.

VI

Monday, Vangie was going back to school and Hortense with her, into war work. The Saturday before there was a box social and dance at Ned Salzer's, proceeds to go to the Red Cross. Rutherford Bills was away, but Hippy chaperoned the girls, as they called it, chaperoned his own good grub, he insisted, as he sat stiffly on the outside in the roadster, his game leg cramped, holding the girls' twin box in a bleached sugar sack on his good knee. Every mile or so he pretended to steal a look inside the sack by the dim light of the dash, with Vangie grabbing at the box in mock horror that he really might see it.

"I bet you let them Piller boys get a eyeful," he protested.

Vangie shook her pale head of curls at him, but Hortense held the wheel and kept her face to the crooked trail.

"The boys are leaving for overseas tomorrow," she finally said.

At Salzer's they climbed the ladder into the long hayloft smelling clean of alfalfa, saddle leather, and kerosene from the row of lanterns hung along the gable. They were greeted noisily by the early comers, the fiddlers beginning to tune up, and the hay waddies shouting, "Let 'er go!"

With the organ unfolded, the musicians swung into "Tipperary," and the two Piller boys, tall and strange in uniform, came over. Easily they moved out upon the candle-waxed floor with the girls from the Bills ranch in ruffled voile dresses, Hortense in Alice blue, Vangie in pink; smoothly they dropped into Eastern steps the boys had picked up in college last spring. Struttin' city stuff, the home boys called it; showing off with glides, hesitations, dips, and whirling turns on the ball of the foot.

Toward midnight, the floor manager got out the broom and, pounding the bald-headed end on the floor for attention, announced the sale of the supper boxes. "One hundred per cent goes for the Red Cross an' the Yanks goin' overseas, so bid 'em up, boys, bid 'em up—"

The girls and women settled along the benches, the men gathering at the far end of the loft, for there were to be no nudgings, no signs now. And when the first box was fetched out from behind the curtain across the corner, Bone Joe came pushing forward, using his sharp elbows against the pack of men, until he was clear out in front where he could watch the faces of the girls from Bills and his signals to the auctioneer could be seen plain, for he had planned this evening a long, long time.

One box after another was held high, cried while the owner tried to look unconcerned, and sold for two, three, even eight or nine dollars.

When a red-satin box with sea shells on the edges came up, Vangie nudged Hortense and then they both pretended to look around for the blushing owner. Paying no further attention to the girls, Bone Joe began to bid. One after another the younger fellows got in against him, the older men yelling advice to their contemporary. The box went to twenty dollars. Joe hesitated, but when one of the Piller boys bid an extra quarter, he began again, slowly, thinking each bid out carefully, hanging on like a badger to a hound's throat, not saying a word, just holding up a finger or nodding woodenly for the extra quarter.

At fifty dollars he stopped again, and the other Piller boy bid a dollar raise. Once more the bone-picker started, went to sixty-three dollars, with Hortense shaking her head hard at the boys. Everybody else dropped out, and in a great rumpus of stomping and yells and calls, Bone Joe went forward to receive the box on his two open palms. Holding it like a jewel case, he slipped away to the wall through the path that opened for him. All through the rest of the bidding he stood there, straight and secure, not bothering to open the box, even to lift the lid a bit for the name inside.

When the children's boxes were gone, and $310.75 had been taken in, the crowd scattered over the loft, men with boxes finding their partners, the stags lining up to buy sandwiches and coffee, usually free at barn dances but sold by the Red Cross tonight. When everybody was settled to eat, Bone Joe once more pushed forward, this time to Hortense and Vangie sitting on a car cushion on the floor, the Piller boys before them on a dust robe, the box with the cattails between them.

"I—I guess maybe I got your box," he said to Hortense, his teeth bucking out through his little grinning mouth. He repeated the words doggedly, despite the roar of laughing that went up from the bar-wide circle watching as the girl shook her short hair.

"Isn't there a name inside?" she asked as kindly as she could, sorry that he made her do this so publicly. The bone-picker looked all around him, swiftly, as a coyote ringed in by hounds, and saw what the girl meant in their faces. Once more he plowed through the crowd, this time clear to the ladder and out to his wagon to sit on the tongue in the dim moonlight while a bunch of young squirts sneaked after him, humming the bone-picker's song from behind shadowy cars and wagons until those fathers who owed the lone man money came out angrily to send the boys flying. And inside the loft sixteen-year-old Alice Mason cried into her handkerchief. She had lost the pretty red box Hortense had given her, and the first social of her whole life was spoiled, even though her box brought the most of any.

VII

Sunday evening the girls went to Gaylor to see the Piller boys off, kissing them and wishing them great good luck with a gaiety that did not cover foreboding. By the next summer both the boys were gone, one in action, the other of gangrene; and Bone Joe had a breach-of-promise suit on his hands, one of the mail-order widows, the one Hortense said would make a good Prussian general. But she hadn't a scrap of paper to prove anything, and no jury would ever believe that she pinned Joe down to a definite promise, even though the widow was a determined woman. She walked clear out to the dugout and might have walked back for all of Joe Leems if the mail carrier hadn't felt sorry for her—thick feet stuffed into high-heeled pumps, a suitcase and something over two hundred pounds of meat to lug. Nothing came of the case because a fellow up at Gaylor who owed Joe some money and couldn't pay married the woman.

VIII

For the first time in ten years Hortense didn't come home that summer. Hippy's rare notes were full of meatless, wheatless days and bread made with black flour and potatoes, not fit for a hound dog's belly. Cap Bills, thinking of Bone Joe in a new suit, with a big car and big ways, didn't urge the girl.

The rancher had put the last cent he could raise into potash, the new wartime industry. Neglecting the interest and the taxes, he even considered mortgaging Bills Pocket, the quarter left to Hortense by her mother. But he couldn't ask the girl, and so that remained free. Everything else went into potash. Fortunes were made down at Sully. Bone Joe had sold the fifty acres of his dirty lake for ten thousand dollars, cash, it was rumored. And his interest in the potash works for a hundred thousand. That was just like a bone-picker, selling out for small potatoes, some said. Another year or two, and he'd been a millionaire. Got scared at the talk of one side or the other in the War caving in. Germany could keep going, Cap Bills thought, now that Russia was out. Another year—that was all he needed.

Then, suddenly, the hysteria of the Armistice was upon them. Hortense's work was over and so she came home for a while. Cap met her at Gaylor, much older, but full of ideas. He was working hard for a tariff on German potash, hoping for an extension on his long overdue mortgages. Hortense tried to talk to him of these things, but he drew himself up tall as ever. "It has never been necessary for a Bills woman to worry her pretty head—" So the daughter kissed his softening cheek and saddled up her pinto for a hard ride in the hills.

IX

The next day Joe Leems came to the Bills yard, not in his bone wagon this time, but in a new yellow roadster, a long, low one he took in on a foreclosure from a potash man. He wore a new wide-striped suit—like one he saw on an actor in Sully the winter before—yellow, bumper-toe shoes and a cap. He stopped his new car alongside the house that hadn't seen paint for twelve years and went in, his bright shoes straight up on the ranch-house porch. Without knocking, he pulled the door open and walked boldly into the Bills living room.

At his step Hortense was up from the piano, to stand alone, straight and tall, against this intruder. Joe Leems tried to hold his ground, say he had a right there, but before the daughter of Rutherford Bills he was once more only a dirty bone-picker.

That night Rutherford Bills sat late before the fire in the old ranch house. Young Hortense didn't seem to have much luck with her men, he mused: her father a gut-shot old critter just hanging onto his place by his toenails, hoping; that Piller boy of hers buried in France; and then she went and fell in love with a poetry fellow. And all the time there was old Bone Joe Leems, waiting around like a bare-necked buzzard on a fence.

He had always hoped to spare the girl but now at last he saw he must tell her something of his difficulties. Of course the market would go up as soon as a tariff was put on potash. It had to come. America protected her industries. Until then he would be busy as a sheep-herder in lambing time, couldn't be beauing his handsome daughter around as was proper. Now he hoped she would go to her aunt for a spell. Later, maybe, they'd take a long trip together.

And so, as though there was nothing but the thought of a holiday for the girl between them, no long knowledge of the ranch failure, no Bone Joe walking unasked into the old living room, Hortense packed. In the morning, Hippy sat over a cup of coffee in the cook-house with the girl and then hobbled to the door to watch her go. Yeh, he'd see to Cap, see to him as well as any man alive.

X

It wasn't until the second summer that Bone Joe realized that Hortense Bills wasn't coming back, even with Cap down sick. A straw boss was running the place, with Hippy living in the ranch house and the doctor coming out every week. Kidney trouble, some said. They could tell. Old Cap'd been walking stooped below the middle for months and looking the color of underdone biscuits. That cigarette-smoking girl of his belonged to home. Somebody had ought to tell her what was what. Then it got around that Bone Joe had a man look her up in New York, found her married, or that she'd better be. The next week he took over the Bills ranch.

The day Joe Leems came out, Hippy padded the back seat of the old touring car with quilts and bedding, helped Cap in and let him hold the portrait of Diane. The front seat and the running board he loaded with stovepipe and pots and pans. Behind them came one of Ned Salzer's trucks with an old stove, a few books, and the piano that hadn't been opened for two years.

By evening they were settled in Bills Pocket, with the first smoke coming from the old shack that was thrown together over twenty years ago and was now mighty leaky and airish. Cap Bills wouldn't let Hippy take out his pencil to write to the daughter. But some of the women folks saw to it that she knew, and so Hortense Bills came home. She must have brought a little money, because Hippy drove in to Gaylor, hired carpenters, and had lumber hauled out for an ell of two rooms. Saturday night, the loafers were waiting thick along the street as the carpenters drew up in the center parking. Yeh, Tensy Bills was a-comin' due, all right. They'd seen her man, too, one of them there pale potato sprouts, with hair light as a meadow full of tickle grass a-blowing, and wax-beany fingers.

The night the baby came, Cap Bills' tired old heart stopped. "The Lord giveth and the Lord taketh away," the preacher said at the funeral. Everyone in the county able to be out seemed to be there, those who had worked for Cap standing in a knot off to the side, remembering the man he was.

At the grave the old ranch cook and Nickie stood alone, the light wind lifting the thin gray hair of Hippy's bowed head, ruffling the heavy blond waves above the boyish face of the young husband. At the end, Joe Leems came edging up to stand beside them, his head sticking forward on his neck, his hat held against his stomach. As the old cook guided the sobbing Nickie away, he thought of those days when Hortense rode free over the hills. Even then the bone-picker's little eyes were after her, even before he had any paper against her father, long before he started wearing a tie to the ranch, a buzzard trying to fly as high as an eagle.

Now Rutherford Bills was gone, and his fine, wide ranch was in the hands of Bone Joe, Mr. Joseph P. Leems. By the time the potash companies were all broke, he had taken over a county-seat bank, and foreclosed the paper until he owned half a dozen of the smaller ranches that just couldn't seem to compete with South American beef. He got most of the town of Gaylor, too, including the buildings housing the post office, the city headquarters, and the fire department.

The backs of the menus at Leems Café listed the Leems hotel, pool hall, barber shop, filling station, garage, grocery and drygoods, hardware and undertaking, livery and feed, lumber and coal, insurance, loans and investments.

Although he held himself fairly straight when he remembered, inside he was still Bone Joe, even in his dark-green, belted-back suit, with a pink silk shirt, gray cowman's hat, and a bulge in the back of his pants that was said to be twenty-dollar bills, although nobody ever saw him break one.

He had a room at the hotel, offices at the bank and the city hall, and a sort of a hole in the wall with outside stairs above the feed store. Inside was an old leather davenport, a rusty two-hole stove, much like that of his old dugout, and several pictures of Theda Bara on the wall.

Women were giving him the eye now. Now and then a girl even slipped up the outside stairs to the room over the feed store, though it was generally some frightened little thing, sent because interest was due on a mortgage.

Around the livery stable there was a lot of laughing. By golly, it sure looked like old Bone Joe couldn't stand comparison, keepin' to them scared kids like he did. The story ran from the pitch players to the five-hundred club and the bridge-whist circle, growing as it went. Some thought it a mean shame, such young girls, but they weren't in a position to do much complaining, just now, owing the man money themselves. The weekly paper at the county seat, where Bone Joe was horning in, gave half a column to the story, mostly just hinting, calling it "The Shame of Our Sister City." By Thursday evening the paper was sold out. Those on the Friday mail deliveries got nothing, and the next week there was an apology, boxed in black, like an obituary, headed "UPRIGHT CITIZEN MALIGNED BY IDLE GOSSIP."

After that, Joe Leems had no more frightened night visitors in his room. Instead, he took to driving out alone in the evenings. He was walking cockier, too, as though the far pastures were pretty good. Then one night young Singer came tearing up the rickety stairs, kicked the door in, and with his fingers on Bone's scrawny throat, told him he'd cut his dirty heart out and throw it in his face if he didn't let Ellie Melkorn alone.

The next Sunday evening two cars full of white-robed figures stopped at the Melkorn place, dragged young Singer out of the kitchen where he was helping Ellie with the supper dishes, and later dumped him on his father's porch, the skin stripped from his back with a bull whip.

Hortense heard little about the excitement that swept Gaylor and the county seat. She did know that times were hard, farm produce down, war mortgages coming due, ex-servicemen out of work, and everybody looking for a whipping boy, somebody to blame. But thoughts of half-soles and sugar and flour in Bills Pocket shut out the world as surely as its ring of hills stood against the far sky. They might sell the place, have a five-hundred-dollar debt left over, no home, and no carfare to Nickie's old job in New York. And even when he could work steady, it wasn't much. If they stayed here his white skin might darken, his body grow stronger, his heart pound less. And Hippy needn't be weaned off the range.

By the time baby Diane was six months old, Hortense was back in overalls, much like all the other summers out here. But this time it wasn't play; this time she was out showing a hired man where to break up spring sod for a big garden, a plot of potatoes, sweet corn, and an acre of white beans against the doctor's bills and the undertaker's. She watched the man closely, for after this there would be no money for help.

Evenings, she worked out the plantings with Hippy, crippled up with rheumatism, not getting around much in damp weather any more, and talking as though he hadn't been limping for thirty years. But even in a wheel chair, Hippy would be handy as a silver dollar.

Sometimes, after a good day, Nickie sang a gay little song or two that his mother had taught him, his mother who died wishing for her native Pyrenees. Sometimes he played a little, too, Chopin or Debussy, reaching out suddenly to pull Hortense from her sewing to the piano bench. Her hands were clumsy now, and calloused, but she learned not to object, since the time Nickie snatched up his cap and ran out into the night.

"I can't bear to see these things happening to you," he cried out to the darkness when Hortense came to bring him in from the cold. And although he sat quietly enough the rest of the evening, his heart pounded like Hippy's hammer on the old plowshare.

He couldn't do much heavy work, but with all the new-turned breaking handy, he finally got a sod fireplace and chimney up at the far end of the living room, snaking the blocks into place with the old pinto that once carried Hortense over all the hills. Well-plastered, inside and out, with alkali mud, it was nice for the long evenings. They made a party of the first fire, and a poem.

But Nickie knew such things wouldn't buy so much as a box of matches or a pound of sugar and so he tried desperately to learn to be helpful outside. Without money for coal and with almost no trees in the country, he became the fuel provider of Bills Pocket, vice-president in charge of cow chips, as he called it. During the summer he dotted the old feed grounds west of the valley with neat little cocks to be hauled in when the team was free. The land belonged to Joe Leems now, and several times he drove around that way to see the cow-chip-picker Tensy Bills had married. But Nickie just waved his hand in greeting and dragged his old tub on.

In spite of all the care and hoeing Hortense could give to her gardening, the first years didn't yield much for sale except sweet corn and potatoes, the surer crops. One September an early frost blackened half her beans, making a long job of sorting for winter evenings. Next, the hail took all the early planting, pounding the melon vines into the ground. Then the drouth. Yet they managed, even paid a little on the debts, until the fall Nickie got sick.

One cold fall day he stayed out cow chip-picking through a slow drizzle that chilled him completely before Hortense came to the hill to call. Scolding that he hadn't hurried home to get dry, she held his hand under the warm sleeve of her jacket, his fingers ice against her side, until she couldn't stand it any longer. Yet as soon as she started to run she remembered and tried to slow down, but Nickie jogged right along to the crest of the road turning into Bills Pocket. Puffing a little, he stopped to point ahead for Hortense to see. Across from them, the smoke of Hippy's baking spread in a thin blue haze along the hills, while over it the breaking clouds of evening hung in yellow folds, burning the windows of their home to a golden light. In a flood of happiness Hortense pressed her cheek to Nickie's wet coat as he held her against him. Then she hurried him along the wet road to the house.

That night Nickie was restless and by morning he was feverish and sick. Two days later it was pneumonia, with Hortense having to admit to the doctor that he had been refused by the army—wet lungs and an unreliable heart.

It was late spring before Nickie was out again, keeping to the sunny side of the house pretty much of the time, with a knitted scarf crossed over his chest, the skin of his high, thin nose stretched tight and shiny. By this time Hortense showed the strain of the winter-long nursing, even with all the help Hippy, limping around on a cane, could give. While Nickie was still only a long skeleton under the blankets, little Diane came down with the whooping cough, and the doctor, not paid out yet for Cap Bills' illness, needed money. Hortense picked over the screenings of her beans, sold her hens and the potatoes, down to the barest necessities, even the calf she had hoped to hold for a couple of years. She looked through Nickie's writing once more, and without hope used up the last of her stamps sending the poems out. Half a dozen were accepted, bringing in fifteen dollars and a half, all in one mail. That was a grand, happy evening with a little music not too badly played.

But finally Hortense had to mortgage Bills Pocket, even though to her it meant giving the bank her home. By her twenty-seventh birthday she was looking pretty sprangly, as Hippy called it, with here and there a wiry thread of gray creeping through her dark hair.

Even now Nickie tried to write a little, a pad of paper always beside him, the desperate need of Bills Pocket a shadow about his bowing shoulder. More and more he wrote of the things he was leaving behind, soil and air and sky, a salty old friend, a daughter that he could never kiss again, a woman long and deeply loved.

And then one day Hortense ran to the old car and tried frantically to start it. Failing, she ran to the ridge road to wave down the first passer-by, send him hurrying for a telephone.

The doctor came in time to pull the sheet up over the white face of the poet, waxy as the soapweed blossoms Hortense had brought to him from the hills that morning.

And when the doctor was gone, Hortense threw an old denim jumper around the girl and, with her arm about the shaking little shoulder, went up the road to where it turned into Bills Pocket. There, off to the west, was the old feed ground where, two years before, Nickie had stayed out in the cold rain because he was so anxious to be of help. Together they had looked toward the little house, with its blue smoke clinging to the hill behind it, the clouds of evening turning the windows to gold. Once more the woman felt the rough, wet cold of Nickie's coat against her cheek, knew the loud thumping of his laboring heart.

And now she must explain death to his child.

XI

When the six months of mourning were up, Bone Joe and his driver stopped beside the garden patch where Hortense was going through the tomato vines bowed to the earth with reddening fruit. At the sound of the car the woman stopped and rose stiffly, her gunny-sack apron heavy before her as Joe Leems came uncertainly through the patch, trying to keep out of the down vines with his new shoes.

"Howdy, Tensy," he said.

"Nice day," she told him.

"Yeh—" opening his mouth several times, closing it, and finally starting, "Yeh, Tensy, I guess maybe I could let you have a house in town cheap—"

"Thank you, but we'll be all right here," she said.

The man pushed the sand around a little with a shoe and finally lifted his eyes to the strong woman figure before him, the leather brown of her face, her high, fine nose.

Once more he started. "Maybe I could let you have a little extra on the place—"

"We're better off here—"

That brought the red to his neck. "You can't go on a-living here like you been doin', with a busted-down cow cook—"

A long time the woman looked at the little man before her, once even started to lift her hand against him, knowing he was no match for her field arm. But behind the things she had suffered from him she remembered his own life-long indignities. She had upset his wagon, pushed herself into his dugout, brought him long ridicule with that matrimonial-paper advertisement. She had helped sing the bone-picker's song, make a fool of him at a box social. Anger was not her right, and so she thanked the man for his interest and turned back to her work. But when the car pulled out of the yard, Tensy Bills looked after it a long time, her hand shading her eyes uneasily.

She was right. Bone Joe had other ways of persuasion. One rainy evening there was a pounding on the door at Bills Pocket. Hortense put aside her mending and went to the door. In the rectangle of light before her stood three white-robed men, a smallish one in the middle, a wide, husky one on each side, and behind them, across the farther fringe of light, was a solid white wall.

The woman started to close the door, but one of the men poked a rifle against it. They were not here to trouble her, he said, but to protect her from a wolf, a human wolf.

"Yes, a human wolf," the other big fellow added. "We've come for him," thumbing toward the crippled man in his chair beside the lamp.

Hortense looked slowly from one masked face to another and back to the little man in the middle. So that was it. Smiling a little, with the light behind her, she reached as though for support to the door casing. Swiftly she grasped the twenty-two rifle hanging beside it, threw the gun to her shoulder, holding the barrel down upon the little man in the center, directly between the holes of his mask, her hand steady and cold.

"Now get out!" she said. "Get out, you dirty, bone-picking buzzards!"

A moment they were motionless, then there was a shift forward among those in the shadow, but the center man waved them back from him. Slowly they obeyed, until they were only a vague patch of white in the darkness, the leader scuttling into their shelter. Then, even before they were gone, Hortense set the gun down, and leaving the door wide open, she went to the table, to sit there at her work, until all the cars were gone and the last of the robed men.

It was Hippy who spoke first, from the shadows of his sunken face.

"You mighta let them bastards take these here old bones a mine," he said, in disgust at his helplessness.

Swiftly the woman was beside him. She tucked the robe in around him and slapped his arm.

"We wouldn't let those bed-sheet paraders take so much as a pants button away from a Bills. And anyway, your bones aren't bleached worth a cent—"

Somehow the story got out, was repeated around the barns, the hardware stores, and the pool halls. By golly, that Tensy Bills was the daughter of old Cap, all right, old Cap who bluffed them horse thieves out up to Wyoming and fetched back all their take. Soon after that, when the Sula girl got in trouble, the new district judge told Bone Joe right out that he was a bird of prey, and the county-seat paper came out against him and his night riders both, without apology. Times seemed to be getting pretty good.

Since Hortense laid Nickie's writing pad away in her trunk, she carried a lantern at both ends of the day. With Hippy sitting in his chair to tell her what to do, she repaired the old car, put a big box on behind, and on spring mornings she was the first at the Gaylor back doors, neat in starched calico or denim, with fresh rhubarb and asparagus, later radishes, lettuce, gooseberries, and so on, until melon and squash time.

In the afternoons Tensy worked with the ditching that brought a little water from the lake to the lower part of her cabbage patch, or hoed, weeded, and gleaned for the next morning. Gradually Bills Pocket became what the real-estate agents called a garden spot, and they began to bring their prospects around that way to show them what the country would grow. But they didn't say that Tensy Bills had learned to watch the romping of her calf and the fluttering whirl of snowbirds for storms, the first coming of the swallow to her eaves to date the season.

The first bad year in Bills Pocket, Hippy had insisted that they buy a shoat and fatten it on scraps, garden truck, and sweet-corn leavings. Cheapest meat in the world and, smoked up, was always handy for the frying pan. So Hortense consented, writing to Vangie's mother where she had tasted ham and side meat cured with the molasses and herb mixture of the old smokin' man of the community and smoked with his secret prep'ration. The recipe for the prep'ration finally came, written out with a stub pencil on a paper sack by the smokin' man himself. After that, there was always good meat, well cured, in the dry sand cave against the hill.

That summer, Ned Salzer and his young wife snapped off a car axle in a sand pass and walked to Bills Pocket to be taken home in the old topless pickup. While they rested and cooled off, Tensy set out a lunch. At first, Lillibelle just poked at the cold sliced ham, looking around at the bare little house, with nothing much but a square piano and an oil painting of a pale young woman with a harp. But when she finally tasted a bit, at the urging of old Ned, who ate zestfully with knife and fork, she found it nice, yes, quite nice. And so, finally, she suggested that, since it would soon be fall meat-making time and that what they seemed to have was just yellowing dried salt pork, suppose this—this woman came over to do the meat curing?

Ned Salzer turned red all down his bald streak behind, but without seeming to notice, Hortense refilled his coffee cup and said she would be very grateful for the opportunity.

Late that evening old Ned drove back to Bills Pocket and made his stiff, bowlegged way to Hortense watering her cabbage. He had come to say that Lillibelle didn't mean nothing today. She just didn't know.

Why, Cap Bills had given him his start in stock, let him have cows on shares, and lent him haying tools, way back thirty-five years ago. And now her asking his daughter to come over like a hired woman—

But Hortense insisted that she would be glad to come. It might be a start of something, especially if they liked the meat. Might start a little business for her.

So Tensy Bills, the smokin' gal of ten years ago, became the smokin' woman, busy for weeks in the early spring and some in the fall too, swinging around the ranches and the stock farms, cutting up new pork, unjointing a ham with a twist of her knife and her strong wrist, sawing the head in two like so much wood, putting down the clean, firm meat well-rubbed with salt and the brown mixture of her jug.

By the time Diane was nine, times were getting hard again, so desperately hard that even the few ranchers left were curing their meat themselves. But Hortense and Hippy kept up the fiction of security pretty well around Diane. Not that either believed in rearing house plants, but there was no denying the girl was timid. She had even been afraid of the little brown-eyed collie Ned Salzer sent over for her sixth birthday, so afraid they gave the dog back.

Because it was eight miles to school, Tensy got a set of books from the district and a course of study, and taught the girl herself. Perhaps it was better so, better than exposing the reticent child to the taunts her made-over clothes and her isolation would bring her.

At night, when the supper dishes were done and a few sticks of chokecherry wood or a handful of silvery sage were on the fire, Diane played over the day's lesson, played so well that Tensy Bills longed to send her away to study with her own teacher Kozal, who would bring out all the sensitiveness of the girl, her delicacy, and develop the power and strength the mother believed lay latent in the slim young body. A scholarship might be managed, but she could never hope to pay the fare and the living expenses of the girl.

These things were never spoken of before Diane, though she grew long, and skinny as a horseweed.

XII

When Diane was twelve, her mother made her a new gingham dress, pretty green and blue plaid, and took her up to Gaylor for the eighth-grade examinations. As they passed the bank, Joe Leems came out. Tensy Bills nodded and went on, but she knew that he stopped to look after them, after the straight young Diane as he had after the mother twenty-five years before. He was clean now, even in the deepest checks of his wrinkled neck, but it was still the same.

While she was trading out the last of her asparagus, Lesper Killey, Joe's bookkeeper, came whispering that Mr. Leems would see her in his bank office right away. But Tensy Bills didn't go, and so the next day the man came out to the Pocket to offer the woman a house once more. She could keep right on with her smokin' work, and the girl could go to high school. He had heard her play as he went by the place at night, sometimes. Maybe—why, maybe she could learn to play pretty good, even good enough for his moving-picture show.

Although Hortense Bills refused with friendliness enough, she leaned on her hoe until the Pocket was quiet and clean again, and all the dust had settled on the Gaylor road.

The next day a string of machinery and wagons, long as a threshing crew on the move, crept down the road into the pocket below Tensy's line. Here it broke up, and before noon a ditching machine was eating into the earth, cutting a deep trench along the fence that crossed the lower end of the little lake, piling up a high ridge along the far side. From the protection of her old shed Hortense watched, knowing that it was to draw her water away, dry out her little valley, her bit of lake and her irrigation ditches, destroy her alfalfa and her fine garden.

Then she saw Diane come in from her flower picking in the hills, running to see this new thing near her home, and so Hortense had to leave the shed, with Bone Joe there to see, and walk calmly to the house. In the doorway she stopped. Hippy had hitched his chair to the window and across his knees was the old Bills rifle.

"It ain't heavy enough to carry clear down there nohow," the man complained in disgust as Hortense took the gun from him. "But some day I'll get that buzzard from clost—"

Before the middle of August the lake was a cracking stretch of gray mud, with only a few green-scummed pools down the center. Below the fence the Leems ditch carried a steady little flow of seepage water to the winding creek bed, usually dry long before this.

Hortense considered digging a ditch across the entire lower end of the valley, deep enough to cut the seepage table and fill it with alkali mud, tamped and dried into hardpan. But that would take months, and she had to save every pound of tomatoes, every head of cabbage now, with prices down to nothing. So she carried water from the pump late into the nights, a bucket in each hand.

As the depression deepened, the best land in the region, land he had long waited for, fell into the hands of Joe Leems like wild plums, ripe and sweet. Busy with these things, he let his ditch fill with Russian thistles and mud until the water started to lay in the lower end of Tensy's lake again, and creep toward the old irrigation ditches, even with the rains slow and the winter black. In town it was said that Bone Joe was buying purple pajamas, keeping a red-headed girl up at the hotel, and walking big as when he used to lead the long, white-robed parade.

When Joe Leems took over the second county-seat bank, he began foreclosing again. Here and there an old-timer discovered that the galluses of his tattered overalls were still stout enough for a noose. But others were discovering that a common calamity becomes a common bond, and talked of organizing and rioting like in the papers, with delegations to march on the State Capitol. Lesper Killey came to tell Joe Leems that there might be rough stuff, knucks and shooting, with mobs breaking up his sheriff sales. But the foreclosure notices appeared, pages at a time, and knots of dark-faced men began to gather wherever Bone Joe was.

So Joe stayed in his hotel room and kept Lesper Killey running back and forth with a briefcase. But across the street from his window a row of men still waited, the February wind whipping their thin old overalls.

The first sale scheduled was Bills Pocket. Ned Salzer came down to see Hippy about it, the two old cowhands sitting in the window with the sandbox between them. There'd been talk of holding up Tensy's sale, Ned said, a little talk, but not enough. Too many was a-looking on it like a grudge fight between the old bone-picker and the Billses, and more had women folks who thought of Tensy as that high-flyin' smokin' gal, or that old smokin' woman.

"Yeh." Hippy shot a pale little splatter into the sandbox and wiped his mouth. "Little fellows a-fightin' amongst theirselves over matchsticks while the big fellows steals their pants—"

For the first time in her life Tensy Bills was unable to plan so much as a shelter in the wind for her two. The morning of her sale there was no gasoline, and so she walked the two miles of gray March prairie to the grave of Rutherford Bills and was glad that he hadn't lagged too long after his time. It was at the unmarked spot beside him, where Nickie lay, that Hortense stood so still, a lone bowed figure, with no moving thing anywhere in sight.

If she hadn't come out of the West and taken Nickie from his little publishing-house job into this hard environment, he would be alive,

writing words that would bring to others the beautiful things his
eyes saw, his heart knew. But it had seemed so right to them, their
coming together, right and beautiful as the wind and the sun they
found on the slopes of their little home.

Wearily the woman started back, through the winter-bleached
grass, the chill gray sky low about her. Then, far out on the road,
Diane came running, crying, jumping up and down about her mother,
whirling her in a witches' dance. Oh, no, it wasn't Hippy. It was a
boy, a fine big boy who had come riding, bringing news. There was
a farm-mortgage moratorium. Their place wouldn't be sold today.

Suddenly Hortense understood and dropping to the grass, dizzy,
looked up at her daughter. "Child, child," she cried, only now realiz-
ing that she hadn't spared the girl anything at all.

But the moratorium was true, and so that night they used the last
of the sugar to make a plate of fudge and stayed up until the lamp
went dry. Early the next morning, Hortense walked across her garden
ground, her plow shoes sinking into the warming earth, dark, frost-
mellowed, and rich. With her fingers she cleared aside a bit of the old
hay covering the rhubarb, and called aloud for Diane. Together
they dug deeper into the covering, baring the first hard knuckles
of the pieplant pushing through, young and pink, pink as a pretty
girl's dress. Then arm in arm they went to the house to put on the
coffee, to bring out all the seed catalogues Tensy had hidden from
Hippy and herself as they came. Now they would look them through,
every one, plan for another spring.

Joe Leems took the mortgage moratorium hard, and talked of
going into politics at last. The country was run by a lot of Reds,
taking a man's liberty away, cheating him out of his rightful property, out of things he'd worked years for. Yeh, that was right enough,
old-timers admitted. Bone Joe'd sure been working to bust the Billses
for twenty-five years.

A test case was started, but it might be years before it reached the
Supreme Court. Until then, so long as the interest and taxes were
paid up, Tensy's place was safe. So she dug in harder than ever,
planted more sweet corn, more beans, and with the first five dollars
she took Hippy to the doctor to give his joints some relief.

Farm prices went up a little, but the reluctant summer rains barely
splattered the fields, and the winter earth lay bare and gray. Although
the dust storms that filled the papers with alarming stories were
seldom more than a red haze on the evening sun, the water table
of the region was falling, the seepage springs of Bills pocket no more

than a wet spot on the outcroppings of sandstone by August. Gradually the grass moved in on the little lake until a bit of rushes in the middle was all that remained where ducks once swam over six feet of water.

When things were pretty thin, the thinnest they had ever been, because now the interest had to be paid on the dot, a woman came out and Hortense discovered that Hippy had applied for old-age pension.

At that, Hortense Bills left the house, and when she finally came back into the lamplight of the supper table, Hippy saw the first sign of tears on her face since the day, almost thirty years before, when he told her some of the things she needed to know. But the woman was calm now, listening sensibly to the practical side of the arrangement. It would be about fifteen dollars a month—the difference between enough to eat and not enough, particularly for Diane and for herself. "You got to feed a plow horse," Hippy pointed out. It would keep the interest and taxes paid, a roof against the sun.

XIII

Spring was back once more, with wind and seed catalogues and interest due. Before the heavy work was upon her, Hortense overhauled the old car, tightening the connecting rods until she couldn't turn the engine over and had to hitch up the team to start it. But today the air lay moist and still, early geese honked high overhead somewhere, and in the garden the parsnip rows were sprouting their first tips of green. Shouting a good-by to Hippy at the window, Hortense started the car off toward Gaylor and the bank. And as she drove, she hummed a little, for the motor ran sweet and in her pocket was every cent of Bone Joe's interest money.

At the hill line she waved back to Diane. The girl was fanning alfalfa seed with a screened salt-barrel hoop, tossing the sieve with slim grace, the blue of her calico skirt billowing, the pile of golden seed on the old canvas on the ground gleaming in the sun. Alfalfa prices were coming up a little. One more crop and she could send the girl away. It was time, for she was seventeen and getting valentines from Joe Leems too, just as she had at that age, when she slipped up behind his wagon, scared his horses, and upset his wagon. But Diane could never be the independent flip she had been, and besides, Joe's wheels were running pretty solid these days.

As Hortense neared Gaylor there seemed more cars on the road than usual, and in town there was a crowd, the streets parked solid, knots of men along the walks, standing thick about the bank. Hortense wondered about them, loafing in the middle of a spring week, and without the women folks, their dark faces silent, giving her no more than a nod today, even old acquaintances.

When she finally got parked, Ned Salzer separated himself from the fringe of the crowd and came over to the car. With his foot on the old running board, the sun on his bald head, he told her, keeping his eyes to the battered hat in his hand as he talked. It was the moratorium. Off, thrown out, pronounced unconstitutional by the State Supreme Court. Foreclosures were starting today where they left off five years ago. Several of the old-timers' places already gone.

So that was it. After all the years of skinning hard work, of planning and saving and fighting the man off, now it was all gone like snow before one blast of a chinook. Everything.

A long time the woman sat behind the steering wheel, gripping the bare old wood with her knotted hands, her eyes straight before her, the wind lines at her mouth deep as folds in old gray leather.

"They're a-needin' somebody educated for a few weeks, for the guide book, somebody what can wrangle a little history stuff—" Old Ned started to say. But he didn't finish, for the woman's face gave him no recognition now, drained of all life before his eyes. Touching her arm with an awkward paw, he stumbled away on his bowed old legs.

At last the woman roused to look about her. Lesper Killey was at her shoulder, jerking at the wash-faded denim of her jumper to get her attention.

"The boss'll be up there to see you after a bit," he said, nodding toward the old feed stable.

The woman only shook her head, not at him but at this moment that would be sweet as meadow honey, time-ripened and warm to the tongue of the old bone-picker.

But in the end Tensy Bills had to go, to climb the rickety old stairs to the room above the feed store, her heavy feet scarcely lifting her from step to step. Meekly, as one come new to begging, she rapped on the old door and waited, her gray hair blowing from under her hat on the platform in the rising wind, her body thin in its blue denim.

But there was no reply, and after a long time she noticed that men in the street were staring up at her, one of them saying something.

"—He's gone. I saw him drive outa town awhile ago."

So Tensy went back to the car, turned the stiff crank with dull persistence and took the road back to Bills Pocket, Leems Pocket in a day or so now. As she drove she thought once more over all the man's long wait, since she was a girl, a child, much younger than Diane—

Suddenly she pulled the gas feed down, gripping the wheel as the engine roared, hoping that the old boot in the front tire would hold. As she turned off the main road into Bills Pocket she caught the sun on a car drawn up at the shed, a new roadster, like Joe Leems'.

Even before she stopped she saw Diane, white as bone, in the corner of the ell. The girl was flattened hard to the wall, her open palms against the boards. On the ground before her lay a man in a blue-green suit, small as a boy, with one arm thrown out, crumpled and gray and old.

Jerking the car to a screeching stop, the woman ran to her daughter, held her close, and looked down upon the man. It was Bone Joe, with a dark little bullet hole in his temple, his open eyes skinning over with gray, like a dead bird's.

Inside the window Hippy sat in his chair, his slack jaw moving slowly, his fingers like claws on the old rifle across his knees.

XIX
Far Looker

An Indian tale of and for the blind, written for the Catholic blind work . . . (71).

WHEN THE SON OF TALL DEER was born, the Sioux warrior gave away many ponies. He gave ponies to all those of his village who were poor, for was not his son, No Eyes, of the Chosen Ones? Many children came every year to the tipis of the great Sioux people, but only a few were set off from the rest because they would never hear the barking of the village dogs, or learn to make words, or see the sun on the buffalo grass. These, it was well known, were the bearers of great gifts for the preservation of their people. And so Tall Deer made all the village glad with him.

Soon this boy of the Chosen Ones learned to know many things beyond common man. He could feel spring on his cheek when the tipis were yet in snow, could smell the smokeless enemy fire that none could see, could hear the far crunch of the ice under the feet of the elk when meat was low in the village. Often in the night he was allowed to roam, for darkness and day were as one to him.

Then one night the fall he was nine, when the ponies were fat and the village full of winter meat, he smelled the burning of the smokeless fire. He was away from his village, up the wind, and his own people had no reason to burn the fire of the sneaker of the night. Swiftly he thought. It must be an enemy war party, out for horses, meat, and scalps. He sniffed the air, slipped off his moccasins and circled out wide, like the bow of a great man. Then his feet felt pony tracks, many times his toes in number, and the broken earth still moist. He followed the trail, losing the fire smell, finding it again. Several times he put his ear to the earth for the sound of pony feet. At last he found them, many ponies feeding, two men on guard, making low words he did not know, and many sleeping men breathing nearby, many men and no women—a war party.

No Eyes knew what this meant—attack at the first small wind of dawn upon his unsuspecting village, robes waved to scatter the pony herd, whooping warriors riding up the canyon to cut off escape, riding down the tipis of his people, with the twanging of the bow string, the swinging of the war club. Swiftly the boy dropped his robe, slipped into his moccasins and began to run. He ran lightly, not swiftly, knowing he must last, avoiding bush and stone and tree, running along the crest of the ridge as the coyote lopes.

An hour later, before the time for the enemy's coming, there was robe-waving among the ponies of the enemy herd, and wild young Sioux riding the surprised sleepers down. By the time the sun was warm on the face, and the cooking fires burning fine before the tipis, the captured ponies were all admired and divided. Then Tall Deer walked slowly through the village in his noblest blanket of blue cloth with a white banding of beads. He was making a song, calling for his friends to feast with him, for now his son who had been No Eyes would be Far Looker, one whose far seeing had indeed saved his village and his people.

XX

Peachstone Basket

During the last seven years, art, particularly mural painting, has gone to the people. It has been placed on walls available to the people, portrays them in all their virtues and absurdities. So literature . . . is to come or has come to the people with renewed insistence upon human values, an anger with smugness, stupidity, intolerance, cruelty, injustice, and the oppression of the common man. It is to be in his language, available to him as the murals are available (19).

I consider greed the most degrading, devastating force in the world today. I must cry out against it. I could not encompass the whole world, so I made my protest articulate by writing of a single segment of the world with which I was familiar and peopled it with fictitious characters (59).

THE TOWN OF GILLROOD lay warm and friendly as a field of vine-ripening muskmelons in the September sun. There was a pleasant buzzing in the air too, and the banners and bunting along the streets hung limp and still. In the business section the walks were filled far beyond any Saturday or holiday trade, and this only Wednesday morning. Even the farmers from down on the bottoms were in, though their fall work was barely started, the wheat plowing still tawny stubble, the bleaching cornfields heavy with drooping ears.
But this was Gillrood's big day, the biggest in all her time, as the posters announced, for the town wasn't just having an anniversary, she was honoring the memory of her founder, Justin Gillrood, paying due tribute to one of the state's great men. So today all the flag-hung main street was one moving, neighborly crowd, with even important people like Russell Cole, the banker, standing out in the sun where anybody could push right up and shake hands, common as a campaigning politician. Nobody was an outsider today, not even old

Hedi, the goatwoman, or her Lunky of a grandson, walking free outside of the alleys for the first time in thirty years, since the day Judge
Gillrood told her that her very presence in the streets of man was an
offense.

At first nobody even considered asking the goatwoman to take part
in the celebration, but it was to be an old settlers' day and Hedi
Fessner was undeniably the earliest settler within a hundred miles
around. So a week ago a delegation of the younger businessmen drove
over to the shack against the bluffs. They found the old woman in
the whitewashed milk shed and stood awkwardly around while she
stripped at a nanny goat. When the heavy-shouldered grandson came
clumping up to fill the doorway, the men moved a little closer together
but kept on with their persuasive talk of the plans for Gillrood Day.
The town would be all decorated up fine and pretty, everybody in
costume, with a mammoth historical parade and barbecue at noon,
speeches and a big barn dance at night. Old Hedi kept stripping away
at the rubbery bag of the goat without lifting her head, even when
one of the newer men forgot and told about the statue of Judge Gillrood to be unveiled. Only when somebody finally mentioned the
window displays of heirlooms and keepsakes, with Len Hutt offering
her a little space if she had anything to show, the old woman pushed
the goat aside.

"We will come," she said.

So today Hedi Fessner and her Lunky openly walked the unaccustomed street, with no faces turning from them and even people
like old Mrs. Cole speaking friendly. "Fine day, Hedi, a fine day for
snake-killing—" calling out loud and free, as she would have fifty years
back, when she was one of the bone-picking Sugers instead of the
widow of old Russell Cole and just up from Florida for the celebration, with a maid and a chauffeur. And when the goatwoman and her
grandson slipped away without answering, Old Stew Brewster, out of
jail for the day, took up the greeting as though it were for him.

"Yeh, you're right, Maggie Suger—" he shouted for all the street to
hear, "—a hell of a fine, warm day it is, but a weather-breeder—time to
be sewing the young uns up for the winter."

A rustle of laughing swept over the crowd like a night wind starting
up in a green cornpatch. By golly, that was a real old-time way to
talk. And very fitting for the ninetieth birthday of Judge Gillrood, the
box-jawed man who stared down from the streamers along the street,
asking everybody to HONOR GILLROOD WITH GILLROOD.

Yes, the town sure had strained a tug for this day, everybody admitted, working on it for months, with some big names on the program and the main speaker, Chief Justice Weedon of the state supreme court, safely in a back room at the hotel with the dedication address sticking out of his hip pocket and somebody there every minute to keep him in shape. They had Senator Bell too, got him to swing his campaign around that way and borrowed his sound car to keep people posted on the progression of events. Then there were the homecomers like old Maggie Cole and, of course, Connilynne Gillrood, the guest of honor, back from California just to witness this tribute to the memory of her husband. And the town was shining for them, as the old high school song promised. The street of the reliefer shacks was closed off and the better homes were all decorated with flags and old-fashioned awnings, iron grilling or cardboard gingerbread. The Castle, the Gillrood residence, was reticent as usual, with only a couple of balloon ascension pennants from the Philadelphia world's fair strung across the high-pillared stone front. Other old places had campaign posters of Garfield and Bryan, while down at the blacksmith shop the picture of Coin Harvey hung in the weatherbeaten horseshoe that was once the sign of the wits and the loafers of the town. Through the business section benches and hitch racks were set up along the walks, and a rusty saloon flytrap stood before the drugstore baited with stale beer as in the old days. Not a window was without its blinds or boardings, as though for an Indian uprising but really only for the grand opening later in the day, when Connilynne Gillrood pressed a button.

First there would be the parade. Old buggies, surreys, and even a velocipede were dragged from their dust and greased up to run from the depot to the courthouse. Carriage harness was spliced out to fit the broad backs of plow horses, and a couple of milk cows were yoked in contrary walk to a wagon fitted up with a cover of moldy binder canvas. Rough old coots like Stew Brewster and Len Hutt would ride in these, with the young people of the town impersonating the better element, the town's handsomest couple sitting elegantly in the side-lighted Gillrood carriage, the boy in the rusty broadcloth of the judge, the girl wearing a slim-waisted dress from the trousseau of Connilynne Carleton of Philadelphia and Saratoga Springs.

For weeks the men of the town had let their hair grow and coaxed their razor-stiffened whiskers along with vaseline, skunk grease, or the more ribald fertilizers suggested around the pool halls. Most of them were in miner's outfits, or cowboy boots and hats of long ago, although a few had to be dragged before the kangaroo court set up in a tent behind the county jail, with small boys hanging around thick for the man-laughing that came from inside.

But the women had needed no such horseplay to get them into bustles and plumes, or calico wrappers and slat sunbonnets. Even Hedi Fessner had dug up something older than generally, the gray cashmere dress she wore when she came to town sixty-three years ago. It still needed no letting out, for although she couldn't have been over sixteen then, she had come "in trouble" as it was called—carrying Big Gillie Fessner, who became the town's one executed murderer.

But this was old settlers' day and the goatwoman was the earliest. Connilynne Gillrood had come through a month or two before but she never stayed long, even as a bride, and today she was only back for the dedication of the statue that waited like some frost-sensitive, winter-wrapped tree in the park. Under the gray cloth stood a towering granite figure of Justin Gillrood, ready for the evening, for the music, the eulogizing, and finally the unveiling in a fountain of lights rigged up by the young mayor who had been waiting to use the ideas he got at the world's fair.

Towards eleven the senator's red sound car swung into the street, the impatient crowd dividing before the blaring voice that called the stragglers to their places at the depot. Then finally the parade came— no sputtering motorcycle escort, no band leading, just a few long cars filled with visiting celebrities: white-haired Connilynne, her back as straight, her thin-fleshed nose as fine and high as when she galloped over the hills over sixty years ago. Beside her was Chief Justice Weedon, red-faced but sitting straight enough. Then came the senator and the other campaigners, a railroad president, the local oil promoter, and finally Maggie Cole, her son Russell and other big bugs of the town. Amid gawks, greetings, and a little scattered cheering they passed on, making room for the real parade, which the watchers in the upper windows could already see, and were announcing with whoops and laughter.

Down the middle of the hard street a handful of pony-mounted Indians clattered slowly along. In the lead rode two gaunt old buffalo-hunting chiefs, their eagle headdresses blowing in the rising wind, their feather-flagged lances erect. They were followed by painted, bare-breasted warriors, jaw ropes on the horses, their bow arms free. Behind them rode half a dozen women, plump in their beaded buckskin, their ponies dragging travois loaded with bundles, children, and one old, old woman, her wrinkles yellow with powder, her eyes milky blind.

Close upon the Indians marched the younger men of town dressed as the fur brigade, new beards dark, their hair curling under the skin caps, guns laid across their forearms as directed by old Mitch Perno, who claimed he had seen both Bridger and California Joe. As in history, the missionaries came next, with blue-coated soldiers marching hard upon their heels. They were followed by the gold-seekers and cowboys and then the early settlers, headed by the Gill-rood float, with impersonations of the judge in youth, in manhood, and in age.

For weeks the paper had been running stories about the town's great man, of his honor and his courage, his stern allegiance to duty and his loyalty to his community. Each time the oldsters got together down at the blacksmith shop or the jail and had a good roar about it. Stew Brewster claimed that the Judge was a heller back when he first came West along the railroad survey. Anyway, he seemed to have been fish-pole slim, with sideburns curly and brown as October plum brush. He cut the liveliest figure in the square dances that summer, all there was to do after the grasshoppers hit, and his fingers were fast as flying hail on a guitar. But on the float today he was already the determined young judge, with a miner's pick in one hand, a lawbook in the other, and his eyes lifted over the heads of his fellows. It was a fine sight, and people clapped, or stood still, a wrist or two brushing up across old eyes in memory of days that could only be mimicked by the tall boy on the parade float.

Yes, as the paper said, Justin Gillrood's rise was typically American. He had read a little law before he came West, hoping to find enough trouble in the new country to keep him eating more regularly than that winter of seventy-three in New York City. Even after the grass-hoppers drove out his neighbors he stayed on, finally striking out afoot for the new mining camp of Deadwood, deep in the Indian country. When he came back to his homestead four years later his pockets were full of agates, and money and gold mine stock, accumu-lated by defending holdups and murderers, it was said. Anyway, the young lawyer had turned out smart as the lash of a bullwhip.

Turned out he was looking ahead, too. Confident that the rains were back to stay and the grasshoppers done, young Justin bought up much of his deserted community and got Gillrood post office estab-lished in the little shack with his name over the door. The next week news got around that the railroad was headed through along the survey. That summer the trails were dark with the covered wagons of homeseekers looking for a new start. Justin sold them land and

230 HOSTILES AND FRIENDLIES

lots, gave them advice and got himself elected attorney of the new county. When he started a house, four, five rooms and a verandah, and began to order furniture, the neighbors looked for him to get married, especially with a letter coming every mail day from up in the Black Hills somewhere, and him riding off that way pretty often. He had managed some Eastern connections too, started a branch loan office, and went away to railroad meetings. When the tracks were finally laid through, President Carleton and his daughter Connilynne stopped by on an inspection tour. Young Justin took the whole party antelope hunting and was asked to dinner at the private car. That evening the cowboys watched the slicked-up attorney pick his way through the crowd towards the tracks, but none of them dared put a hole into his plug hat or even to spurt up a little dust around his feet.

After that there were letters from the East too, and once a package marked PERISHABLE containing a pair of wax-coated peaches big as Rocky Ford melons wrapped in tissue paper. With his house almost finished and the fall roads snow-blocked, Justin put in his extra time around the office carving a basket from one of the peach pits. At first he laughed too about the society girl and her airs, but when he came back from the Black Hills around Christmas and found several telegrams waiting he took the train east. By spring he had married into the railroad money; the little house behind the office was rented and a new one, the Castle, was put up of native limestone, with long brown columns across the front.

After a while somebody brought a story back from the East. It seemed that the Carleton girl had taken to running around with a divorced man and that the father, up from track-layer himself, grabbed at the young lawyer for his daughter like a snake-bit old maid reaching for the whisky jug.

Seems he'd had some trouble getting the girl's Saratoga Springs mother to agree. But it turned out they were drawing to a good hand as the Gillroodians had predicted, for while the Judge remained pretty close in both residence and loyalty to his little town, he managed to reach the state supreme court bench—the supreme court and half a dozen directorships before his hair was white as the powdered head of the boy who impersonated him in honored age today.

So the main float of the parade moved on, rocking a little in the rising wind, followed by the proper applause, controlled and moderate, as was due the memory of a great judicial figure. It gave way to a ripple of higher cheering when the women saw the Gillrood carriage, with the pretty dark-haired girl in Connilynne's reception dress of gray brocade. Looking back now it seemed inevitable that Justin Gillrood should bring his town such a fine lady. To be sure, she was away most of the time, health-seeking, the Judge called it, at the Springs or Newport, or maybe Nice or Florence. But she always came back in the spring, between the wind of April and the heat of June, to gallop her sorrel mare over the hills, her hair netted close under a plumed hat, her riding habit a flying cloud of black against the windy sky. But soon her cheeks seemed to pale, her step grow listless, and then she would be gone once more. There was some talk around the livery barn about a woman's place being with her husband, but the wits at the blacksmith shop agreed it would be better to look ahead to Connilynne for a few weeks a year than across the table at the liveryman's slob of a wife every day. Besides, it kept even the better women of the town switching their skirts a bit to have the Judge alone among them. It was worth the trouble, too, for with the prematurely graying lock at his temple and the growing dignity of his office, Justin Gillrood was handsomer every year. But if any woman ever got more than a bow and a compliment for her venison dinners or her less open attempts at favor, not even the livery stable crowd heard of it.

The first year or two Connilynne brought guests out for the fall hunting, a cousin and a couple of his friends that set the town to talking. They were dashing young men with bold eyes, drake-tail curls at their foreheads, and a taste for champagne dinners. That kind of visiting didn't last long. But in the springtime the Gillroods still made the same elegant, high-headed couple behind the bays that the Judge drove with close leather and dangling whip, the tassel dropping lightly to a satin back now and then, just to let the horses know the cutting edge was waiting. It was so he handled the lawbreakers of his district, and brought the record of petty crime in Gillrood County 'way down, although its murder rate stayed high. Killers, men or horses, couldn't be reformed, the Judge maintained, and must be destroyed, swiftly, ruthlessly. He practiced that too. The time his finest colt got scared and kicked the stable boy in the face he shot the animal right there in the stall even before the doctor was sure the boy was dead. Not that the Judge had liked to do it. The last time he told the story, just before he died, his eyes still leaked tears, but without any softening.

It was this sternness against the promptings of his own heart, the paper said, that had sustained young Justin Gillrood in his long fight against rustlers, horse-thieves, and murderers. It carried him through

the office of county judge to the district court and got him called
Justice Gillrood long before he reached the state bench. He was as
firm against tears and beggings as against threats of vengeance at the
polls or by a quicker slug of lead in the back. He sent Russell Cole,
only son of his law partner, to jail for breaking windows Hallowe'en
as quick as he had sent the cattle rustlers to the penitentiary and Hedi
Fessner, too, for harboring them. As he had set himself against the
tears of Maggie Cole so he held out against those who came to remind
him that Hedi was a poor, strayed creature, little more than a child
herself, with a fatherless boy at her skirts. Probably she really didn't
know what those rustlers were and was glad to make an extra penny
doing a little washing for them, cooking an extra meal. But the Judge
was set. So her four-year-old boy was sent to the detention home, and
because nobody wanted a jail brat, he was still there when Hedi got
out. Against the friendly advice of the warden and the stern protest
of Judge Gillrood, she brought the seven-year-old boy back to the
shack against the bluff.

But Big Gillie, as he was already called, soon got himself sent away
to the reformatory for trapping muskrats on one of the Cole places. By
his eighteenth birthday he was out again, grown so strong he could lift
the hind end of a mud-stuck grain wagon.

"No keeping his kind out of the fouled nest—" everybody said, when
it got around that he was back in the shack with Hedi.

After that Big Gillie was picked up every few weeks, every time a
storekeeper missed a stick of candy or somebody lost a dominick hen,
although he was always turned loose in the end. At first his mouth was
silent, only his gray eyes darkening. But gradually he got surly, told
the sheriff that they'd better leave him be. People noticed the change
and predicted that he'd get himself killed one of these days, resisting
arrest. About that time he went to work up in the ranch district, and
only got back to Gillrood once a month or so. But he ended just as
everybody had predicted: he killed an officer who tried to bring him
in for questioning.

This time the Judge got his name into all the papers, even made an
inch in the New York *Times* with his instructions to the jury. It was
later, to the mother's plea for clemency for her son, that he told old
Hedi her very presence in the streets of man was an offense.

So Big Gillie was hanged and the next day the town found out more
against him. The chambermaid at the Commercial Hotel was dead of
iodine and her fatherless boy had disappeared. By the time it got
around that he was out in the Fessner shack it was clear that Big Gillie

was guilty of other things besides murder, for old Hedi met the officers with her upraised hoe, claiming the boy by right of blood. So
they let her keep him. Save the county tax money, and besides the boy
would come to no good anyway, not the son of a murderer and a loose
woman. A few people insisted that such an uncomplaining little
worker as the chambermaid couldn't be bad. The big brute must
have taken advantage of her. It turned out all right though, just very
foolish, with Gillie only making twenty dollars a month. The two
had been married all along, but Judge Gillrood, who owned the hotel,
was a gallant man and kept his jobs for single girls, not those with
husbands to support them; so they had kept it a secret.

That was thirty years ago. Since then Hedi's grandson had grown
into a manhood as powerful as his father's, but without Gillie's
straight, defiant bearing. Instead, Lunky shambled guiltily along, his
pale, mild eyes always down before his fellows, the crown hair curling protectively about his ears. Today in the parade he was hunched
low beside Hedi in the old slat cart that was so familiar to the road
and the alleys all the years she delivered her goat milk to the hospital.
There were no cheers as the old roan mare plodded slowly along between the two walls of people—mostly just whisperings and silence,
with here and there a boy's high jeering, "Look at Lunky! Old
Monkey-Lunky!" to be shushed by those around him. Hedi Fessner's
head was not down. She sat up straight before the eyes of all Gillrood
County, her lined and leathery old face flushed beyond its usual ruddy
windburn, the dove-gray of her dress not much yellowed in the years
since she came to town. She had been pretty then, her cheeks paper-
white, her blue eyes disturbed as the April sky, but there had been
no place in a parade for her that year, and no banners along the street
carrying the picture of the great man who was to take away the son
she was bearing.

After the old settler section of the parade came the historical floats
representing the early business houses of the town, the White Ribbon
Temperance Club, and the football team as first organized. Last there
was the finest float of all, representing the World of Tomorrow. It
was built like a chromium rocket with a mounted map of the United
States standing across the back, the center of the country covered by
a plaque labeled The Constitution and six young men in costume
uniforms of the army, the navy and the marines defending it with
machine guns on every side.

"By God, wouldn't old Jefferson snort if he could see that layout!
Every one o' them pseudo-patriotic outfits around here's represented

except maybe the Klan, and I guess Billy Baylor's one—" a loafer from
the blacksmith shop said.

But most people barely noticed the young men. They were looking
at the group of pretty girls on the front of the float: Miss Aviation,
Miss Streamliner, Miss Air Conditioning, Miss Oil Wells, Miss Hybrid
Corn and Miss Certified Seed Potato, all looking pretty chilly in their
bathing suits but smiling bravely upon all the town as the band behind them played and the crowd whistled and cheered.

With a rising gust of wind that flapped the banners and swirled
the blue capes of the band, the parade was done, and the crowd
turned to the windows. The historical displays were ready, the boarding all gone, the draperies of Cole's department store sweeping back
by the pressure of Connilynne Gillrood's finger on an electric button.
Everyone pushed towards Cole's with its fine, rounded corner of
plate glass filled by the Gillrood display. In the center were two figures in the wedding clothes of Justin and Connilynne against a background of family photographs. Beside each were the things that belonged there: the lawbooks, the certificates of election, the mining
outfit, old broadcloths greening and rusty, and the inky black of later
judicial garments for the Judge. On the wide, hand-carved desk from
his supreme court office was a pile of open clipping books and the
dusty old American eagle from his first law office, one eye gone.

On Connilynne's side were pieces from her trousseau: the plum-
colored going away suit; the opera cloak and gown of deep ruby red;
the short-trained infair dress of yellow satin that she wore her first
evening in Gillrood, with her hair shiny as a blackbird's wing. There
were trailing tea gowns in sea-green and canary with foamings of
ecru lace; summer dresses with hats and parasols to match; mink-
trimmed winter costumes; neckpieces and muffs of beaver and mink
and seal and a cape of sable—all things that the town had never seen.
And on the little square piano brought down from The Castle were
things to please the romantic: vases, scent bottles, fans of ivory and
plume and lace, yellowed invitations to the Carleton-Gillrood wedding, and dance programs with the Judge's strong, legible initials op-
posite all the polkas.

It was magnificent, as the papers had promised, this display of the
town's great couple, and the crowd pushed and shoved until the
marshal had to set himself and several boy scouts with their striped
poles along the windows to keep the people from pushing the glass
in. "There are other exhibits, many fine exhibits—" he kept shouting
through a cupped hand.

It was true that every window along the street was full, even at the pool halls and Len Hutt's old livery stable. Before everybody had made the rounds it would be time to drift off towards the barbecue pits, where the big dinner, the band, and the speakers would be waiting.

At the barbecue grounds the special guests and the old-timers were seated at one long table, from Connilynne Gillrood in her silver foxes, between the governor and Justice Weedon, down to Old Hedi and her grandson. Lunky never lifted his head, the back of his thick neck reddened by the jibes of the roving boys, the sly pebbles that hit his back. But the old woman sat dark and silent as she always had before these people, even when they took her son away.

The dinner went very well. The barbecued meat was good and the hot coffee welcome, now that bits of flying cloud grayed the sky and the paper napkins fluttered in the vest fronts or slid away entirely in the wind.

By the time everybody had been fed, the singing done, the guests of honor welcomed, and the crowd invited to the park for the six o'clock dedication, the clouds had thickened unmistakably. Perhaps old Stew's prediction to Maggie Cole was coming true; the still, warm morning had been a weather-breeder. At least the air was dampening, the wind so chilly that the main table emptied itself fast, some to rest a little for the evening unveiling, Hedi and her Lunky to get at their chores so they could be back early. Those who stayed for the band concert dug out wraps or hurried boys away for them. Afterward the senator began his speech from the sound car but it was loud and would probably be only campaign stuff anyway; so those who were used to washing and churning or even driving a tractor with the radio going visited around the picnic ground, talking about the children and fall plowing and what a big day this was. Too bad the Judge couldn't be here, particularly tonight, to see himself in that statue out there in the park. Some talked with concern about the boys having to register for the draft before three weeks and some of these wandered over to hear the senator although he was a jackass. But he was against the third term and the warmongers in Washington, and so they'd vote him in again.

Here and there a few spoke of the London bombings and the rumor that Japan was joining the Axis, and then perhaps slipped away to their cars to listen to the news that was never good any more, but not even these talked overmuch about the war, afraid of being thought warmongers too, and uncouth. That's what Maggie Cole called those who mentioned the bombings at the dinner last night. Uncouth.

"Maggie Cole?—and her one of the bone-picking Sugers?" Len Hutt said when he heard about it.

By now the sky was darkening fast and here and there a farmer lifted his face into the wind. Yes, there was a big rain coming for the fall plowing—make next year's crop. So they followed their women good-naturedly towards the stores, open for business now. Many stopped at the Gillrood windows once more. With the marshal gone and fewer pushing from behind there was really time to look.

It was a woman who noticed the little peachstone basket on the floor of the corner window, close up to the glass—a tiny brown basket just large enough to hold the little finger ring it carried. The set fitting snugly under the basket handle was a heart-shaped rose agate banded in dusky gray, like strips of morning cloud against a sunrise sky. On the side of the basket were a J and a C, entwined, and against the pillow lay a little card:

> Peachstone basket carved by
> Justin Gillrood
> for his future wife from fruit
> picked and waxed by her. Gold
> and the sunrise agate in ring
> were brought from Black Hills
> by the Judge.

"Isn't that just darling!" the women exclaimed, saying it to each other over and over, perhaps thinking of their own plodding husbands. Finally old Stew Brewster came pushing his head between the impeding shoulders. He had met a crony with a jug and now a patriotic fervor for his town's greatness was beginning to burn in his breast. With the marshal gone, he would size up the Gillrood display, maybe make a little speech. Then, before his slow-focusing eyes, he saw the satin pillow with its peachstone basket.

"By the dickety damn!" he spluttered out in surprise, yanking at anybody in reach. "See that there basket fixing? It's just like old Hedi's down to the livery barn, and them rings is alike as two swallows outa the same jug!"

At first nobody listened to the old jail bum, not even the marshal strolling past. But Stew kept nudging, blowing his breath around, insisting that the baskets were the same, the Widow Gillrood's and old Hedi Fessner's. The crowd exchanged looks among themselves, pitying grins, some of the more delicate turning offended noses away. Then a couple of boys took up the pointing. The Stew was right. The baskets were the very same. Of course old Hedi's had an H with the J instead of the C, but the stones in the rings were both the pinky color, and the stripes were the same too. Old Judge Gillrood's wife and the goatwoman had rings cut off the same chunk of rock in the same peachstone baskets!

As the story spread there was an increasing push towards the window, a hurrying away to the old livery stable and back, with bewildered nods of agreement. The baskets were alike, all right, rings, sets and all, and somebody better be telling them, meaning the big people of the day. By now there was a rising giggle among the younger people, a little shamedly at first, but picking up and spreading fast. The older people still stood back, clinging to the silence between them, or making a few low words and whisperings, perhaps a few headshakings that were heavy and serious. Some of them began to remember things they couldn't recall having heard or seen, or even known. It was true that the young Justin had carved at a peachstone basket all the fall before he was married, all the time that he was building the little house everybody thought was for a girl up in the Black Hills somewhere. Then the chance at the railroad money had come along and so the house went to renters.

While some still argued that the baskets were an accident, a mere coincidence, fewer and fewer stood against the crowd, until finally all the street under the flapping Gillrood banners was quiet, as quiet and still as when the storm wind dies before the lightning. And suddenly from among them a man climbed up to one of the Gillrood posters and jerked a corner free. Then deliberately he tore it across the face.

"Son-killer!" he cried, and dropped the piece down upon the watching crowd. Someone clutched at it, tore it to bits and flung them into the air. Now others began ripping at the posters, pulling down the strings of banners stretched across the street and only the marshal and his deputies saved the Gillrood windows themselves from being smashed in.

It was almost dusk when the rain started, lightly at first, then quickened until the deserted streets ran curbful and were swept clean of all the litter except the heavier of the storm-torn branches. Dedication time came and passed and in the park the wind still whipped at the gray cloth about the tall granite figure of Judge Gillrood. Before it, huddled under an old tarpaulin, Hedi and her grandson waited, silent and alone, the rain beating quieter around them as the darkness came.

A NOTE ON EDITED PIECES

IN THE RECOLLECTIONS, minor cuts were made in "The Kinkaider Comes and Goes," "Musky," "The Son," and "The Neighbor" to avoid repetition of detail and incident. In "The Kinkaider Comes and Goes," the name Jules, Junior, which appeared in the piece on its first publication, was changed back to Young Jules, as it was in the original manuscript. "Marlizzie" was originally titled "The New Frontier Woman." "The Son" is the author's original title for this piece, which appeared as "What the Sioux Taught Me."

In the Indian Studies, three paragraphs of "Some Oddities of the American Indian" were extracted and used in the commentary which introduces it. One paragraph was deleted. "The Lost Sitting Bull" is the author's original title for the study which appeared as "There Were Two Sitting Bulls." The opening section was slightly expanded by the author from the original unabridged manuscript. Topical matter pertaining to a 1954 expedition to search for the bones of Crazy Horse was deleted from "The Burial of Crazy Horse," which was originally titled "The Search for the Bones of Crazy Horse."

In the Short Fiction, there were no changes in the previously published stories. The author made some slight alterations in the text of "The Smart Man," which was unpublished at the time of its selection for inclusion in HOSTILES AND FRIENDLIES.

All the selections were copyedited for consistency in spelling and punctuation.

"The Son" and "The Lost Sitting Bull" were previously published only in abridged form. "The Kinkaider Comes and Goes" originally appeared as a two-part piece.

CHRONOLOGICAL BIBLIOGRAPHY OF THE WRITINGS OF MARI SANDOZ

The number at the left is that used in the text to identify material quoted or referred to. The *date of writing* is given after the title and the *date of first publication* after the name of the outlet in which the work appeared.

1. Fearbitten. 1925. Short story. Honorable mention, Harper's Intercollegiate Short Story Contest, 1926.
   Unpublished.
2. The Vine. 1925. Short story. Signed "Marie Macumber."
   Prairie Schooner, I, 1 (January 1927).
3. Old Potato Face. 1926. Short story. Signed "Marie Macumber."
   Prairie Schooner, II, 1 (January 1928).
4. Dumb Cattle. 1926. Short story. Signed "Marie Macumber."
   Prairie Schooner, III, 1 (January 1929).
5. The Smart Man. 1928. Short story.
   Prairie Schooner, XXXIII, 1 (Spring 1959).
6. The Kinkaider Comes and Goes. 1929. Nonfiction.
   North American Review, CCXXIX, 4 and 5 (April and May 1930).
7. Sandhill Sundays. 1930. Nonfiction.
   Folk-Say: A Regional Miscellany, ed. B. A. Botkin. Norman: University of Oklahoma Press, 1931.
8. What Should Be Considered When Choosing a Profession? 1932. Essay. Signed "Marie Macumber." Second prize, contest sponsored by Chancellor of University of Nebraska.
   Daily Nebraskan, April 3, 1932.
9. Pieces to a Quilt. 1932. Short story.
   North American Review, CCXXXV, 5 (May 1933).
10. Musky, the narrative of a muskrat. 1932. Nonfiction.
    Nature, XXII, 5 (November 1933).
11. *Old Jules*. 1932–1933. Biography. Atlantic Nonfiction Prize, 1935.
    Boston: Little, Brown & Co., 1935.
12. White Meteor. 1933. Short story.
    Ladies' Home Journal, LIV, 1 (January 1937).
13. Pioneer Women. 1934. Nonfiction. Paper written for Fremont Women's Club.
    Unpublished.
14. The Birdman. 1934–1935. Indian tale.
    Omaha *Sunday World-Herald Magazine*, February 10, 1935.

15. River Polak. 1935. Short story.
    Atlantic Monthly, CLX, 3 (September 1937).
16. I Wrote a Book. 1935. Nonfiction.
    Nebraska Alumnus, XXXI, 9 (November 1935).
17. The New Frontier Woman. 1935–1936. Nonfiction.
    Country Gentleman, CVI, 9 (September 1936).
18. Mist and the Tall White Tower. 1936. Short story.
    Story, IX, 50 (September 1936).
19. Stay Home, Young Writer. 1937. Nonfiction. Paper for Nebraska
    Writers Guild, May 1937.
    The Quill, XXV, 6 (June 1937).
20. *Slogum House*. 1933–1937. Novel.
    Boston: Little, Brown & Co., 1937.
21. The Devil's Lane. 1937–1938. Short story.
    Ladies' Home Journal, LV, 4 (April 1938).
22. The Girl in the Humbert. 1938–1939. Short story.
    Saturday Evening Post, CCXI, 36 (March 4, 1939).
23. Bone Joe and the Smokin' Woman. 1938–1939. Novelette.
    Scribner's Magazine, CV, 3 (March 1939).
24. Far Looker. 1939. Indian tale.
    The Sight-Giver, VIII, 2 (February 1939).
25. *Capital City*. 1939. Novel.
    Boston: Little, Brown & Co., 1939.
26. Peachstone Basket. 1939. Short story.
    Prairie Schooner, XVII, 3 (Fall 1943).
27. *Crazy Horse: The Strange Man of the Oglalas*. 1942. Biography.
    New York: Alfred A. Knopf, Inc., 1942.
28. Anybody Can Write. 1943. Nonfiction.
    The Writer, LVII, 4 (April 1944).
29. Sit Your Saddle Solid. 1944. Short story.
    Saturday Evening Post, CCXVII, 33 (February 10, 1945).
30. The Spike-Eared Dog. 1945. Short story.
    Saturday Evening Post, CCXVIII, 6 (August 11, 1945).
31. Martha of the Yellow Braids. 1945. Nonfiction.
    Prairie Schooner, XXI, 2 (Summer 1947).
32. The Neighbor. 1945. Nonfiction.
    Prairie Schooner, XXX, 4 (Winter 1956).
33. *The Tom-Walker*. 1947. Novel.
    New York: The Dial Press, Inc., 1947.
34. Yuletide Saga of a Lone Tree. 1947. Allegory.
    Philadelphia *Inquirer* Book Review Supplement, December 7, 1947.
35. The Lost Sitting Bull. 1949. Nonfiction. Published as: There Were
    Two Sitting Bulls.
    Blue Book, XC, 1 (November 1949).
36. The Lost School Bus. 1950–1951. Novelette.
    Saturday Evening Post, CCXXIII, 47 (May 19, 1951).
37. *Winter Thunder*. Unabridged version of above.
    Philadelphia: Westminster Press, 1954.

38. The Son. 1951. Nonfiction. Published as: What the Sioux Taught Me. *Reader's Digest*, LX, 5 (May 1952), reprinted from *Empire*, February 24, 1952.
39. *Cheyenne Autumn*. 1952. Biography. New York: McGraw-Hill, 1953.
40. *Miss Morissa: Doctor of the Gold Trail*. 1952–1953. Novel. New York: McGraw-Hill, 1955.
41. The Indian Looks at His Future. 1954. Nonfiction. *Family Weekly*, April 11, 1954.
42. *The Buffalo Hunters: The Story of the Hide Men*. 1954. Nonfiction. New York: Hastings House, 1954.
43. The Search for the Bones of Crazy Horse. 1954. Retitled in this collection The Burial of Crazy Horse. *The Westerners' Brand Book*, New York Posse, I, 4 (Autumn 1954).
44. Look of the West—1854. 1954. Nonfiction. *Nebraska History*, XXXV, 4 (December 1954).
45. Some Oddities of the American Indian. 1954. Nonfiction. *The Westerners' Brand Book*, Denver Posse, 1955.
46. Acceptance Speech, Distinguished Achievement Award. 1955. *The Westerners' Brand Book*, Chicago Corral, XII, 1 (January 1956).
47. Nebraska. 1956. Nonfiction. *Holiday*, XIX, 5 (May 1956).
48. December 2006 A.D. 1956. Nonfiction. Enclosed in the cornerstone of KETV, Omaha, Nebraska, to be opened in fifty years. Unpublished.
49. *The Horsecatcher*. 1956. Novel. Philadelphia: Westminster Press, 1957.
50. *The Cattlemen: From the Rio Grande across the Far Marias*. 1957–1958. Nonfiction. New York: Hastings House, 1958.
51. Tyrant of the Plains. Adaptation of a section of the above. *Saturday Evening Post*, CCXXX, 49 (June 7, 1958).

OTHER SOURCES

55. Interview by Saare Erickson, Lincoln, Nebraska, *Sunday Journal and Star*, June 23, 1935.
56. "Mari Sandoz Discusses Writing" by Donald MacCampbell, *The Writer*, XLVIII, 11 (November 1935).
57. Letter to Mamie J. Meredith, n.d., 1936.
58. "Nebraskan" in Keeping Posted, *Saturday Evening Post*, CCXI, 36 (March 4, 1939).
59. Interview by Eva Mahoney, Omaha *World-Herald*, November 26, 1939.
60. Letter to Mamie J. Meredith, n.d., Summer 1943.
61. Reply to a questionaire from the Dial Press, 1947.
62. Note to the editor of the *Reader's Digest* accompanying "The Son," December 19, 1951.

63. Statement in "Guerra Ideologica y Militar, Cutaro Novelistas Contemporaneos de Norteamerica" (Mari Sandoz, pp. 241–245) por Tomás Bledsoe, *Cuadernos Americanos,* Mexico I, Enero-Febrero 1952.
64. Interview by Bernard Kalb, *Saturday Review,* XXXVI, 11 (August 21, 1954).
65. Interview by Rochelle Girson, Saturday Review Syndicate, August 28, 1954.
66. Unpublished paper, "Mari Sandoz, Daughter of Old Jules" by Felie Woodrow Clark, submitted to the Graduate Council of the Florida State University, May 1956. Quoted by permission of Florida State University and the author.
67. Notes written for the editor by Mamie J. Meredith, October 1956.
68. "Turning Points" by Roger Langenheim, *Nebraska Alumnus,* June 1957.
69. Letter to the editor, June 3, 1957.
70. Letter to the editor, June 15, 1957.
71. Letter to the editor, June 19, 1957.
72. Postcard to the editor, August 2, 1957.
73. Letter to the editor, August 8, 1957.
74. Letter to the editor, August 10, 1957.
75. Letter to the editor, August 24, 1957.
76. Letter to the editor, February 7, 1958.
77. Letter to the editor, February 16, 1958.
78. Letter to Mamie J. Meredith, February 21, 1958.
79. Letter to the editor, July 25, 1958.

THE TRANS-MISSOURI SERIES

I should like to understand as much as possible about man, shaped by and shaping his world. I decided early that most writers do their best work in material with which they have emotional identity. Therefore I restricted myself to the trans-Missouri country—and its nearer settlement origins—examining modern man's occupancy in the region from the stone axe to the A-bomb and jet propulsion. Through the discovery of this one region, this one drop of water, I hope to discover something of the nature of the ocean (61).

THE TRANS-MISSOURI SERIES, which is likely to stand as Mari Sandoz' central achievement, was conceived before the author was twenty. It was originally intended as a six-book project, but at the time of writing (July 1958) the author believes she will also include *The Buffalo Hunters,* thus expanding it to seven (76). Her plans call for the book on oil to be undertaken some time after 1960. After that will come the final volume, which will be the first of the series chronologically.

The books in the series are:

I. Untitled. The coming of iron and powder to stone-age man of the Great Plains. To be written.

II. *Crazy Horse: The Strange Man of the Oglalas*

III. *The Buffalo Hunters: The Story of the Hide Men*

IV. *Cheyenne Autumn*

V. *Old Jules*

VI. *The Cattlemen: From the Rio Grande across the Far Marias*

VII. Untitled. The story of oil in the Great Plains region. To be written.

PROFESSIONAL ACTIVITIES AND AWARDS

1935   *Old Jules* awarded Atlantic $5,000 nonfiction prize.

1941   On staff of Writers Conference, University of Colorado.

1946   On staff of Writers Conference, University of Indiana.

1947–1956   In charge of Advanced Novel Writing, Writers Institute, Eight Weeks Summer Session, University of Wisconsin.

1950   Honorary degree, University of Nebraska. "Doctor of Literature: Mari Sandoz, distinguished Nebraska historian, biographer, novelist, story writer, authority on Indians of the Nebraska territory and neighboring states. Published two books of a six-volume study of the trans-Missouri country. Author of three novels and many stories of Nebraska frontier life. Winner of the Atlantic nonfiction award. Recognized nationally as a representative midwest writer: cited for contributions to the Saga of Crazy Horse and other Indian history. Widely-known teacher in creative writing at several state universities."

1954   August 23: Mari Sandoz Day in Nebraska. "WHEREAS, the indomitable pioneer spirit has been typical of Nebraskans since the first settlement of this State, and WHEREAS, we Nebraskans are extremely proud of our fine heritage left to us by our pioneering forefathers, and WHEREAS, a native Nebraskan, Mari Sandoz, has immortalized the spirit and history of Nebraska and the Midwest by her writings, Now, THEREFORE, I, Robert B. Crosby, as Governor of the State of Nebraska, do hereby proclaim August 23, 1954, as MARI SANDOZ DAY."

September 23: Received the Nebraska Native Sons and

Daughters Award for Distinguished Achievement—the first such award made.

Crazy Horse named one of the Ten Best Serious Books of the West.

1955   National Achievement Award, The Westerners, Chicago Corral. "In recognition of her contribution to the preservation of the cultural background of the American West through her writing, and for her unequalled achievement in having four of her books selected by Westerners in a nationwide poll as ranking in the One Hundred Best Books on the West, this award is unanimously conferred by the Chicago Corral of The Westerners. Given this nineteenth day of December, One Thousand Nine Hundred and Fifty-Five. HERBERT O. BRAYER, President; L. P. JERRARD, Secretary."

1957   Headliner Award, Theta Sigma Phi.

1958   Made a life member of the Nebraska State Historical Society.

ACKNOWLEDGMENTS

THE AUTHOR wishes to thank the following publications in which material in this book first appeared: *The Atlantic Monthly; Blue Book; Country Gentleman; Cuadernos Americanos; Folk-Say: A Regional Miscellany; Ladies' Home Journal; Nature Magazine; Nebraska Alumnus; North American Review;* Omaha *World-Herald Magazine; Prairie Schooner; The Quill; The Reader's Digest; Saturday Evening Post; Saturday Review; Scribner's Magazine; The Sight-Giver; Story; The Westerners' Brand Book,* Chicago Corral; *The Westerners' Brand Book,* Denver Posse; *The Westerners' Brand Book,* New York Posse; and *The Writer.*

The University of Nebraska Press wishes to thank Felie Woodrow Clark, Librarian, King College, Bristol, Tennessee, for permission to quote from her unpublished study "Mari Sandoz, Daughter of Old Jules"; and Miss Nancy Bird, Interlibrary Loan Librarian, and Miss Mary Alice Hunt, Librarian, Materials Center, Florida State University, for facilitating our procuring this study. We wish also to thank Mr. J. E. Molloy, Librarian, the Philadelphia *Inquirer;* Mr. Frank Donohoe, Librarian, the Philadelphia *Bulletin;* Miss Bernice Kauffman, Reference Librarian, Lincoln City Library; Mr. John W. White, Librarian, Nebraska State Historical Society Library; and Mr. Richard Shugrue, Editor, *Daily Nebraskan,* for assistance in checking bibliographical data.

We are indebted to Professor James E. Miller, Jr., Chairman of the Department of English, University of Nebraska, and Professor Wallace Stegner, the Department of English, Stanford University, for reading the book in manuscript; to Professor Boyd G. Carter, Department of Romance Languages, University of Nebraska, for translating the author's statement in *Cuadernos Americanos;* and to Professor Bernice Slote, Department of English, University of Nebraska, for a number of useful editorial suggestions.

Finally, we wish to express our particular thanks to Professor-emeritus Mamie J. Meredith, Department of English, University of

249

Nebraska, for the loan of letters, clippings, and other material; for personal reminiscences of the author; and for her invaluable help in locating and securing stories and articles and in checking biographical and bibliographical data.